ANTIQUE GAMBLING CHIPS

REVISED EDITION

ANTIQUE GAMBLING CHIPS

REVISED EDITION

by

Dale Seymour

Contributing Authors:

Derek Cowan
Mother-of-Pearl

Allan Myers
Old Code Assignments

Ken Chopping
Ivory Manufacturing

John Benedict
European Chips

PAST PLEASURES
P.O. BOX 50863
PALO ALTO, CA 94303

ACKNOWLEDGMENTS: Special thanks to Allan Myers, who agreed to assign identification codes to new chip finds from 1986-1996. This task required a few hundred hours of his time. In addition to contributing authors Cowan, Chopping and Benedict, the following collectors provided *major* input into the development of this manuscript: **Jack Boberg, Steve Bowling, Ken Craig, Robert Eisenstadt, Benj Fauver, Tom French, Gene Grossblatt, Howdy Herz, Ron Kusel, Travis Lewin, Steve Passalaqua, Ralph Strandwold, Ernie Wheelden and Stan Wilker.**

In addition, the following people made helpful contributions: Mike Auterson, Roger Baker, Betty & Bill Barnard, Phil Beguhl, R.C. Bell, Joe Benedek, Steve Berg, Archie Black, Dick Brach, Kate Burt, Jeff Busby, Mike Butler, Fred Chapman, Tony Citko, R. W. Colbert, A. B. Corciluis, Rick Crandall, Mrs. H. W. Crowell, Ron & Elaine Daniels, Tony Davis, Tom & Judy Dawson, Russ Diaz, Gary De Dontney, John Dodds, Bryan Eggers, Jack Ferrell, Doc Finstuen, C. E. Fitzsimmons, Phil Flannagan, Jim Fondren, Henry Garrett, Walt Gonski, Charlie Gooden, Jack Gregory, Len Gratteri, H. C. Hall, Ken Hollenbeck, Bill Hamilton, Kregg Herz, David Howard, Steve Howard, Dean Ives, Phil Jensen, Mel Jung, Edward Karolick, Michael Knapp, Bruce Landau, Ernie Long, Larry Lubliner, Bob Matthews, Ernie Meador, Wini Michael, Kenneth Miller, Richard & Linda Miller, Ernie Modlin, John Moore, Michael Moore, Jim Myers, Crash McQueen, Colin Narbeth, Kevin Norris, Dennis Owen, Armin Pfaender, Chuck Pilgrim, Jane Pitman, Will Posthumos, Mrs. Thomas Powers, Dick Race, John Rauzy, Jim Reynolds, Dean Richman, Chuck Rodgers, Albert Rollins, Bob Rosenberger, Terry Roses, Doug Saito, Lenny Schneir, Paul Schweizer, John Simpson, Charlie Smith, Jodi Sones, Fred Sweeney, Russ Umbraco, Jim Vanek, Larry Watson, Bettye & Vic Williams, Bill Williamson and David Wilson.

CREDITS: *Production:* David Woods, Cathy Rutman and Ruth Cottrell
Edit: Lorri Ungaretti, Ruth Cottrell and Margo Seymour
Photography: Steve Talmadge and Margaret Lyons
Printing: Jim Knight and Malloy Litho, Inc.

ISBN: 0-9614273-3-7

CONTENTS

Part III ILLUSTRATED CHIPS (continued)

PREFACE TO THE SECOND EDITION

When this book was first published in 1985, the number of serious gambling chip collectors was probably less than 100. Now, little more than a decade later, the number is in the 3,000 to 5,000 range. Many new collectors are discovering the fascination of this hobby. (Some casinos have taken advantage of the fast-growing number of chip collectors and have flooded the market with new chips. Collectors of antique chips escape this frustration.)

Chip collectors have discovered many new antique chip designs that did not appear in the first edition of *Antique Gambling Chips*. For example, in 1985, I was aware of about 260 different ivory chip designs. You will find more than 1300 ivory designs in this new edition. Undoubtedly, several hundred more designs are still to be discovered.

"Clay" chips, which were made in quantity lots for sale to the general public, are another matter. Although this second edition contains 550 more clay poker chip designs than were in the first edition, it is doubtful that more than two dozen "new" designs will ever be discovered. Unlike ivory sets, which were designed to be unique, clay chips were mass-produced.

A revision of the book was necessary for reasons other than the addition of new chip designs. Discoveries about various categories of chip collecting have made it possible to be more accurate and authoritative in this edition.

A major addition to the book is an expanded description of 18th and 19th century mother-of-pearl gaming counters. This section was written by Derek Cowan of Bath, England. Derek is the primary authority on these gaming counters, which were made in China and used mainly in England during the period 1750–1900. Although several hundred specific mother-of-pearl counter designs are known, no attempt is made to identify each individually as that would require at least an additional hundred pages. At this time, the number of mother-of-pearl collectors is few, even though many of the counters are incredible works of art.

Another improvement to the first edition is a section on the history of the manufacture of ivory chips used primarily in the United States during the period 1840–1910. Ken Chopping, a collector from San Rafael, California, researched and wrote this section.

By adding more than 2000 new chips, I had to create a new coding system for chip identification. Collectors who have been using the codes from the first edition may begrudge recoding, but the new system should handle all future finds in every chip category. A separate, inexpensive chip code conversion listing, as well as a chip inventory checklist, will be available soon.

INTRODUCTION

It is difficult for some people to understand the obsession of a collector. For me, it is a simple fascination. Collecting offers a chance to seek undiscovered treasures, to explore a part of the past by accumulating bits and pieces of information and then assembling them as one would a puzzle. A collector shares an anthropologist's excitement, an historian's sense of wonder, an artist' or craftsman's appreciation of design and technique, and even a speculator' or investor's anticipation of potential profit. Since my youth, I have had collections of one type or another, but when I saw my first antique poker chip, I knew that I must find out more about these fascinating little works of art.

This book began the day I found an embossed clay chip with a design of a jockey on a racing horse. I was curious. How old was this chip? How many other designs were there? Who made them? Were books available on the subject? Did anyone collect them?

Obviously there was a period of time when the design, manufacture, and marketing of fancy poker chips was a viable livelihood for some people. My curiosity compelled me to find out more. The first edition of this book was the result of that search.

Some signs indicate that people collected chips in the first half of the century. (Records show a collector purchasing a large group of different chips.) The earliest known serious collector of poker chips was Carl M. Strandwold of Pasadena, California. Strandwold, father of current collector, Ralph Strandwold, claimed the largest known collection in the 1930's and 1940's. He entered his 450 different chip varieties in several southern California hobby shows. Today, collecting gambling chips and game counters is one of the fastest growing hobbies in the United States.

This book is designed for the collector of antique chips. For the most part it addresses chips that were made and used in the period 1775–1940.

Part I provides an historical perspective of the manufacture of chips and counters, starting in the 15th century.

Part II gives tips for beginning collectors, including advice on how to get started collecting, where to find chips, how to display a collection, and how to clean, repair, and care for chips. A new Seymour Chip Identification Code system will facilitate communication with other chip collectors. A section explaining the price guide used here should be helpful to antique dealers and collectors in determining the value of their chips.

In most cases, information is not available to determine the exact date a given chip was made, as manufacturing records have been destroyed. Nearly all of the information that is available on chips made since the Civil War comes from old catalogs. Part III of this book contains a selection of interesting pages taken from some of the first catalogs known to have advertised the sale of chips. This section also includes some sample chips from the era of casinos and illegal clubs that existed in the U.S. before 1931.

The manufacturer's section also contains an illustrated list of every chip that received a design patent from the U.S. Patent Office. A topic and chip code index appears at the end of the book for the reader's convenience. The bibliography lists articles, books, and booklets on specialized areas of chip or counter collecting.

For this book, the cut-off date is 1940. Of course, certain chips (particularly inlaid ones) were molded before and after 1940. Legalized gambling began in the United States in 1931. Since this book is already quite extensive in scope, I decided not to include casino chips. Books are available about casino and club chips in Nevada, Atlantic City, Colorado, and Florida. Other books specializing in illegal clubs, California clubs, and gambling ships are in preparation. See the bibliography at the back of this book for information about these publications.

For the most part, this book contains information about chips in the U.S. Few of the mother-of-pearl chips are American, and only a few of the ivories are not American. While there are several collectors of non-American chips, a catalog of foreign chips is beyond the scope of this book.

In addition to showing more than 2000 additional chips than appeared in the first edition, this book also has eight pages with color photographs that show the beauty of gaming chips and some rare new finds.

The broad scope of collector interests makes chip collecting a fascinating hobby. A collector may specialize in one of dozens of collecting categories, choosing a category that matches his or her interests and financial situation. Collecting ivory chips can be expensive, but the chips are beautiful and it is possible to discover the history of a given chip. Clay poker chips are cheaper, and collecting them provides the same challenge of finding all of the hundreds of designs and color variations.

If you are not yet a collector, perhaps this book will help entice you into collecting chips. If you are already a collector, I hope it enhances your enjoyment of the hobby. Please communicate with me about new chip finds or other aspects of this book or this hobby. Enjoy.

PART I

HISTORICAL PERSPECTIVE

GAME COUNTERS

The oldest counters manufactured were small metal discs. These objects were originally used for reckoning in the marketplace or in Roman counting houses. The counters in Rome were called *tesserae* and were used for such things as admission tokens to the Roman games. Metal pieces were also produced in private mints in Europe in the 14th to 18th centuries. Nuremberg became the center for the manufacture of game counters in the 18th and 19th centuries. Most of the early American game counters were made in Europe.

The counters made in Birmingham, England by Henry Kettle were dated 1803 and closely resembled the U.S. quarter-eagle and half-eagle gold coins of that period. The counters used during the period 1850–1870 were made largely in Nuremberg, Germany by the die sinking firm of Ludwig Christoph Lauer. Hundreds of varieties of American game counters have been identified.

Store card counters that resembled U.S. gold.

Game counter collectors have identified and classified, coded and valued game counters used in America during the period from 1790 to the mid 1900s. The most comprehensive publication on metallic U.S. counters is *American Counters Part I, Double Eagle & Eagle Gold,* by L. B. Fauver. Others are listed in the bibliography in the back of this book. The Token and Medal Society (TAMS) is an organization of collectors who communicate through a bimonthly journal (*TAMS JOURNAL*) and meet at various auctions and shows. For information, write to the Token and Medal Society, Box One, Tecumseh, MI 49286.

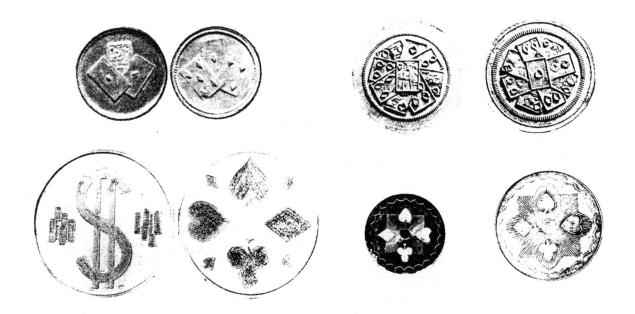

Metal card counters inscribed with playing cards or card suits.

"Keep Your Temper" whist markers.

Metal poker marks are dated 1882. Roman numerals were used
rather than Arabic numerals.

Spiel Mark is German for game counter.

According to L. B. Fauver, in spite of their close resemblance to gold coins which have a fixed value, it is likely that the counters were assigned a value representing some fraction of "face value" by the players before the game commenced.

Another type of metal game counter called a whist marker was also used in Western Europe and the United States largely in the period between 1820 and 1860. Whist markers were normally sold in sets of four and were used to keep score by individual players. (Non-coin-type whist markers exist in an amazing variety of styles and materials. An interesting book could be written on this subject.)

Representative whist markers that were used in America.

Still another type of metal gambling token appeared in the United States in the 1880s. These trade tokens were ordered by individual saloons, pool halls, stores, or manufacturers. They carried both an advertisement for that individual firm and a fixed value, such as "good for one drink," or "good for one cigar." These pieces were used for gambling largely in areas of the United States where there were legal restrictions against gambling for cash. To circumvent these restrictions, gambling was conducted with these tokens which were good for merchandise. Their use also provided the proprietor a ready means of getting his cut when the tokens were redeemed. The use of "good for" gambling tokens was most widespread in the United States during the first quarter of the 20th century. Many other types of "good for" tokens, concurrently in use in this country, were circulated by other kinds of businesses and were not generally used for gambling purposes.

Prices on above Checks
--IN--

BRASS, per 100 . . . $1.50
NICKEL, per 100 . . $1.75
ALUM'NUM, per 100 . . $2.00

BRASS OR GERMAN SILVER

No. 4600. No. 4601. No. 4602. No. 4603.

STAMPED ON ONE SIDE ONLY.
PRICE OF CHECKS.

BRASS, per 100 . . . . . $1.50
GERMAN SILVER $2.00

No. 4604.

TRADE CHECKS.
Price per 100 in Brass.

No. 4605. Size 3-4 Inch - - $1.90
No. 4606. Size 1 Inch - - 2.00
No. 4607. Size 1 1-8 Inch - - 2.90
No. 4608. Size 1 1-4 Inch - - 3.90
No. 4609. Size 1 3-8 Inch - - 4.90

Numerals 5, 10, 20, 25, 50 and 1.00.

Prices quoted on Trade Checks are for one numeral only.

BONE CHIPS

During the 19th century, before the manufacture of inexpensive composition chips, game counters were often made from animal bone. It is fairly easy to distinguish bone from ivory, as bone has a more porous surface. Genuine ivory is extremely smooth and will usually, but not always, display a grain or striation, whereas bone has little grain and will usually display some areas of small cracks or fractures that look much like whiskers in the surface.

Bone Chip   **Ivory Chip**

Bone chips are generally thinner and are rarely decorated as extensively as the engraved ivory chips. In fact, the majority of chips made from bone are plain with no color or design. Many of the bone chip sets are composed of chips of different shapes and/or size. Square, rectangular, and circular chips appear in many sets. Sometimes the the chips appear in the shape of fish. These bone chips were used in playing the games of *Pope Joan* or *loo*. Bone counters were the less-expensive alternative to chips that were inticately carved from shells. The author's research unearthed no information on who manufactured bone chips or how they were made or sold. Pictured below is an enlargement of a rare, highly decorated chip (*circa* 1800).

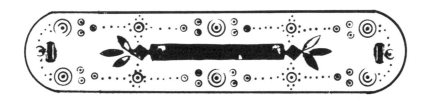

Ornate bone chip decorated with inlaid mother-of-pearl (enlarged).

MOTHER-OF-PEARL COUNTERS

Easily the most beautiful of game counters are those intricately carved from mother-of-pearl in China in the early 1800s. These counters were made in various shapes such as ovals, rectangles, circles, squares, and fish shapes. Many of the sets of chips are incredible works of art in miniature. A set of 140 chips must have required hundreds of person-hours of work. Often a set of chips was custom-made for a European customer, depicting the customer's initials or even a coat of arms.

The quality of the engraving varies, but most chips show scenes of Chinese gardens. The details on some of the finer chips can only be appreciated when viewed through a 25X magnifying glass. In some sets, every carving on the 100 plus chips shows a different scene of two to three characters. There is speculation that a set of chips may have depicted a story in the carver's imagination.

Some elaborate borders appear to have been cut out with a fret saw. Most of these chips were probably made to be sold in Europe for use in the games of *Pope Joan, loo, ombre,* and *quadrille.*

It has just been in recent years that the full value of these chips has been realized. The more elaborately carved, thicker chips sell for $50–$90. This is especially true of chips that contain an identifiable coat of arms. Mother-of-pearl game counters are frequently sold mounted as necklaces at the finer antique shows. (See Part III for more detail on Chinese mother-of-pearl chips.)

PORCELAIN COUNTERS

Game counters of porcelain were made and used in Thailand and perhaps elsewhere in Asia in the 19th century. One report dates their manufacture as during 1761–1870; another as 1821–1870. The counters were officially illegal after 1908. The collector should beware when purchasing these counters, as modern reproductions are hard to distinguish from original counters.

Examples of porcelain game counters.

IVORY CHIPS

During the last half of the 19th century in America, the games of *poker* and *faro* provided the main gambling fare in saloons and gambling halls. Mississippi River steamboats were seldom without a "game." Although the stakes in these games were sometimes gold dust or coins, checks or chips were much easier to manage.

Poker is essentially an American game that evolved from the French game of *pogue* and the English game of *brag*. Poker started in the New Orleans area and moved up and down the Mississippi in the mid 1800s. The need for counters or chips to manage the banking in poker and faro coincided with the golden age of whaling (1820–1870) so ivory was a natural choice as a material for gambling chips.

Ivory gambling chips used on river boats (*circa* 1870).

COMPOSITION CHIPS

As gambling games requiring chips became more popular, the impracticality of supplying the needs of the market place with ivory chips became apparent. In the 1880s, a new "composition" chip made from clay and shellac was manufactured quite inexpensively. The Will & Finck catalog of 1896 advertised these chips as "Compressed Ivory" and used the subtitle, "such as the country is flooded with."

The composition chips were molded into steel molds (usually 25 to a tray) and baked for 2 to 3 minutes in furnaces heated to around 3000° Fahrenheit. The chips were popped out of the molds like cookies, then the ridges on the edge of the chip where the two sides of the mold met were polished. The faces were also polished or sandblasted. Customers could buy these chips for about one-tenth of what they would have to pay for the ivory chips.

(*Above*) A salesman's chip sample book. (*Right*) Metal mold used to form an embossed composition chip. Courtesy U.S. Playing Card Co., Cincinnati, Ohio.

14

The biggest problem with plain composition chips was "ringing in." "Ringing in" is when a player, unbeknownst to the other players, slips some of his chips, identical to those being used, into the game. With the plain, three- or four-color composition chips that were easily purchased from catalogs or stores, ringing in was a cinch. To counter this problem, composition chip manufacturers began to offer their customers a number of alternative chip styles and designs. These chip options included "paste-ons" engraved chips, embossed chips, inlaid chips, and machined chips.

Paste-on chips were simply plain composition chips with a colored, lithographed sticker pasted on the chip. There was no indentation for the design that was to be pasted on, but the stickers seemed to be well sealed to the chip with adhesive and a shellac covering. These paste-on chips were first made in the mid 1880s and soon evolved to an "inlaid litho" chip. The inlaid litho chip differed from the paste-on in that a very thin recess was molded into the chip and the printed design was set in this recess in the face of the chip. It is often difficult to tell a paste-on chip from an inlaid litho chip without peeling off or extracting the piece of paper from the chip.

Engraved Chip   **Embossed Chip**   **Paste-on Chip**   **Inlaid Chip**

The more common alternatives to plain chips were the engraved or embossed chips. Engraved chips are known to have been cataloged as early as 1880. Embossed chips followed a few years later. In the manufacture of engraved chips, the design was stamped into the plain surface of the chip after it was molded. The embossed chips, on the other hand, were created by a carved die or mold.

Most engraved chips came with the engravings filled with paint of contrasting color. Some engraved chips contained no paint and it is often difficult to see their design clearly.

Embossed and engraved composition chip sets generally came in sets of 100. A set included 50 white chips, 25 red chips, and 25 blue chips. Yellow chips could be ordered separately. Embossed chips may have lasted longer as one 1908 ad stated that "long use does not deface the design (embossed)."

A chip that was much more common than the inlaid litho chip was the regular inlaid chip. Inlaid chips contained an inlaid design of one color set into a chip of contrasting color. These chips were amazingly indestructible. It is unusual to find the inlaid piece out of one of these chips, even when they are nearly 100 years old and quite worn. In general, inlaid chips were made from a slightly higher quality composition material than were the embossed and engraved chips. Since chips were needed in many colors for games such as roulette, manufacturers chose to make the inlaid chips in 12 colors. Purchasers of inlaid chips had a choice of square edges, round edges, or sometimes semi-round edges. A few inlaid chips were made with serrated edges. Some of the designs on the inlaid chips made in the 1890s are identical to those used as roulette chips in some casinos today.

One kind of composition chip that is distinctively different from the others described here is a chip we shall call the "machined chip." Machined chips appear like a miniature musical records in that the chip face is covered with concentric grooves.

Examples of "machined" chips. Tiny grooves make the chips look like miniature records.

Every manufacturer of gaming chips advertised that its company used the "finest indestructible material." Other oft-used terms included: non-duplicate, uniform thickness and color, polished edges, sand-blast finish, and permits easier cutting and stacking. In the late 1800s the chips were often referred to as "Paranoid Chips." The use of this name continued well into the mid 1900s. The name was more descriptive of chip users than of the chips themselves; it was merely a brand name denoting a better quality.

Most chips measured 1½" in diameter, but some manufacturers made chips an eighth of an inch smaller or larger. Miniature chips with a diameter of ⅞" also were common, but they were never engraved or embossed.

One popular, high-quality chip that appeared about the turn of the century was called the *Crest and Seal* chip. Other manufacturers later called it the *Crest or Seal* and the *Seal and Crest*. As one ad stated, "The design in Seal and Crest Checks is printed on the reverse side of a transparent celluloid inlay which prevents discoloration and wear of the design." Crest and Seal chips could be custom made for anyone in any design the customer chose. The special order could be one's own design or photograph or, as they suggested, "our artist will do it."

MASON'S CREST AND SEAL NON-DUPLICATE "HUB" CHECKS

For the particular operator who desires the finest non-duplicate crap check made, we mould to order, Hub checks with specially printed Crest and Seal inlay. The check illustrated is but one of thousands of designs. Mason can develop a check for every occasion . . . a check that will carry a printed reproduction of letters, numbers, numerals, photographs or any design that will portray any specific characteristics of the particular individual. All the fine features of our well known Hub check are incorporated in the Crest and Seal check. And with all these marvelous features goes a distinctive design! Colors and prices are listed below.

MASON'S PLAIN ROUND OR SQUARE EDGE INLAID CREST AND SEAL CHECKS

The inlay in these checks have the identical unlimited possibilities as Mason's Crest and Seal checks, described above. The big difference lies in the fact that these checks are supplied with a plain design, with both round and square edge. We recommend our plain square edge non-duplicate Crest and Seal Inlaid checks for the smart club that wants the last word in fine checks.

When placing an order, simply send us an outline of what you have in mind for the inlay design. Mason's artists will prepare several sketches and submit them to you for the final selection. The prices we have listed below, are based on ONE COLOR printing of the inlay. Where more than one color is desired, add $15.00 per 1000 checks for each additional color. Each order for Crest and Seal Inlaid checks requires a deposit of 50%. Two to three weeks for delivery is necessary on checks of this type.

Supplied in twelve distinctive colors: Red, White, Blue, Yellow, Green, Orange, Chocolate, Light Blue, Pink, Lavender, Black and Vermilion.

No. B-41 "Hub" Inlaid
Crest and Seal

Note: The prices listed apply to B-41, Mason's Inlaid Crest and Seal Hub Checks or B-42, Mason's Plain Thick Square Edge Inlaid Crest and Seal Checks. If B-43 Mason's Plain Inlaid Round Edge Crest and Seal Checks are desired, deduct $5.00 per thousand from the list price.

1000	$125.00
2000	240.00
3000	345.00
4000	440.00
5000	525.00

No. B-42 Plain Inlaid
Crest and Seal

Copy from early catalog describing Crest and Seal "Checks."

Each catalog promoted its efforts to provide the buyer with unique chips. One catalog proudly swore, "under no circumstances will we use your design or die for anyone else." Another read, "We only send this check to one person in a locality." The importance of using unique chips in a game is confirmed by an old timer's story about a gambling venture in Colorado Springs, Colorado in the depression days. A local, who was unemployed, decided to open a game in a vacant motel. The entrepreneur bought a supply of chips and other materials and soon business was booming. But inexplicably, things went bad and after a few months he closed down the operation, having lost his initial stake. To his chagrin, he had nearly twice as many chips when he closed his game as he did when he started. Many chip designs were easy to acquire and slip into the game.

Each manufacturer or well-known chip supplier had its own chip design or distinctive border. In the sample catalog advertisements elsewhere in this book, you can see many examples of this. Probably the best-known special chip was the Monarch chip that was made by the Harris Company. The Harris Company claimed to be the first manufacturer of composition chips. Harris' ad about its Monarch chip stated that it was "disked in the center, that is, the centers are made so they do not touch." Harris called its Monarch chip the "live chip" and advertised that the contact only on the outer rim allowed for higher stacking of chips. As was the case with designs and other chip features, other manufacturers copied the Monarch. Other special borders included the *Winner* and the *Chain*.

Monarch Border   **Winner Border**   **Chain Border**

Chip designs incorporated such things as gambling motifs (playing cards and horse racing), good luck symbols (swastika, clover leaf, horseshoes, and bees), patriotic symbols (flags, stars, and eagles). In many cases, chip designers or manufacturers seemed to prefer to copy a competitor's design rather than to create a new design of their own, which resulted in a number of slight design variations on many chips.

SELECTED CHIP BORDER TRADE MARKS OF MANUFACTURERS

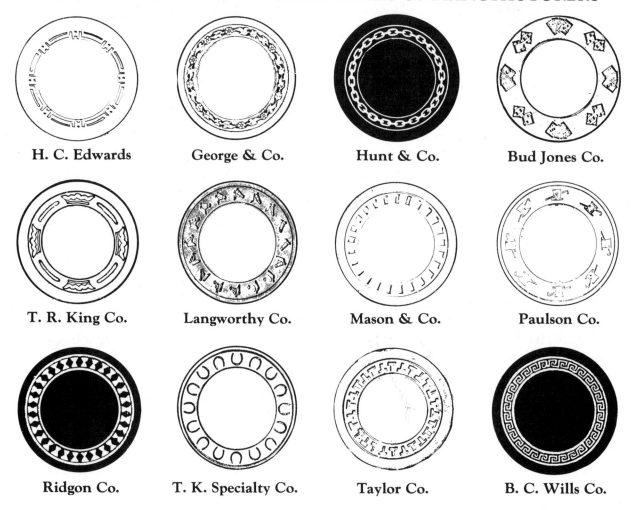

H. C. Edwards   George & Co.   Hunt & Co.   Bud Jones Co.

T. R. King Co.   Langworthy Co.   Mason & Co.   Paulson Co.

Ridgon Co.   T. K. Specialty Co.   Taylor Co.   B. C. Wills Co.

One kind of composition chip seems to be a transition from the ivory chip designs to the composition designs. These chips differ from other composition chips in their size. Some of the designs on these chips are identical to ivory chip designs, and others are identical to other larger composition chip designs.

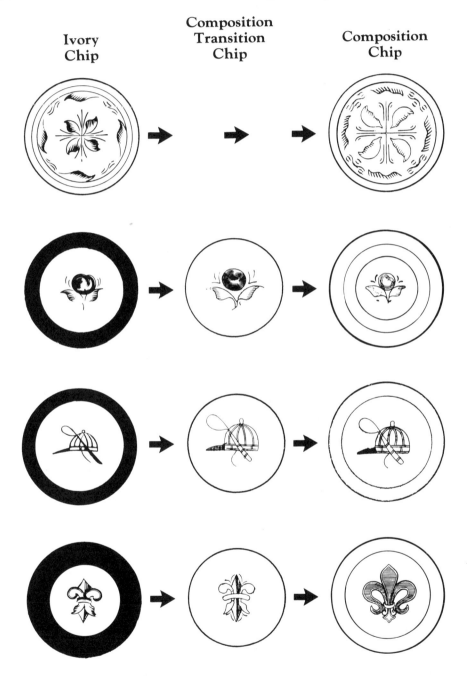

Ivory
Chip

Composition
Transition
Chip

Composition
Chip

Examples of designs that evolved from engraved ivory chips to a smaller hand-crafted composition chip to a standard 1 1/2" machine engraved, mass-produced, composition chip.

19

CELLULOID CHIPS

Celluloid was invented in 1869 in Newark, New Jersey. It is difficult to determine when the first celluloid gambling chips were made because very few catalogs ever offered celluloid chips for sale. Apparently it was more difficult to engrave or emboss designs in the celluloid than in the composition material.

Celluloid chips were sold under the name of *Catalin*. One ad for these chips claimed "All Catalin Chips listed below are beautifully mottled, with a lasting, high polish which accentuates the delicate mottled lines. Catalin Chips are guaranteed not to warp, break or burn." The Popper Adult Games catalog advertised that they would engrave the chips with a deep engraving and fill them with paint, leaving a permanent design. Many of the celluloid chips were two-tone chips with dark colors on the rim of the 1½″ chip and a light-colored 1″ solid center.

PAPER, RUBBER, AND WOOD CHIPS

If a game was to be kept secret, quiet chips were helpful. Paper, wood, and rubber chips served this purpose, but they probably existed more because they were a cheap alternative to the composition chips. These quiet chips are also less aesthetically pleasing than their clay counterparts and, consequently, they are less collectible. Both paper and rubber chips were made before the turn of the century. Rubber chips turn brittle with age and are sometimes indistinguishable from plain clay chips.

PLASTIC CHIPS

In the late 1930s, plastic was a new and exciting material. It was considered ideal for poker chips — ideal, that is, for the *manufacturer* of poker chips —because plastic was stronger and less expensive than clay. The first plastic chips were not light in weight as are today's plastic chips. They probably contained a sizeable quantity of composition material. Some of the interlocking composition chips from the late 1930s seem to be about half plastic and half composition material.

After World War II, most chips were made from plastic. Chip design had sunk to an all-time low; the plastic chip was a far cry from the beautiful hand carved mother-of-pearl chip or the scrimshawed ivory piece. The elegant gambling chip had become a thing of the past.

CASINO AND CLUB CHIPS

Many collectors of gambling chips specialize in casino and/or club chips and tokens. Most of these chips or tokens were used in Nevada casinos; however, private club chips were made for a number of clubs throughout the country. Collecting foreign casino chips and chips from ocean liners is another collecting specialty. Chips generally display the value, casino name, and often the casino location. These chips are inlaid, engraved, embossed, or a combination of all three. Most foreign casino chips are made of celluloid, while American casino chips are composition, metal, or composition with metal insets.

Manufacture of chips or tokens containing Nevada casino names began in the 1920s even though gambling was not legalized until 1931. The most desirable chips to collect are those used in casinos that are no longer open. Collectors prize old chips from the El Rancho Casino in Las Vegas because it burned to the ground one night in 1960, destroying nearly all the chips. Only the few that were left in players' pockets seem to have survived.

When a casino is closed it is often difficult to determine just how many of the chips were not destroyed. Collectors speculate and wait to see if a box of them will turn up years later and affect the "going value" of the chips. Collectors naturally treasure the higher-value chips such as the $50, $100, $500, or $1000 chips.

Because of the shortage of the U.S. dollar coins, a number of casinos began to have their own metal tokens made in the 1960s. Many of these tokens were struck by the Franklin Mint and have been cataloged in Franklin Mint publications. In addition to the Franklin Mint, more than a dozen other private minting companies are involved in manufacturing metal gaming tokens. A small booklet published as part of the Hewitt's Numismatic Information Series lists all tokens minted in the United States from 1965 to 1970.

Metal casino tokens are mostly dollar tokens; however, some of them were made in denominations of 50¢, $2, $2.50, and $5. With the advent of legalized gambling in Atlantic City, New Jersey, the scope of collectible casino chips expanded.

Collectors often refer to club chips as a separate collecting category from casino chips. Club chips were used in private clubs or clubs having limited gambling privileges. Some of these clubs were legal; others weren't. The most common private clubs issuing chips are the service clubs such as the Elks Lodge, Moose Lodge, and Eagle Lodge. California and other states have legalized poker or low-ball card clubs that are a source of chips.

The bibliography refers to several excellent up-to-date sources of information on casino and club chips.

DEALER CHIPS AND MARKERS

Dealer chips were special chips that were used to indicate which player was to deal next. These chips were often very special in design. In the case of ivory dealer chips, the chips were much larger than the regular chips, and they sometimes contained silver inlays. These chips were frequently elliptical or rectangular in shape. Part III shows many examples.

Markers were used to indicate debts to the house or to other players. Some markers were made with specific numerical values on them whereas others contained designs. Ivory chips less than 1¼″ in diameter were made as markers and were usually included with a "set" of chips. Ivory markers generally had a design of two or more concentric circles. Markers sometimes served as dealer chips and vice versa.

DESIGN-PATENTED GAME CHIPS

Design patents registered with the United States Patent Office reveal some interesting information regarding the history of the development of game chips and their design and manufacture. Twenty-five design patents were registered from 1887 to 1964.

Some of the chip designs that were patented have not been seen by collectors. This may be because they are scarce, or it may be because they were never manufactured even though a patent was awarded.

It is interesting to speculate why so few designs were registered for protection. It may have been the expense, or it may have been that designs were so easy to come by that it was a waste of time and money to bother with the application. In any case, it is quite obvious that designers and manufacturers frequently copied each other's designs.

The information from the Patent Office included the name and address of the designer, the assignor of the design, and the dates the design application was submitted and awarded. A rather lengthy technical description of the design was also reported. Illustrations of the design accompanied the preceding information in the Patent Design logs starting in 1899. None of the 25 chip design descriptions made any mention of the material the chips were to be made from, nor was there any mention of the dimensions of the chips.

A summary of the essential information on patented chips is given on the following pages. It is interesting to note that the first person to receive a design patent on a chip design was a woman, Annie Ball, from Chicago. The well-known Spalding brothers sporting goods' company was one of the first manufacturers of game chips.

DESIGN PATENTED GAME CHIPS

1. Pat. # D 17,249 (April 12, 1887)
    Annie Ball, Chicago, Illinois
    "two circular concentric grooves"

2. Pat. # D 18,122 (Feb. 29, 1888)
    William M. Welling, New York,
    N.Y.
    "endless coil of rope with circular
    lines inside and outside the figure"

3. Pat. # D 18,411 (June 26, 1888)
    J. Walter Spalding, N.Y., N.Y.
    for A. G. Spalding Bros., Chicago

4. Pat. # D 18,412 (June 26, 1888)
    J. Walter Spalding, N.Y., N.Y.
    for A. G. Spalding Bros., Chicago
    "A hound with one of its fore legs
    on a log and the other lifted. Foliage
    in background."

5. Pat. # D 18,470 (July 17, 1888)
    J. Walter Spalding, N.Y., N.Y.
    for A. G. Spalding Bros., Chicago
    "Head and bust of a female tennis
    player. Racket in hand and ball on
    racket."

6. Pat. # D 20,709 (May 5, 1891)
    Louis Steinberger, N.Y., N.Y.
    for George Kuehl, Chicago

7. Pat. # D 20,710 (May 5, 1891)
    Louis Steinberger, N.Y., N.Y.
    for George Kuehl, Chicago
    "Horseshoe in foreground centered
    on clover-leaf in background. Single
    circular border."

8. Pat. # D 20,713 (May 12, 1891)
    Hiram W. Harris, N.Y., N.Y.

9. Pat. # D 30,208 (Feb. 14, 1899)
    Godfrey H. Harris, N.Y., N.Y.
    for Dickinson Hard Rubber Co.,
    Massachusetts

10. Pat. # D 30,209 (Feb. 14, 1899)
Godfrey H. Harris, N.Y., N.Y.
for Dickinson Hard Rubber Co.,
Massachusetts

13. Pat. #D 34,593 (May 28, 1901)
Peter A. Schaefer, Cincinnati, Oh.
for U.S. Playing Card Co., Cincin.

11. Pat. # D 33,715 (Dec. 11, 1900)
Peter A. Schaefer, Cincinnati, Oh.
for U.S. Playing Card Co., Cincin.

14. Pat. # D 36,151 (Dec. 9, 1902)
Stanley A. Cohen, N.Y., N.Y.

12. Pat. # D 33,716 (Dec. 11, 1900)
Peter A. Schaefer, Cincinnati, Oh.
for U.S. Playing Card Co., Cincin.

15. Pat. # D 36,242 (March 10, 1903)
Stanley A. Cohen, N.Y., N.Y.

16. Pat. # D 61,340 (Aug. 8, 1922)
Godfrey H. Harris, N.Y., N.Y.

19. Pat. # D 118,623 (Jan. 23, 1940)
Victor E. Hofmann, Toledo, Oh.
for Owens-Illinois Glass, Toledo

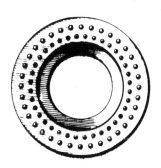

17. Pat. # D 100,853 (Aug. 18, 1936)
George J. Crosman, Irvington, N.J.

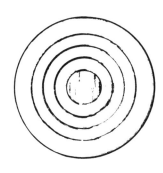

20. Pat. # D 136,394 (Sept. 21, 1943)
James F. Cooper, Darby, Mont.

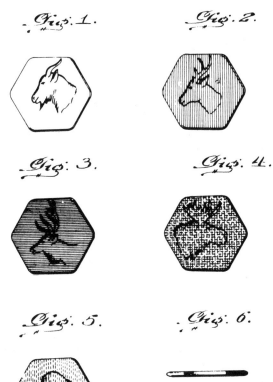

18. Pat. # D 111,273 (Sept. 13, 1938)
Fred W. Voges, Ozone Park, N.Y.

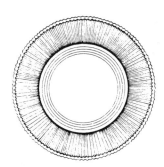

21. Pat. # D 137,608 (April 4, 1944)
Kenneth Tator, Fairfax, Va.
Gustave Halmgren, Washington, D. C.

24. Pat. # D 150,099 (June 29, 1948)
Walter W. Taylor and Leo McMenemy,
Kansas City, KS

22. Pat. # D 149,533 (1947)
Cecil B. Woofter, St. Paul, MN
for Brown & Bigelow, St. Paul

25. Pat. # D 162,020 (Feb. 20, 1951)
Stanley F. Fuchs, Janesville, WI

23. Pat. # D 149,613 (May 18, 1948)
Chas. E. Caestecer, Kenilworth, IL
for Amer. Molded Prod., Chicago

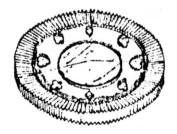

MANUFACTURERS AND DISTRIBUTORS

Manufacturers' and distributors' catalogs provide the best source of information about which chips were made when and by whom. Dozens of catalogs printed in the late 1800's and early 1900's have been very helpful in identifying when various composition chips were made. This is not true, however, with ivory chips made between 1860 and 1900. No known catalogs contain illustrations of ivory chips. William Suydam Co. and the Will & Finck Co. both advertised ivory checks in their catalogs, but they included no illustrations. The Grote Co. of New York is known to have sold sets of ivory chips.

Harris claims to have been the first to manufacture composition chips. The U.S. Playing Card Company was the largest manufacturer of composition chips in the first half of the 20th century. The USPCC started manufacturing chips around the turn of the century. The company decided to get out of the chip-making business right after World War II, as they were faced with problems of (1) employees pilfering custom chips which were, in effect, like money and, (2) manufacturing decisions regarding increased costs of manufacturing composition (high-quality) chips vs. cheaper plastic molding (low-quality) product.

It is difficult to determine from catalogs which companies manufactured chips as opposed to just distributing chips made by others. A selected number of catalog pages depicting chips advertised for sale are included in Part III.

OTHER MATERIALS

Chips were also made from imitation ivory, compressed ivory, French Ivory, leather, glass, Bakelite, gold, Tunbridge Ware, cardboard, Tupperware, tortoise shell, catalin, and even jet stone (coal). It seems as if chips have been made from nearly every substance but potatoes and silicon.

French Ivory is neither French nor ivory. It is a type of celluloid that was patented for use by an American company. French Ivory was an inexpensive substitute for ivory. It may not be true that French Ivory contained powdered ivory, as commonly thought. Many of the silver inlay chips from early Monte Carlo days appear to be ivory but are actually French Ivory.

In the second quarter of the 20th century, the field of plastics exploded. Trade names like "Lucite," "Catalin," and "Bakelite" were popular and were used to make chips. Invented in 1907 by Dr. Leo Baekeland, Bakelite was strong, insulating, and anti-corrosive. It was the "material of a thousand uses." Bakelite was made in plain colors, but chip manufacturers combined colors to create a popular marbleized look. Today, art deco collectors pay high prices ($200–$400) for a set of Bakelite chips in a Bakelite holder.

Other variations to differentiate chips from one another included serrated edges, square edges, machined (having grooves, as on a phonograph record), non-duplicate, noiseless, non-skid, interlocking (from 1938 on), oval edges, no-roll, durable, etched, semi-round, fibret inlaid, paste-on, and inlaid litho.

FOREIGN MANUFACTURING

Each country seems to have had its own preferences for styles of chips. Americans and Canadians used ivory for high-end chips and clay for low-end chips. Europe seemed to prefer mother-of-pearl at the high end and bone at the low end. Early in the 20th century, plastic chips replaced the bone chips in Europe.

American chips were nearly all round, but chip sets in Europe usually contained squares, rectangles, and sometimes oval or elliptical shapes. Chips with high denominations in Europe were called *plaques*, and they were often very large and rectangular in shape. (Part III shows examples of these chips.)

Bourgogne & Grasset, one of the oldest and largest casino chip producers, is located in Beaune, a peaceful town in the heart of Burgundy, France. During the beginning years of the company, Mr. Bourgogne and Mr. Grasset, two brothers-in-law, used lithography on celluloid to supply jewelers and eyeglass manufacturers. When it became evident that celluloid presented too great a danger, they began using cellulose acetate.

In 1927, a huge scandal erupted in Monte Carlo: ivory and mother-of-pearl chips were being counterfeited, resulting in great losses for the casinos. After reading the story in the newspaper, the Bourgogne & Grasset partners decided to apply their technical skills to producing a new generation of gambling chips and plaques that would offer security to casinos around the world. Their solution was ingenious, as they perfected a process by which the impression made on a chip is protected by a thin film of plastic that makes imitation impossible. Each chip and plaque comprises up to 15 layers of plastic, with color effects that cannot be duplicated. In fact, some of the chips and plaques found in collections today have been in use for more than thirty years at some casinos in Europe.

Today, more than 400 casinos around the world use Bourgogne & Grasset chips and plaques. In the United States, such casinos as Caesar's Palace in Atlantic City, Del Webb's Sahara in Las Vegas, and the El Dorado in Reno have used this type of chip. The Sands in Las Vegas had a complete series, and the MGM Grand uses a complete series in their European games section.

MAKING CLAY POKER CHIPS

The traditional process of making clay gambling chips was a well-kept secret for more than 40 years, until 1985 when the new owner of The Burt Company in Portland, Maine, agreed to open the company's doors to a reporter for the *Evening Express* newspaper.

The Burt Co. was founded as Portland Billiard Ball Co. in 1895 by Alonzo Burt. At one time, the company was the largest billiard ball producer in the world. It also produced poker chips for casinos. Burt's sons took over the business when their father died and ran it until 1985 when it was sold to John M. Kendall. Renamed Chipco, the company is now one of the leading chipmaking companies in the world, using modern techniques and graphics. Below is a description, taken from the *Evening Express* article, explaining how The Burt Co. made clay gambling chips.

The traditional process of making ceramic chips didn't change for more than 40 years. First, workers bleached the clay white. Then they mixed and dyed it the color of the final chip. They heated the clay on steam tables, then spread it into long, hot, wafer-size strips. As the strips cooled, a press punched out the chips. The Burt Co. had more than 20 presses, each with a different casino's mold.

Poker chips had to meet strict thickness specifications so that they stacked well at gambling tables. The margin of error was .004 of an inch — about the width of a human hair.

The chip-making process allowed little wastage. If a chip was imperfect, it was reground and the clay used again to create other chips of the same color. Also, when chips were punched out, the leftover clay was reused.

Preventing counterfeiting was an important part of making chips. A casino's chip was distinguished by the molding around the edge and the design inlay.

The Burt Co. chips contained anywhere from two to eight colored "spots" that were punched out by the presses and inserted into chips of a different color. Sometimes casinos wanted two halves of two different colors adhered together for an individual look.

Chips were made in French francs, English pounds, and from $1 to $100,000 in U.S. dollars. A chip was worthless until a piece of clay indicating the denomination was placed in the center. At that point, the chip was as good as money and was shipped immediately to the customer.

From "Poker Chips Good Deal for Local Firm" by Frank Sleeper, *Evening Express*, September 16, 1985. Photo by Doug Jones. Used with permission.

SPECIAL SEAL and CREST CHECKS
manufactured by
The Burt Company

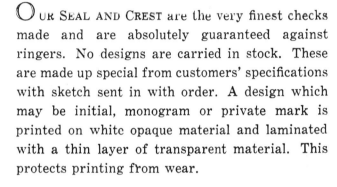

OUR SEAL AND CREST are the very finest checks made and are absolutely guaranteed against ringers. No designs are carried in stock. These are made up special from customers' specifications with sketch sent in with order. A design which may be initial, monogram or private mark is printed on white opaque material and laminated with a thin layer of transparent material. This protects printing from wear.

These checks can be supplied in square edge, dull linen finish or supplied in a round edge polished check.

We can supply these checks in ten different standard colors and the price for design like shown on the left, printed in black on a white background, is $154.00 per thousand.

On special designs, send sketch of design with quantity of checks desired for quotation.

THE BURT COMPANY
Morrill Street   Portland, Maine

GAMING CHIPS BELONGING TO VERY IMPORTANT PEOPLE

Obverse   Reverse

This beautiful mother-of-pearl chip belonged to Queen Charlotte, wife of King George III of England. Maybe "Mad King George" was mad because his wife played cards so often. (enlarged 29%)

These two chips belonged to Napoleon. They are made from mother-of-pearl (light color) and tortoise shell (dark color). The scalloped edges, inner scallop and the bee's legs are gold. These chips are the rarest known, valued at over $10,000 each. (enlarged 38%)

These ivory chips belonged to Edwin Booth, famous actor and brother of John Wilkes Booth, Lincoln's assassin.

GAMING CHIPS BELONGING TO VERY IMPORTANT PEOPLE

Richard Canfield, owner of the casino at Saratoga Springs, New York in the 1890's, owned these ivory chips. Canfield was the Bugsy Siegel of the late 19th Century when much of the action was in the eastern United States.

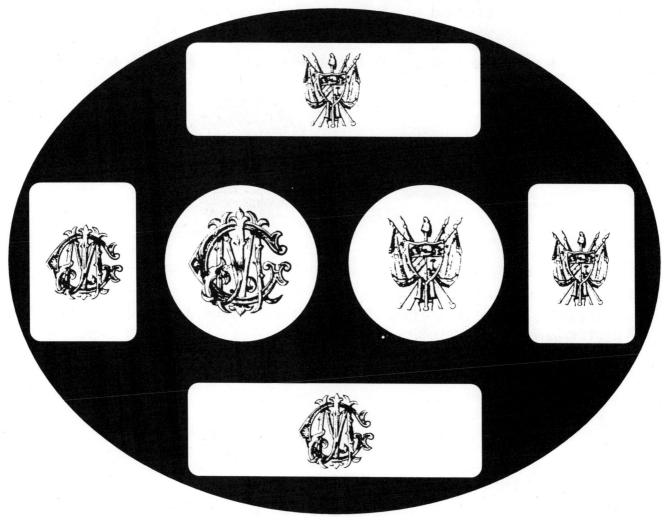

French style mother-of-pearl chips belonging to the president of Cuba, Jose Miguel Gomez, 1909-1913 (JMG). (enlarged 29%)

GAMING CHIPS BELONGING TO VERY IMPORTANT PEOPLE

These ivory chips belonged to President Chester A. Arthur at one time.

✤ ✤

A chip that belonged to President Herbert Hoover. These chips had black, yellow and red rims and were made of catlin. The presidential seal was stamped on opaque, cream-colored inlay in gold. (enlarged 29%)

✤ ✤

Chip made for President Dwight D. Eisenhower with the presidential seal inlay for use on Air Force One. Chips were made by T.R. King in white, red, blue and yellow. They were ordered from King on June 23, 1954. (enlarged 29%)

GAMING CHIPS BELONGING TO VERY IMPORTANT PEOPLE

Copy of a pen and ink inventory letter found in a box with the ivory chips.
Chips were supposedly used on a riverboat by Mark Twain.

⚜ ⚜

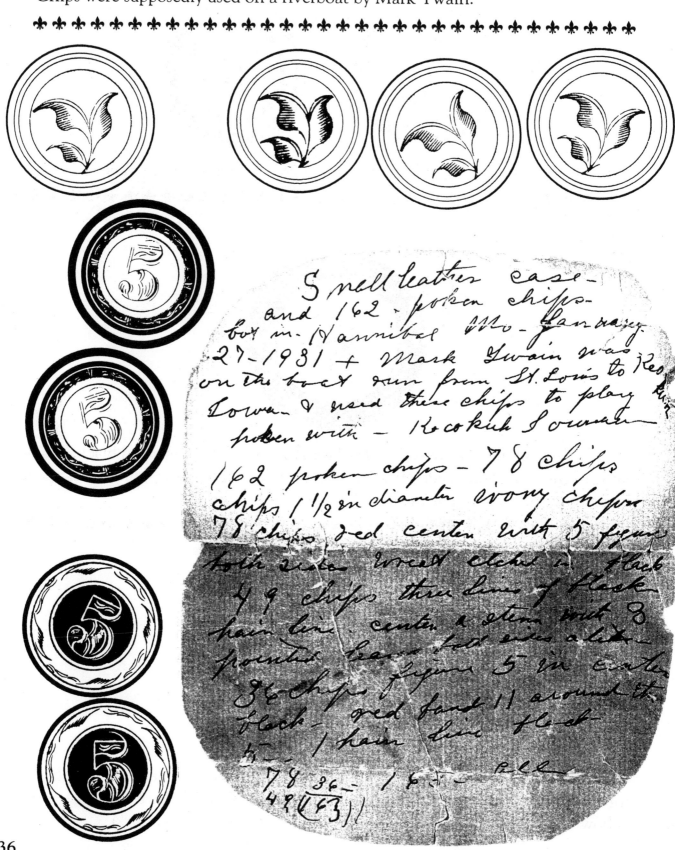

PART II

COLLECTING
CHIPS

CHIP COLLECTING

People who purchase Antique Gambling Chips often inquire about various aspects of chip collecting — i.e., How do I get started? How do I trade? Where do I find chips? This section will try to answer some of those questions.

What are my collecting options?

Most chip collectors narrow their focus to a few of the many types of chips. Collecting all types of chips can be very expensive and time consuming.

Below is a list of various options for collectors and important factors relating to each one. In some cases, these figures are very rough estimates.

SOME CHIP COLLECTING OPTIONS*

Type of chip	Time period	Dif. chips (incl. colors)	Difficulty finding	Chip Expense		Comments
1. M-of-Pearl	1730–1900	6000+	very diff. (Qual.)	$2–$500	($15)	Qual. varies greatly
2. Ivory	1850–1910	2000+	difficult	$25–$3000	($50)	Hard to find
3. Bone	1700–1900	500+	hard	50¢–$20	($4)	Few collectors
4. Clay	1880–1940	15,000+	easy–difficult	50¢–$30	($3)	Interesting, inexp.
5. Casino (US)	1930–	50,000+	easy–difficult	$1–$1,000	($10)	Big undertaking
5a. Nevada	1930–	25,000	easy–difficult	$1–$3,000	($15)	Still big challenge
5b. Las Vegas	1930–	13,000+	easy–difficult	$1–$3,000	($15)	Several specialize
5c. Reno	1930–	7,000+	easy–difficult	$1–$3,000	($15)	Several specialize
5d. Atlantic City	1930–	500+	easy–difficult	$1–$2,000	($10)	Several specialize
5e. Card Clubs	1930–	10,000+	easy–difficult	$1–$200	($5)	Calif. alone is huge
5f. Roulette	1880–	10,000+	easy–difficult	$1–$40	($6)	Hard to get them all
6. Foreign	1730–	10,000+	easy–difficult	$3–$500	($12)	Few U.S. collectors

*Some collectors also specialize in Colorado, South Dakota, or in a given denomination of chip, such as 10¢, $1, etc.

How do I acquire chips?

You can buy and trade chips from other collectors and dealers. There are several chip-collecting groups in the United States. The largest of these is the Casino Chips and Gaming Tokens Collectors Club. This club has more than 2,000 members and produces a 100+ page quarterly newsletter containing many ads by both collectors and dealers. Dues for this club are $25 a year. To join, write to James Steffner, P.O. Box 368, Wellington, OH 44090. Several smaller local groups are also active in the U.S.

A very informative newsletter on old casino and club chips is called Chip Chat. It is published by Doug Saito, 4056 Front St., San Diego, CA 92103.

You might also attend club meetings, shows, or conventions. The Casino Chips and Gaming Tokens Collectors Club has an annual meeting in Las Vegas in June each year. At this show you will find tens of thousands of chips for sale or trade, and usually 40 to 50 collectors or dealers have exhibit tables. Dealers often sell chips at local coin shows, too.

Dealers at large flea markets often have chip sets for sale. You will rarely find ivory or mother-of-pearl chips at flea markets. You are more likely to find them at large antique shows or in antique shops.

Asking dealers at shows or flea markets will help turn up new finds, as dealers often have chips "back in the store" that they didn't bring. Most collectors have numerous duplicates and are more than willing to help new collectors get started by selling a number of their duplicates at very reasonable prices.

Try your own ad. Advertising in antique journals or papers is an excellent way to find chips. It is surprising how many old sets of chips are still in closets or attics. One often hears the statement, "Oh, poker chips. Yes, we have some at home. I didn't know they were worth anything."

The best price for current chips, of course, is in the casinos or clubs themselves. If you don't gamble, many clubs will sell you chips at the cashier's window. Several clubs, however, will let you buy chips only at the tables. It's okay to buy chips and then walk away. You may get a strange look, but if you aren't a gambler you don't need to lose money just to buy chips.

How do I know the value of chips?

It is important to know the value of chips when buying or trading. Learning the value of chips takes some time. This is another example of the advantage of specializing — you have less to learn and remember. Dealers send out price lists on chips. One can't generalize that $1000 chips are always worth more than 10¢ chips. It depends on their rarity, authenticity, and condition.

Contrary to what you might think, chip collecting does not need to be an expensive hobby. If a collector is patient, diligent, and lucky, he or she may accumulate a reasonably-sized collection that has paid for itself. It is not unusual to find a nice set of pictorial composition chips for sale for $15 to $25 at a local flea market. If these 100–200 chips are not common, the finder has some excellent trading material. It is possible to keep 10 to 12 chips and trade the others. Advanced collectors may be more than willing to trade 50 to 60 different chips for the set. With so many different chip designs in existence, it is not infrequent for a collector to stumble onto an entire set of chips that is new to long-time collectors.

Although most collectors like to find sets of chips, the majority of collectors have as their objective owning one of each kind and color of chip made. If collectors see a chip they want, they may be willing to pay $2 to $5 for it ($40 to $80 for an ivory), but they would not pay a similar unit price for a complete set. The first chip may be worth $3 to the collector, the next few $1 each (for trading), and after that the value to that collector may drop to 25¢ to 50¢ each (for additional trading). The seller trying to get "top dollar" may choose to sell one chip at a time at the $3 price. That seller may take several months to move the chips at that price.

The condition of the chips is, of course, an important factor in price. The prices given here are for chips in good condition.

Antique Chips
Value Rating Code*

a: 50¢   b: $1   c: $2-$3   d: $4-$5   e: $6-$7

f: $8-$9   g: $10-$14   h: $15-$19   i: $20-$29

j: $30-$39   k: $40-$49   l: $50-$69   m: $70-$89

n: $90-$109   o: $110-$149   p: $150-$199

q: $200-$299   r: $300-$399   s: $400-$499

t: $500-$699   u: $700-$999   v: $1000-$1999

w: $2000-$2999   x: $3000-$3999

y: $4000-$499   z: $5000+

*It is important to remember that quantities
of one chip or a set of chips would have
a much lower unit value per chip.

General Comments on Chip Values

Metal Counters: The value of metal game counters varies greatly. For information on price lists and further information, write to: The Token and Medal Society (TAMS), Box One, Tecumseh, MI 49286.

Bone Chips: Bone chips with no designs or coloring are not highly prized by collectors, even though these chips may be more than 100 years old. A set of 100 plain bone chips may sell for $15 to $50. If the chips are colored but without a design, they may be worth twice that amount. If the chips have colored border designs or fancy internal designs, they may bring from $6 to $10 each or from $200 to $400 for a set of 100. These prices do not include the chip case. Many of the old cases that held bone chips were very fancy and may be worth from $50 to $200 themselves.

Mother-of-Pearl Chips: Prices for mother-of-pearl chips rose considerably in the late 1970's when they started appearing as necklaces. The thickest, most intricately carved pieces sell for $40 to $125 each. In contrast, the plainer, thin, worn chips may sell for as little as $1 each. Average chip prices in this category range mostly from $6 to $20.

Porcelain Counters: As mentioned earlier in the manufacturing section, porcelain counters are often counterfeit. *Caveat Emptor* (let the buyer beware). Depending on size, detail, and condition, these chips sell from $5 to $15 each.

Ivory, Inlaid, and Composition Chips: For values in these categories, please refer to the specific sections in this book where chips are pictured; individual chip values are given there.

Celluloid Chips: A set of celluloid (catalin) chips generally sells for $40 to $400. If they are marbleized, they are very desirable to art deco collectors.

Paper, Rubber, and Wood Chips: With a few exceptions, collectors are not interested in these chips. Some collectors seek paper advertising chips. Others look for wood and rubber chips if they contain designs. See specific sections in this book where these chips are pictured.

Plastic Chips: Plastic chips have no value to collectors, and consequently they are not covered in this book. A few of the first interlocking chips made in the late 1930's were a combination of plastic and clay. These chips are included in this book.

Casino and Club Chips and Tokens: To determine values of casino and club chips, it is essential to have a detailed price guide. Several guides cover casino chips in Nevada, New Jersey, Colorado, California, and Florida. See the bibliography at the back of this book.

Monogrammed Chips: Unless a monogram on a chip can be authentically identified with a famous person or a famous gambling establishment, monogrammed chips generate little interest among collectors. A collector may pay $1 or $5 for a particularly interesting monogram design but might be reluctant to purchase a set. If a monogrammed chip can be connected to a specific casino or club, it can bring from $25 to $100.

Numeral Chips: No values have been established.

How do I organize and display my chips?

Probably the best way to store and display chips is in binders designed for collectors of silver dollars. Since most chips are about the same size as silver dollars (1¹/₂"), supplies for displaying chips can be acquired at a local coin collectors' shop. As your collection grows, the binders expand to the point where you may use one binder for each major chip category. It is helpful to arrange chips alphabetically by using the Seymour Chip Identification Code for each chip category. Collectors generally try to collect one chip of each color for each design. Design and color variations are usually displayed next to the chips of the same code.

How do I clean my dirty chips?

Composition, especially old clay poker chips, should not be soaked in water to be cleaned. Soaking clay chips in water dries them out and makes them look faded and "lifeless." (If chips have been cleaned by soaking, they can be revived somewhat by soaking them in vegetable oil.) Chip dealers sell chip cleaning compounds; different collectors prefer different brands. Also, rubbing a clay chip lightly with a damp cloth won't dry it out the way soaking will.

Ivory is porous and will naturally expand and contract as humidity changes. Extremes of humidity are the worse enemies of ivory chips. Wetting will cause rapid swelling of ivory and can dislodge and wash out ink. Wetting also makes rapid drying more probable, which increases internal stress and can cause cracking. To clean an ivory chip, rub it lightly with a rag containing a little bit of mild liquid detergent. Rinse with a damp cloth and pat dry immediately with a soft cloth.

Should I repaint or repair worn or damaged chips?

This is a matter of personal preference. Some collectors do; some never do. Engraved clay chips with no paint are very difficult to see, so you may wish to rub in a contrasting color to bring out the design. If the chip is dark (black, blue, or red), regular white chalk works well and can easily be removed. You can use oil paint sticks to fill in engravings, but it is wise to experiment on an unwanted chip first to be sure the paint doesn't stain the chip. On ivory chips, raw umber may look better than black paint. The "off white" paint stick for dark clay chips may look better than regular white, which may seem too new and bright. Try the color on a chip or two; if you don't like it, use a toothbrush and paint thinner to remove it. When you get it "right," let it dry a week on a flip (a 2-x-2 chip holder), folded in a V so that air gets to both sides. Collector Ken Craig, the ivory enhancement expert, puts the chips in a food dehydrator set at 90° for two days.

SEYMOUR CHIP IDENTIFICATION CODE

Certainly it is not sufficient for a collector proposing a purchase or trade to refer to a "red composition chip with an eagle on it." Composition chips have at least 19 different currently known eagle designs. There is obviously a need to identify different chip designs by picture and code. The Seymour Identification Code is an attempt to satisfy this need. The code is designed to provide some alphabetical listing by designs within various design categories and, at the same time, provide for future expansion to include "yet to be discovered" chips.

It is obvious from looking at the old gambling catalogs that manufacturers of composition, inlaid, and ivory chips were not hesitant about copying each other's designs. It is not certain whether manufacturers were trying to copy designs exactly and couldn't, or they were trying to copy the general design and made minor variations on purpose. In any case, a number of chip designs differ slightly from one another, and these designs have been assigned separate three-letter codes to assist collectors in identifying chips. Where differences in designs are difficult to see, an enlarged close-up of the design is provided to make identification easier.

The original three-letter coding system devised in 1984 and introduced in the first edition of this book was adequate to code the chip designs known at that time. Now, with more than 2000 chips to identify, it is necessary to create a new system. This new system will be expandable to accommodate thousands of chips and should never need to be changed. The first letter of all poker codes begins with the letter P (poker) to differentiate the chips from other types of chips such as ivory. The second letter identifies the major collection category—i.e., animals (A), birds (B), playing cards (C), etc.

Between 1984 and 1996, Allan Myers graciously donated hundreds of hours assigning new codes to all new chip finds. As the three-letter coding system became inadequate it was necessary to add a fourth (lower-case) letter. Some collectors wanted new codes for every minute difference. Communication of new codes to all collectors was difficult, and the system broke down. At one point, some of the expanded codes were given "better" codes so that some chips had two identifying codes. In the new coding system, those variations have been omitted. Minor variations of a chip are given the same code. Many collectors have requested this simplification.

For the collectors who have organized their collections by the old codes (or some of the old codes), a new/old code list is provided in the books *Old Poker Chips* and *19th Century Ivory Gaming Chips*. See the bibliography.

Use of the new codes by all collectors will facilitate communication between collectors and help to provide more accurate identification of chip designs in the future.

COLLECTING CHIP BOXES AND HOLDERS

Poker players often purchased their chips in cardboard boxes from mail order catalogs or local stores. Many of these boxes were colorfully decorated and are considered as collectible items by gambling collector enthusiasts. Most of these boxes contained 100 chips — 50 white chips, 25 red chips, and 25 blue chips. The common fourth color was yellow, and yellow chips were purchased separately, usually in quantities of 100. Boxes that are marked or labeled as containing 100 chips of a special color are naturally more collectible. Among the more desirable chip boxes are the cylindrical cardboard boxes that were manufactured by the U.S. Playing Card Company (see illustration, page 47). These tubes held 12, 16, or 25 chips each.

Chip holders vary greatly in every design aspect. A representative selection of chip holders is pictured on the following pages. Fancy holders may be worth from $50 to $300 without chips. Early cases from the 1800s were sometimes decorated with elaborate ivory inlay.

A variety of chip containers, including a sack of about 200 cowrie shells, which were sold as game counters.

CONTAINERS

Most chip cases held 6 or 8 stacks of 25 chips. Quality varied greatly.

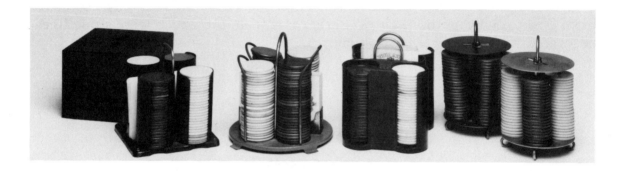

These metal chip cases each held 100 chips.

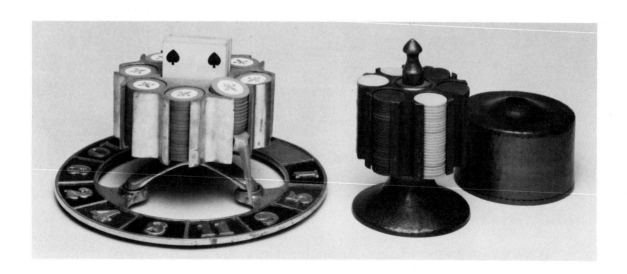

Chip holders made from cast aluminum and copper. The holder at the left doubled as a gambling device.

Cylindrical and miniature chip containers from the U.S. Playing Card Company.

Chip boxes usually gave quantity, brand name, manufacturer or distributor, chip
diameter, material, and sometimes a design name.

CONTAINERS

A cleverly designed chip holder from the 1930s revealed 8 stacks of chips with the twist of a wrist.

An assortment of unusual chip holders from the early 1900s.

Set at the left was a souvenir of the 1895 World's Fair in Chicago. At the right, an advertising piece from a cigar Co. featuring metal chips. Center piece is a premium "Wishing You a Lucky 1912."

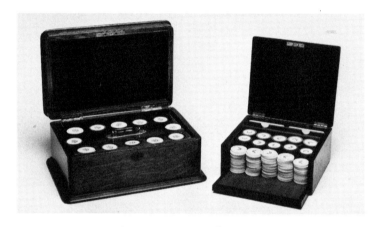

Cases housing sets of ivory chips.

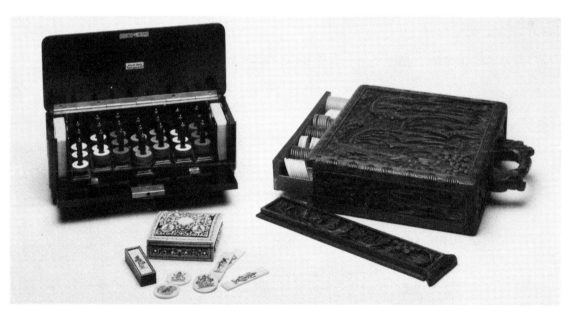

At left, case made in Germany holds enameled metal chips. At right, intricately carved case houses set of chips. Foreground shows hand-carved ivory box with unusual ivory chips.

CONTAINERS

The game tray at left is a Pope Joan tray that was used to hold mother-of-pearl chips (*circa* 1835). Inlaid Bezique card and chip case is shown on the right (*circa* 1890).

Two 19th century chip cases that held fancy bone chips and playing cards.

Four sets of chips were often housed in four separate boxes for players. Both of these sets were made from bone.

**Elaborate chip cases from the 19th century. Pictures courtesy of
William R. Williamson.**

CONTAINERS

More chip cases from William R. Williamson's collection.

CHIP BOX LABELS

1 SET NO. 2037/100

POKER CHIPS

BARON

H. BARON CO. INC.
NEW YORK 3, N. Y.
MADE IN U.S.A.

BREAKNOT
POKER CHIPS

Size 1⁹⁄₁₆   No. 550

THE BURT COMPANY
PORTLAND, MAINE

100   ASSORTED   1½ INCH
CAVENDALE
NON-SKID DESIGN

HARVITE POKER CHIPS

Clarion

100   PAPER CHIPS 1½"
EMBOSSED • ROUND EDGE

100   Embossed   1½
FAMOUS JOCKEY CLUB
(Reg'd) Trade Mark
POKER   CHIPS

COMPO-SITE, Inc.   Newark, N. J.   U. S. A.

100 CONSOLIDATED POKER CHECKS
UNIVERSAL EMBOSSED
ASSORTED COLORS
1½ IN.   THE N.Y. CONSOLIDATED CARD Co
222-228 W. 14TH ST NEW YORK:

ONE
HUNDRED
CROWN

POKER
CHIPS

100   1½ Inch
NOISELESS—UNBREAKABLE
CUTINO
POKER CHIPS
CUTINO SUNDRY CO.
KANSAS CITY, MO.
ASST'D   COLORS

100 ASSORTED NO.4.
Dennison's
GAME COUNTERS.

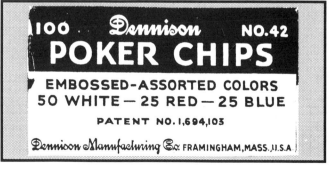

100   *Dennison*   NO.42
POKER CHIPS
EMBOSSED-ASSORTED COLORS
50 WHITE — 25 RED — 25 BLUE
PATENT NO. 1,694,103
Dennison Manufacturing Co. FRAMINGHAM, MASS. U.S.A.

53

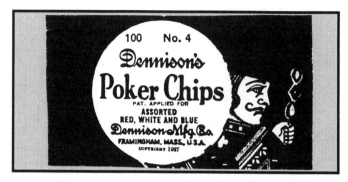

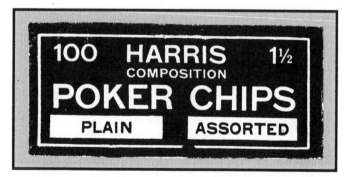

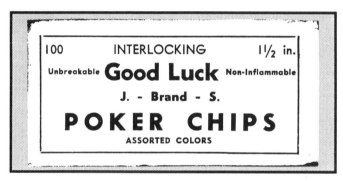

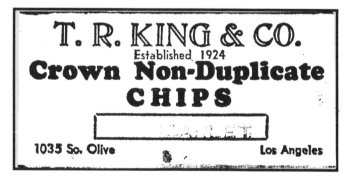

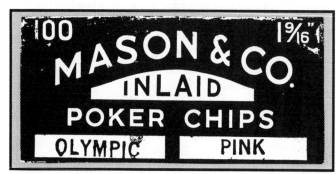

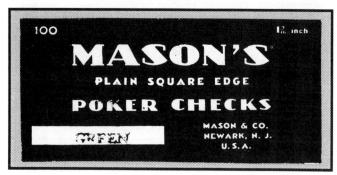

Greetings...
THE OSHKOSH BREWING CO.
1631 DOTY ST.
OSHKOSH, WISCONSIN

DRINK Chief OSHKOSH BEER

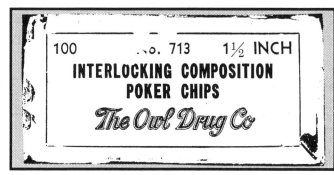

100   No. 713   1½ INCH
INTERLOCKING COMPOSITION POKER CHIPS
The Owl Drug Co

100 Pacific Registered 100
NON-DUPLICATE CRAP CHECKS
PACIFIC CLUB SUPPLY

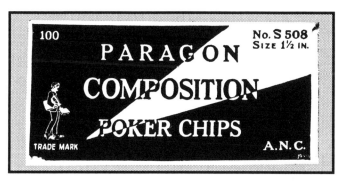

100   No. S 508   SIZE 1½ IN.
PARAGON COMPOSITION POKER CHIPS
TRADE MARK   A.N.C.

POKER CHIPS
No.1250   COMPOSITION-INTERLOCKING
RATTBERG NOVELTY CO.   NEW YORK

100
PLA-M-WEL
POKER CHIPS
UNBREAKABLE
The General Timber & Lumber Co., Cleveland, O., U.S.A.

100
PLA-M-WEL
POKER CHIPS
UNBREAKABLE
Rite-Hite Golf Tee, Inc., Cleveland, Ohio, U. S. A.

100
PLA-M-WEL
POKER CHIPS
UNBREAKABLE
PLA-WOOD PROD. CORP., CLEVELAND, O., U. S. A.

PO DO

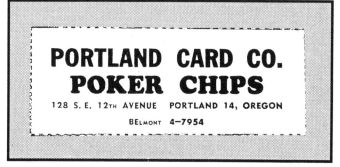

PORTLAND CARD CO.
POKER CHIPS
128 S. E. 12TH AVENUE   PORTLAND 14, OREGON
BElmont 4-7954

100   1½ in.

ST. REGIS

Composition

POKER CHIPS

Embossed   No. 179   Assorted

100   1½"

Assorted Poker Chips

EMBOSSED—ROUND EDGE

SUN RAY DRUG CO.

Stores throughout the East

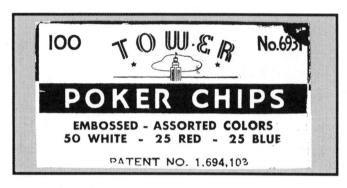

100   T·O·W·E·R   No.6931

POKER CHIPS

EMBOSSED - ASSORTED COLORS
50 WHITE - 25 RED - 25 BLUE

PATENT NO. 1,694,103

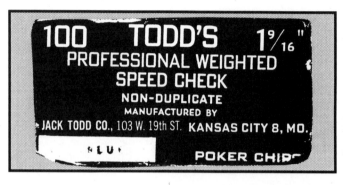

100   TODD'S   1 9/16 "

PROFESSIONAL WEIGHTED
SPEED CHECK

NON-DUPLICATE

MANUFACTURED BY

JACK TODD CO., 103 W. 19th ST.   KANSAS CITY 8, MO.

BLU   POKER CHIPS

100   U. S.   1½ Inch

PAPER POKER CHIPS

PLAIN

ASSORTED

THE U.S. PLAYING CARD CO.
CINCINNATI, U.S.A.

U.S.

Assorted
-Thin-

"U.S."

Rubber Poker Chips
100 ASSORTED

100   U. S.   1¼ Inch

POKER CHIPS

ANCHOR—BRAND

ASSORTED

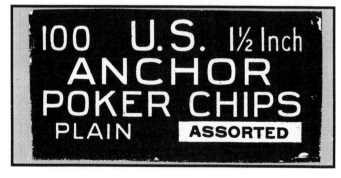

100   U.S.   1½ Inch

ANCHOR
POKER CHIPS

PLAIN   ASSORTED

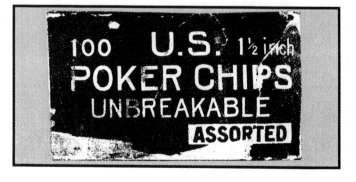

100   U.S.   1½ inch

POKER CHIPS

UNBREAKABLE

ASSORTED

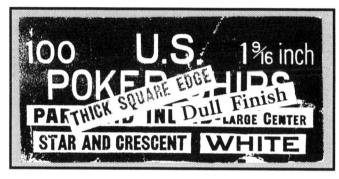

"INTERNATIONAL" SERIES.

FIFTY

BAKELITE COUNTERS

FOR ALL GAMES

H.P. GIBSON & SONS Ltd.,   LONDON E.C.

MADE IN ENGLAND

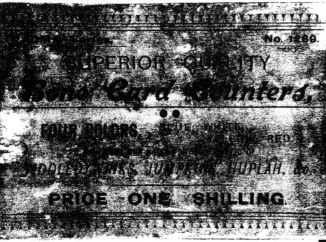

No. 1260.

SUPERIOR QUALITY

Bone Card Counters,

FOUR COLORS. BLUE, WHITE, GREEN, RED.

FIDDLESTICKS, JUMPKINS, HUPLAH, &c.

PRICE ONE SHILLING.

AFRICAN COWRIES

THE MOST POPULAR

CARD COUNTERS.

THE SACK

CONTAINING

ABOUT 200

Embossed
Composition
Poker
Chips

PART III

ILLUSTRATED

CHIPS

MOTHER ⟨of⟩ PEARL

Game Counters

MOTHER-OF-PEARL COUNTERS

The most superb game counters are the better varieties made from mother-of-pearl by the Chinese for the West between 1720 and 1840. The rarity-quality-cost combination is excellent.

Many counter sets were commissioned by individuals, often at the same time as porcelain dinner services, and usually good records exist describing their social and commercial history. Dating is possible within fifteen years by style and within two years from records. Research can involve China trade history and products, heraldry, genealogy, calligraphy, folklore, and symbolism.

The earliest styles of Chinese mother-of-pearl counters showed images of animals and flowers. As the Chinese people began creating counter sets for the West, several other types of images emerged, including:

- Armorial, with coats of arms or emblems
- Monogrammed, with words, phrases, or customers' initials
- Numbers, ranging from 1 to 1000, for use in games
- Games, with suits or names of card games

Analysis of large private collections suggests that 1500 to 2000 armorial and 2000 to 2500 monogrammed counter sets were made. (David Howard, the armorial porcelain expert, estimates that 5000 dinner services were personalized.) Probably there were as many non-personalized sets made as there were personalized.

Counters are given a variety of names around the world. In the United States they are called Chips because they were used in private card games.

In Europe they are now called Mother-of-Pearl Game Counters (Great Britain); Jetons de Jeu en Nacre (France); Jetons de Nacre (Belgium); Gettoni Madreperlati (Italy); Perlmuttermarken (Germany); Parel Moer Fiches (Holland); Ficha Madreperola (Spain); Ficha Nacarado (Portugal). Traditionally, they were called Fiches in France, Italy, Spain, and Portugal.

The key date for Chinese export items is 1699 when Emperor K'ang Hsi encouraged the West to trade with China through the Hongs, or places of business, at Canton. The foreign agencies or "factories" were confined to a quarter-mile strip of land on the banks of the Pearl River. Each nation had one building containing all residences, trading headquarters, and warehouses.

Although their prime responsibility was trading on behalf of the Honourable East India Company (H.E.I.C.), captains and supercargoes (agents) were allowed to trade privately as part of their pay. Since the H.E.I.C. mainly bought large quantities of limited varieties, specialty items such as gaming counters were commissioned through the private traders.

MATERIAL AND TECHNIQUES

Mother-of-pearl, or nacre, the interior shell layer of the pearl oyster, is the same substance as pearls — calcite and calcium carbonate. Its luster results from ridges in which the calcium carbonate deposits. The Chinese used the best shell variety, "gold lip," from Manila and the Persian Gulf.

Even good shells required removal of the hard outer layer by grinding. A full day's work by one person produced only ten shells. After cutting and lapping, the finished material was expensive. To maximize yield, early counters were made flat and thin (typically 1.3mm), with designs carved in low relief into a finely polished surface. The final cleaning polish used goats' milk.

Although designs are often described as etched, this technique was not used to make Chinese mother-of-pearl counters. Etching is a chemical process employing an etch-resistant layer applied to the substrate. The etchant can dissolve only at the designed openings.

While nacre dissolves readily in weak acid, resist pattern line width and spacing cannot produce the fine definition needed for Chinese designs and cross-hatching. That definition is not possible with relatively rough nacre and wax or lacquer resists.

To confirm that the Chinese used physical rather than chemical techniques, counters were subjected to Scanning Electron Microscope (SEM) analysis. A Mass Spectrometer was used to look for etchant chemicals and to predict the engraving implement material. The smooth and rough (decorated) surfaces of "engraved" and "deep carved" counters were examined. High magnification always showed characteristic mechanical cleavage and not undercutting associated with chemical etching.

While we do not know for sure how the Chinese incised their intricate mother-of-pearl designs, the fact that there is no chemical difference between smooth and decorated areas and no iron in decorated areas implies that crafts people used diamond- rather than steel-tipped tools.

The Chinese could produce works of art with exquisite craftsmanship in great numbers. Equally impressive was their ability to organize the many and varied orders from the captains and supercargoes competing for delivery in the one period per year when ships could arrive and depart. A single order for a personalized porcelain service and a boxed set of counters involved coordinating different skills at different locations. Many person-years of production time were needed to make the porcelain, mother-of-pearl, and lacquer boxes and trays in different shapes and quantity with personalized decoration. The supply logistics are as admirable as the workmanship.

Part of a porcelain service, lacquer games box, and counter set for the Herworth family, c.1810. The pot and box are half size, the counter actual size.

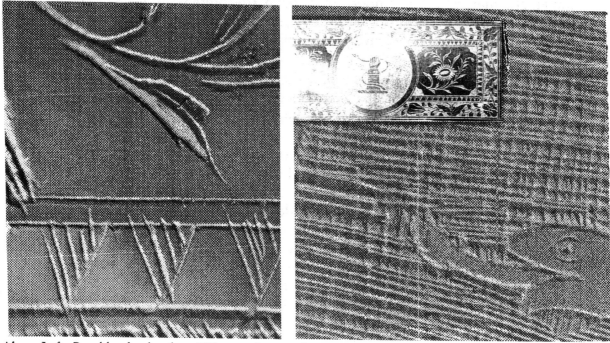

Above Left: Panel border details at 20X magnification showing mechanical scratch-engraving and engraving with a burin or graver.

Above Right: A true-size counter laid upon a 25X magnification of the background hatching around the snake's head and tongue.

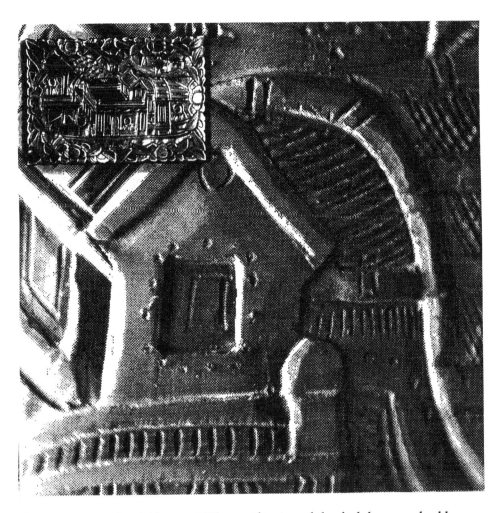

A counter, true size, laid upon 15X magnification of the deck house end gable to show tool marks.

EARLY AND CHINESE-STYLE COUNTERS

The first Chinese armorial porcelain produced for Britain was in 1695. Although some mother-of-pearl counters with roughly interpreted Medici-style arms and crests suggest dates earlier than 1695, most counters were made for the West between 1720 and 1840.

Around 1720, several armorial counter sets were commissioned in a distinctive European style. How many sets and who initiated the demand is unknown, but thereafter the life-cycle and demand mirrored the growth and decline of armorial porcelain services and the number of ships trading to Canton.

Also during the period 1720 to 1840, many sets of Chinese-style counters were exported from Canton, often with workmanship equal to that of armorial counters. Until 1780, the designs employed on the reverse of Chinese-style counters were often used on armorial counters.

From about 1780, large numbers of counters for personalizing, in differing shapes, designs and quality, were made speculatively. All exhibit one of two features: a blank roundel at the center of one side or a roundel completed with a Chinese motif. Counters purchased with a blank roundel and subsequently monogrammed in Europe can be identified in three ways: the absence of cross-hatching around arms or monogram, a distinctive font style, and incisions engraved as opposed to scratched.

Highlights of Facing Page
First Row Left: Counters with coronets and Medici-style arms, made prior to 1695.
First Row, Second from Right: Arms of Hyde, Earls of Clarendon and Rochester, Governor of New York, c.1710.
Second Row Left: Thin, small diameter, engraved with a simple Chinese flower or carp, c.1700 – 1720.
Fourth to Sixth Row: The most popular exported designs included two love-birds, centra star, flora, village landscape, card suits and Chinese symbols.
Sixth Row Bottom Left: Speculative counter with engraved flower roundel and panels. The border is point-in-point.

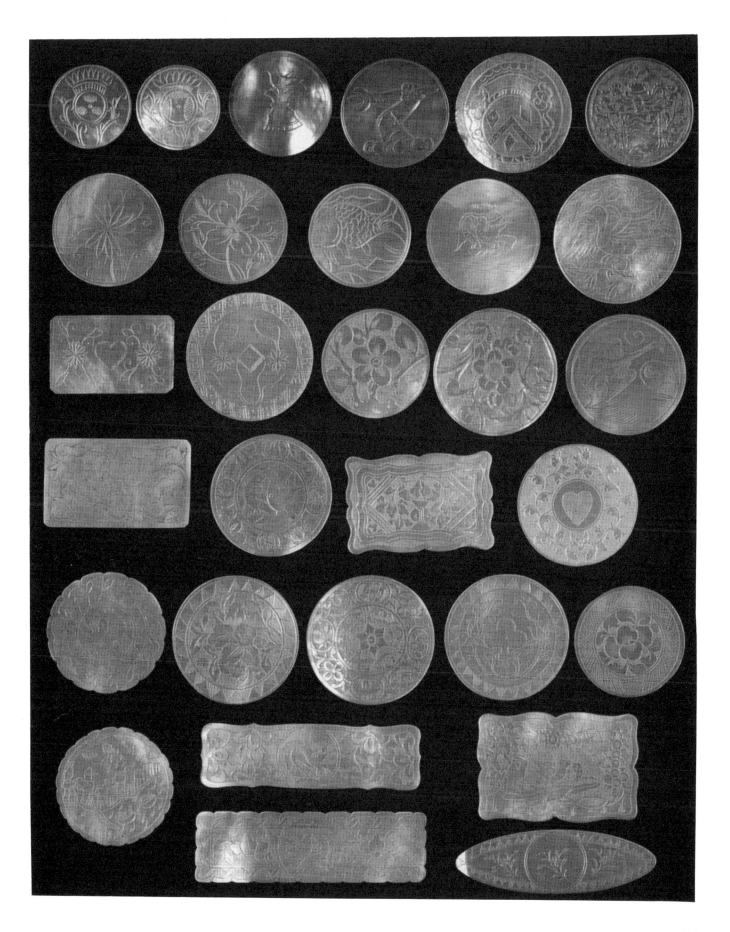

EUROPEAN COUNTERS

From its formation in 1708, The Honourable East India Company (H.E.I.C.) progressively dominated the East India trade. By 1770 the British accounted for almost all Indian and seventy percent of world trade to China. The majority of private items commissioned at Canton were correspondingly British.

Other countries also created East India Companies. After the British, the Dutch were the most successful, then Danish and Swedish companies, followed by Spanish and Portuguese. Supercargoes from each company commissioned porcelain and counter sets.

When any East India Company ceased trading (Austria in 1727, Prussia in 1763, and France 1769), other companies supplied the needs. If British supercargoes were used as alternative agents, they would have influenced the style of any counters ordered because they were already handling large quantities of established designs.

From the coat of arms it is possible to determine which European country commissioned a counter.

Highlights of Facing Page

First Row: A variety of designs not seen in British counters. The two right-hand counters were made before 1700.

Second Row: French. Arms of St. Georges, Marquises de Verac, c.1750. The set was supplied in shaped lacquer boxes with the same arms painted on the lids.

Third Row: Russian or Austrian. Unidentified, c.1740.

Fourth Row Right: Spanish. Arms of Solar de Tejada, c.1790.

Fifth Row: Spanish or Portuguese. Unidentified, c.1810.

FISH

The Chinese had fish-shaped items symbolizing luck long before the West commissioned them as counters. Fish-shaped counters were popular in the West throughout the 18th century. A 1716 reference records Lady Griselle Baillie purchasing three dozen fish at 6 shillings per dozen with six dozen others at 4 shillings per dozen, today's equivalent of UK£10 or US$15 each.

Some fish bearing arms were ordered in the period 1720 – 1735 and are rare. Probably less than seventy families commissioned them.

More rare were armorial crossed-fish, probably fewer than five sets exist. Godfrey, with arms identical to several porcelain services, is a particularly fine example and could predate 1720. Another set for Charles Dubois, Cashier General to the Honourable East India Company from 1708 to 1738, has arms identical to those on a Chinese armorial porcelain service ordered from Canton in 1722 (recorded in the H.E.I.C. accounts), indicating that this set of counters was made at the same time.

In the 18th century, more than 200 varieties of fish-shaped counters were made in ivory, bone, window-pane oyster, or mother-of-pearl. The two most popular shapes in mother-of-pearl, the Carp, which represented placidity, and Crossed Dolphins, still exist in large quantities. Each has a point-engraved roundel with a pseudo-crest of two "billing doves" and background hatching. The remainder of the designs were engraved with a burin or graver tool. Considering the amount of shaping and engraving involved, these counters are undervalued today, often selling for as little as $5.

Sewing winders similar to fish counters were also made. These thread holders are identifiable by the mouth being a deep slit cut in the head/tail axis.

Highlights of Facing Page
First Row Left: Godfrey, c.1720 – 1725. Very rare armorial crossed-fish.
First Row Right and Second Row Left: Charles Dubois, 1723.
Third Row Left: Bolney, c.1726. Right, Tracy, c.1735.
Fourth Row: Hyde of South Denchworth, c.1725. Obverse/reverse.
Fifth Row Center: Crossed Dolphins. (The sides are open mouths.)
Sixth Row Left and Right: Monogrammed, MAL and either I or J.
Seventh Row Left: Carp, pseudo-crest of two love-birds, c. 1740 - 1820.
Seventh Row Right: High quality. Roundel has point-in-point border.
Eighth Row Right: Non-armorial, same as Bolney design, c.1720 – 1730.
Ninth Row Center and Right: Probably predate 1720 and of the type ordered by Lady Griselle Baillie in 1716.

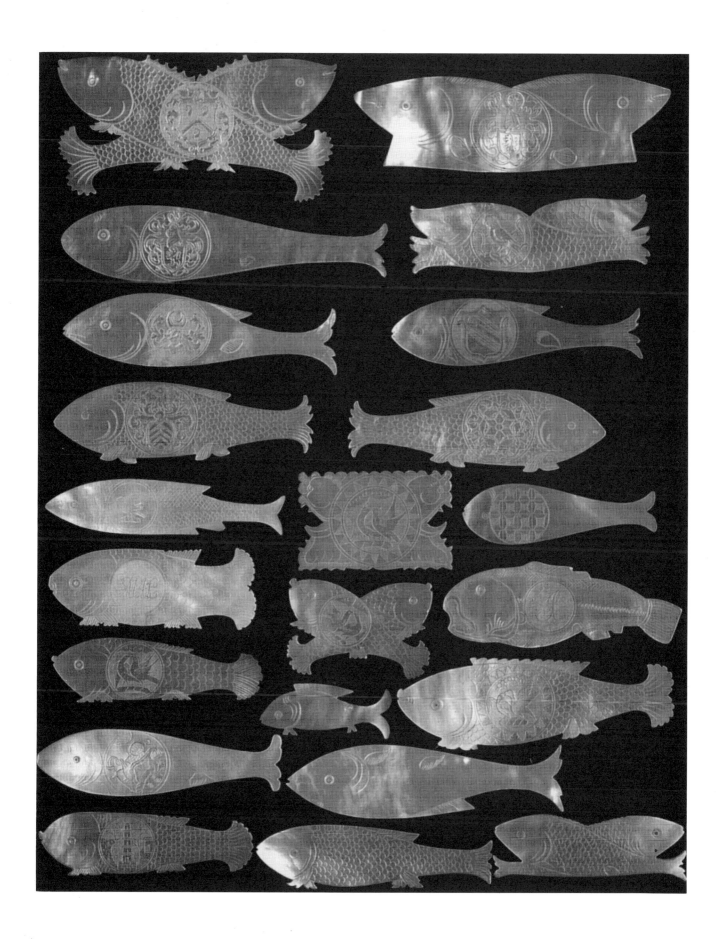

1715 – 1760

Until the 1740s commissioned counters had the same thin substrate as Chinese counters. The obverse (front) was carved in low relief to copy exactly the illustration of arms provided by the private trader for armorial porcelain. The reverse was left blank, shallow-carved with additional arms or the simple flower designs used in Chinese counters. All counters exhibit very fine background cross-hatching, suggesting a long-established skill.

About 1740, the style of personalizing changed. The overall design of a coat of arms within a mantel was replaced by a centered smaller roundel containing the arms or monogram. A popular design for fish shaped and many non-personalized counters was a roundel with a pseudo-crest of two loving birds. From this date, the roundel with a very fine cross-hatched background is a standard feature in all Chinese counters.

Also about 1740, counter thickness increased by about half to 1.8mm, and incisions were a combination of shallow-carved and scratched engraving. In the late 1740s, designs changed to a roundel surrounded by a heavy Chinese floral border. The overall background was also cross-hatched.

There was no standard shape or number of chips in a set. The private traders were flexible to any ideas, but some combinations became popular:

- 1715 – 1730: Round and Fish
- 1730 – 1740: Square and Rectangle
- 1740 – 1760: Round and wavy-sided Square and Rectangle

Highlights of Facing Page

First Row Left and Center: Styleman impaling Danvers, c.1716 – 1718.

First Row Right and Second Row: Godfrey, a supercargo, c.1720 – 1725.

Third Row: Percival, Earl of Egmont, c.1730.

Fourth Row: Maule, Earl of Panmure, c.1744 – 1745.

Fifth Row: Bookey, imp. Peake. Master of Shaftesbury, Canton, 1746.

Sixth Row: Bonham, Captain of Norfolk at Canton, 1757 and 1761.

1745 – 1785

In the late 1740s counters with shaped edges and an engraved central roundel surrounded by deep engraved floral sprays became popular. This style, with minor variations, remained popular until the early 1780s.

In the 1750s the background behind designs was cross-hatched with scratch engraving. By 1780 the design included a narrow inner border copied from European styles being introduced.

The "European" design was short-lived, possibly from 1775 to 1785. It is characterized by a border with a narrow pattern on a hatched background surrounding panels of delicate deep-engraved floral sprays on a plain background. Roundels continued to be scratch-engraved with fine background hatching.

An alternative to the standard square-round-rectangle counter shape was introduced — the oval-round-shuttle (elliptical). Two other styles that were introduced had even shorter lives. They may have been designed and commissioned by a single private trader. One was a thin counter with pierced panels within a point-on-point border. The other was a scalloped-edge style that appears to be more suitable as a thread winder; however, these were definitely counters.

Highlights of Facing Page

First Row: Crest of Bookey. Matthew Bookey was captain of the Shaftesbury at Canton in 1746. He appears to have died during the voyage. The log shows he was succeeded during the return journey by Captain William Bookey. It is not known if William was a brother or son.

Second Row: Arms of Stewart, 7th Lord Blantyre, motto *Sola juvat virtus*; above the initial B is a baron's coronet, c.1760.

Third Row: Same arms as in second row. Sets made for Lord Blantyre's sons, CS for Charles, the younger son, and AS for Alexander who became 8th Lord Blantyre, c.1770.

Fourth Row: Arms of Montague, Duke of Manchester, oval-round-shuttle counters (European style), c.1780.

Fifth Row: Arms of Perreau of London (European style), c.1780.

Sixth Row: Crest of Jones, very rare, c.1760 – 70.

Seventh Row: Unidentified (not thread winders), c.1775.

1785 – 1815

During this period the Chinese produced many of the finest sets of counters in highest quality pearl. Thickness and size were increased and the surface saturated with a wealth of meticulously scratch-engraved minute detail.

Scenes from Chinese legends incorporating up to five figures were enclosed within borders of floral, geometric or traditional animals and birds. The roundels displayed perfect copies of the most complex coat of arms. Milled edges, which appeared in 1780, continued to be standard.

There were two standard shapes for sets—square, round, and rectangle; or oval, round, and shuttle (elliptical).

More varied border designs were used in this period than in any other. Some sets had a border on the reverse different to that on the obverse. The designs included variations of key fret, drilled indent, floral, foliating vine, Chinese animals and symbols, and geometric and reserves.

Highlights of Facing Page

First Row: Arms of White of Poole and Tickleford, Dorset, c.1795. The set has seven rectangular and elliptical shapes.

Second Row: Crest of Dobree of Guernsey, reverse with initials *PED* for Peter Dobree, a merchant and U.S. Consul at Nantes, c.1810.

Third Row: Crest over initials *EB*, for Edmund Byng, Viscount Torrington, c.1815.

Fourth and Fifth Rows. Full Achievement of Arms of Seton of Touch, county Sterling, c.1810. Heraldry scholars would describe the coat of arms as: Quarterly, first and fourth or three crescents within a double tressure flory counterflory gules; second and third, argent three escutcheons gules, for *HAY*, behind the shield two spears in saltire, bearing on their points a royal helmet and shield of the arms of Scotland.

Crest: A boar's head couped or.

Supporters: Two greyhounds proper.

Motto: *Forward ours*

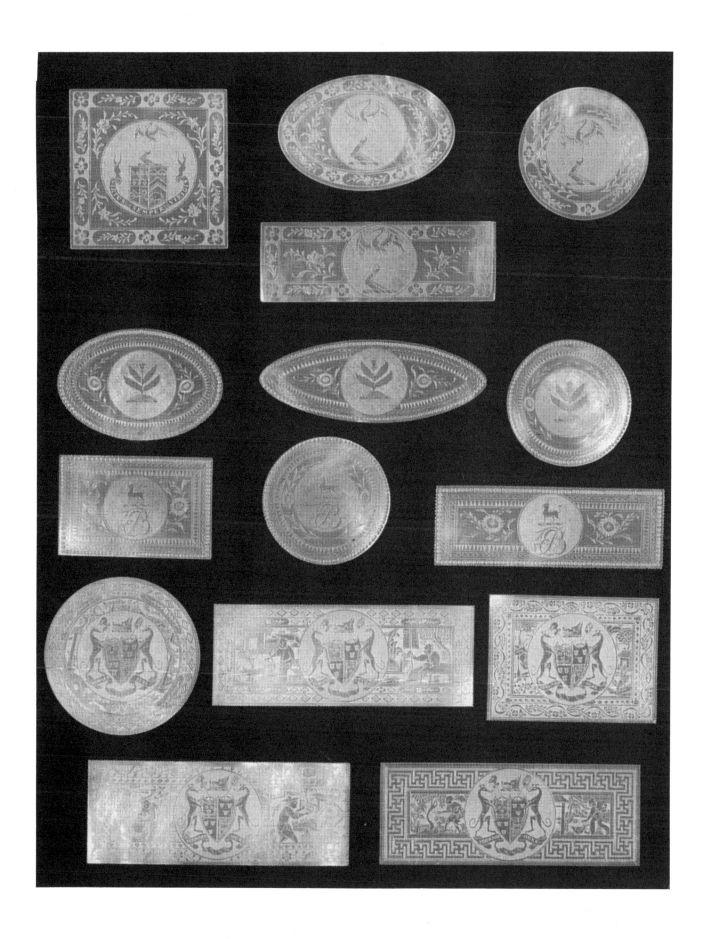

1815 - 1840

Between 1815 and 1840 the tendency was to commission counters that looked obviously expensive. Initially the effect was achieved through combinations and permutations of serrated edges, pierced borders, shallow carving, and fine-scratch engraving. The counters were also thicker and larger and of good quality pearl. This would have taken huge quantities of large shells to yield the large high quality blanks.

As popularity for games requiring counters declined, the private traders made one final attempt to keep the British and American markets. Between 1825 and 1840, very thick counters were produced. Generally exceeding 3mm, sometimes over 5mm, they were cruder and very deep-carved to resemble Chinese silver repoussé. The mother-of-pearl quality became variable, and many sets had a totally striated appearance.

Most sets had the usual combination of square (20), round (40) and rectangle (80) shapes, but other quantities from 4 to 16 were sold in ivory and paper boxes.

Nothing of merit was produced in China after 1840. Instead, the market was flooded with cheap, Chinese-made souvenirs of almost toy-like quality, thin, of poor workmanship and simple design. After 1840, mother-of-pearl plaques and chips for public casinos were made in Europe, not in China.

Highlights of Facing Page

First Row: Arms of Dunlop with motto *Merito*, c.1820. Milled edge, scratch-carved vine and floral border. Shallow-carved panels. Cameo roundel with background hatching.

Second Row: Unidentified. Reverse initialed FCM, c.1820. Smooth edge, pierced border, shallow-carved panels. Scratch-carved roundel with very fine background hatching.

Third Row: Arms of McClintock, reverse with Crest over M, c.1825. Serrated edge and pierced border. Fine-scratch carved design.

Fourth Row: Crest of Baxter of Scotland over WB, c.1830. Serrated edge, deep-carved border and design. Scratch-carved roundel.

Fifth Row: Harry Brown, Gloucester, crest over HB, c. 1835. Serrated edge, scratch-carved design.

HERALDRY

Heraldry is a science that uses mostly Norman French to describe coats of arms (blazons). The order of blazoning is:

- The background or field color called a tincture, usually a fur, metal or color. For printing and engraving these are represented graphically by lines and patterns.

- Tinctures are given from right (dexter) to left (sinister) and top to bottom if the field is divided (partitioned). (Dexter and sinister are right and left for the bearer behind his shield. When seen from the front the opposite applies and the dexter is shown on a counter's left side.)

- The principal object (ordinary) on the field and its tincture. This can be a real or mythical animal or bird, or a shape.

If arms are quartered, impaled (divided in half for husband and wife) or in pretence (on a shield), each coat is blazoned (described) fully before the next coat is blazoned.

The Chinese could copy arms exactly from a bookplate or drawing onto counters or porcelain. This accuracy, the vast literature on heraldry, peerage, genealogy and the account books of the East India Company and American trading ships are the key factors in dating and establishing the provenance for more items than any other field except hallmarked armorial silver. An enlarged photograph of one of these counters can be seen of page 96.

TINCTURES ETC...

argent (silver or white)	*or* (gold)	*gules* (red)	*azure* (blue)	*sable* (black)
vert (green)	*purpure* (purple)	*ermine (white, w/black tufts)*	*vair*	*chequy*

ORDINARIES

bend	*bend sinister*	*fess*	*bars (two)*	*pile*

chief	*pale*	*chevron*	*cross*	*saltire*

MARSHALLING OF ARMS

 The plain coat of a man and his male descendants.

 The coat of a man with that of his wife "in pretence"—she an heraldic heiress.

 The impaled coat of a man and his wife (not borne by his descendants.

 The male descendants of the man and his heiress wife—the coat "quarterly".

PEERS, BARONS, AND LANDED GENTRY

Because the science of heraldry accurately reflects a person's standing in society, it is possible to gain information from an accurately engraved coat of arms. Elevation to or within the peerage, marriage, succession to a title, or an Order bestowed could be cause for commissioning a new porcelain service or set of counters.

The order of precedence is the Sovereign and the Heir-Apparent, then Duke, Marquis, Earl, Viscount, Baron, Knight and Esquire. For each there is an heraldic helm or coronet.

With the wealth of heraldry, peerage, genealogy, and trading records information available, plus David Howard's research and books on armorial porcelain, it is possible to date and determine provenance for many personalized counters, particularly when the counters were ordered at the same time and with the same personalizing design as the commissioned porcelain.

THE HELM

Esquire   *Knight & Baronet*   *Peer, below the rank of Duke*   *Royal Prince & Duke*

duke's coronet   *marquis's coronet*   *earl's coronet*   *viscount's coronet*   *baron's coronet*

Highlights of Facing Page
First Row: Queen Charlotte, Wife of King George III, c.1785. Arms of England before 1801 impaling Meccklenburg-Strelitz. Reverse CR beneath a queen's coronet.
Second Row Left: Russell, Duke of Bedford. Motto: *Che sara sara*, c.1735.
Second Row Right: Brydges, Duke of Chandos, impaling Willoughby of Middleton, c.1725.
Third Row Left: Anne Townshend, Marchioness. Her husband was elevated from Earl to Marquis in 1787, c.1790.
Third Row Right: Stewart, Marquis of Londonderry, c.1800.
Fourth Row Left: Campbell, Earl and Marquis of Breadalbane, c.1775.
Fourth Row Center: Simon Luttrell, created first. Earl of Carhampton in 1785. Reverse, crest and C below an Earl's coronet.
Fourth Row Right: Maule-Ramsay, Earl of Dalhousie, Military Order of the Bath, c.1820.
Fifth Row Left: Viscount Downe, c.1800.
Fifth Row Center: Pitt-Amherst, Viscount Holmesdale, succeeded to the title in 1797.
Fifth Row Right: Bishop of Ely, c.1790.
Sixth Row Left: Sir William Fraser of Ledclune, Baronet, impaling Farquharson, c.1810. Sir William was created a Baronet in 1806 but died in 1816.
Sixth Row Right: Adams of Somerset, an Esquire, c.1800.

DEDICATIONS, MEMENTOS, AND SOUVENIRS

All commissions and purchase of counters at Canton were by captains and supercargoes — the private traders. Many traders commissioned counters for their own or family use. Since they had to be well connected to become a captain or supercargo, many had personal coats of arms. The high cost of a porcelain service or counter set usually ensured that the arms were real and open to admiration in a socially sensitive society — unlike a "fake" signet ring.

Superb counter sets were made for Godfrey, Bookey, Seton, and the Stewart brothers, Charles and Andrew. Charles Deane, captain of "Earl of Sandwich," ordered a simple set for himself when he was at Canton in 1777 and collected it upon his return in 1780.

Counters were made for owners of shipping and livery companies, as gifts from one person to another, as a token of unity for a marriage, or in recognition of a creation or elevation in the peerage.

Some sets had surnames translated into Chinese. Others showed places, such as the set with Napoleon's home "Longwood" and tomb on St. Helena after his death in 1821.

Up to 1776, sets commissioned by East Coast families in America went through British traders. The first American ship, Empress of China, arrived at Canton in 1784, and thereafter American trade became direct. The supply of monogrammed counters is well documented. The Peabody Museum of Salem, MA has some counters with purchases recorded at $10 per set — $4500 at today's rate.

Initially, counters purchased for America were identical to the styles purchased by the British. But by 1830 America dominated the trade at Canton and probably originated some new counter styles such as the thick deep-carved variety. The set inscribed "Keep Your Temper" (see facing page) is American inspired.

Highlights of Facing Page
First Row: Vintners Company, c.1730.
Second Row Left and Right: SS & FG Company and Darien Company.
Third Row: Captain Charles Deane; Mrs. Jones; R. Walker.
Fifth Row Right: American-inspired *"Keep Your Temper."*
Sixth Row Left and Center: Sergent and Johnson in Chinese.
Sixth Row Right: Sha Ti Hua, a rare Chinese commission, c. 1835.
Seventh Row: Napoleon's St. Helena home and tomb, c.1822 – 1840. His remains were returned to France in 1840.

NUMBERS

For all counters, the value for each different shape was decided by participants prior to play. Parson Woodforde's diary for 1777 notes that he played Quadrille at one penny per fish. Sarah, Duchess of Marlborough, wrote of playing Quadrille for half-a-crown (US$60 today) per fish. Generally the shapes and their quantity in a set represented counter denominations. This correlates with the ascending order seen in numbered counters.

The usual configuration for sets was 140 counters in three shapes: 20 square (or squarish), 40 round, and 80 rectangle; or 20 oval, 40 round, and 80 shuttle. It was usual to make rectangle or shuttle worth 1; round worth 5, and squarish or oval worth 10.

Some counters were commissioned with numbers ranging from 1 to 1000. It appears that all numbered counters were made between 1780 and 1810. For the majority, the number was engraved into the roundel in Europe, using a burin or graver. Europeans could not perform the minute background hatching that was standard in Chinese roundels. Also, in Europe the numeral itself was engraved. In contrast, the Chinese outlined the numeral within a background hatching by scratch-engraving.

When numbered counters were personalized, the Chinese in Canton created the monogram or arms on the front of the counter inside a roundel scratch-engraved with background hatching.

Highlights of Facing Page
First Row Right and Fourth Row Right: The pierced and carved counter numbered 15 (first row), and the "square" counter numbered 100 and the round counter numbered 10 (fourth row), were completed in Canton. The numbers on the remaining counters were engraved in Europe. The drilled border pattern on the counters numbered 1, 5, 10, 20, 50, and 100 are part of the set with four large counters — Medallion, Whist, Whist Singelo, and Whist Dobrado — shown on the GAMES page. The front roundels are monogrammed IS within a fine-hatched background.

GAMES

The 18th century was an age of cards. Playing skills were a social must — Hoyle lived by traveling between estates to teach the nobility. Ladies and clergymen indulged. Status was paramount. Gambling became endemic, with stakes ranging from pennies to estates.

At the start of the 18th century, trade with China started in earnest to satisfy the fashion for "the Chinese Style." The British, Spanish and Portuguese dominated trade and the private traders (ship captains and supercargoes) commissioned counters for games played in their own countries.

In Spain and Portugal, Hombre (Ombre) was a popular game and favored by ladies. Played at a triangular table by three people, two against the high bidder, with 40 cards (without cards 8, 9, and 10), it was an early version of Solo. Ombre was introduced into Britain and France and became a four-handed game called *Quadrille*. It became most popular with ladies. Diaries report frequent three-day sessions.

At the same time in England, Whist and Piquet were becoming fashionable, especially with men, and were played almost exclusively at Georgian cities like Bath.

Quadrille was superseded by Pope Joan, which required pre-loading a wheel with counters. Spinado was a simpler version. Today's variants are Newmarket (England) and Stops or Boodle (USA).

By 1820 Whist was becoming dominant. The game used a points system for scoring, and counters were no longer required.

A Spanish variant of Ombre, Tresillo de voltereta (Somersault), reached Portugal in 1780 – 1790. Called *Voltarete*, it was played until the 20th century.

Highlights of Facing Page

First and Second Row: Suits engraved on counters at Canton.

Third Row: Portuguese counter showing rules for Voltarete, c. 1795.

Fourth to Sixth Row: Spanish and Portuguese counters showing the game and stake multiples.

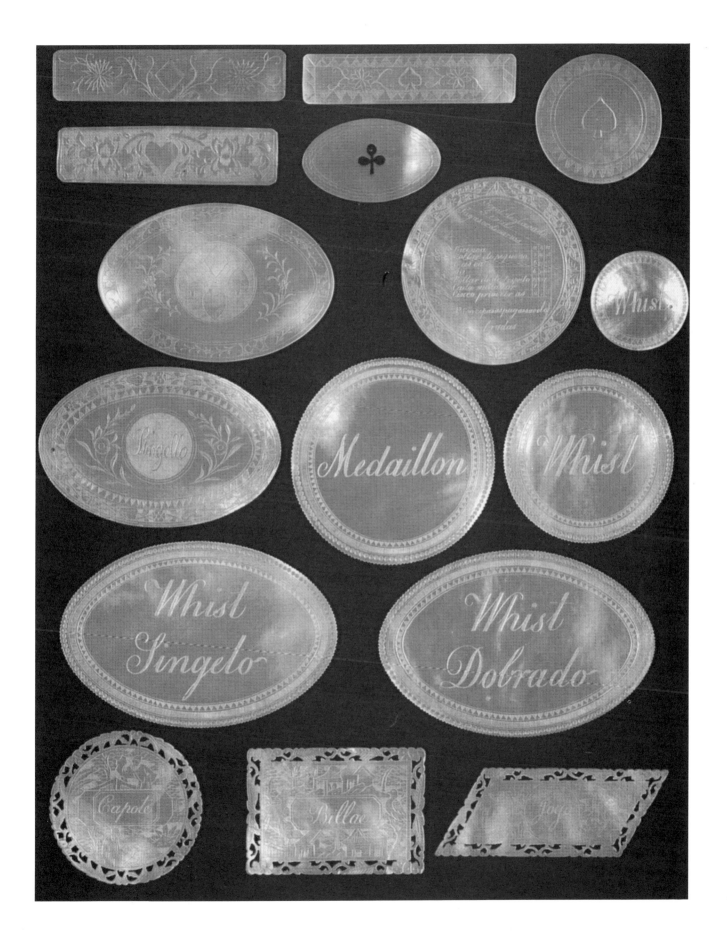

COUNTER REVERSE PATTERNS

Although there are far fewer design varieties on the reverse of counters than on the obverse, they can form an interesting study.

Apart from a brief period in the 1780s, the designs used on the reverse were all Chinese. The Chinese counters that existed prior to 1720 were thin and circular and were either blank or engraved with a simple flower. Later they became more intricate, showing traditional Chinese symbols, patterns, and eventually full scenes.

Full scenes were always different and appear to be unique to each counter. It is conjectured that each set narrated one of the thousands of poems from the teachings of the great philosophers Lao Tzu, Confucius, Mo Tzu, and others, capturing ideologies of the past, the duty structure, and preservation of family customs. Family respect was of utmost importance in the Chinese culture and was usually depicted by three people. The more expensive counters had four or even five people and generally depicted a story involving a visitor.

When the supercargoes first adopted the existing Chinese counters, they had their personal arms shallow-carved into the obverse and kept the same Chinese reverse. Thereafter the decoration of the reverse received more attention until, by about 1815, the reverse required more work to complete than the obverse.

On Facing Page

First Row Center and Left: Existing Chinese designs, c.1720 – 1745.

First Row Right of Center: First customized designs and use of scratch engraving, c.1735 – 1740.

Second Row: Surface saturated with Chinese symbols and flora, scratch-and-burin engraved, c.1740 – 1760.

Third Row and Fourth Row Left: Traditional Chinese diaper (pronounced dye-apper) patterns, scratch-and-burin engraved, c.1750 – 1810.

Fourth Row: Flowers were always engraved with a burin or graver. Note the European influence, c.1760 – 1790.

Fifth Row Right: Surface saturated with a scratch-engraved scene of a man receiving a last drink prior to execution by beheading, c.1800.

Sixth Row: Surfaces saturated with shallow-carved, scratch-engraved and deep-carved scenes, after 1815.

A shallow carved and engraved counter (magnified 4.5X) with the arms of Styleman of Ashton Steeple, Wiltshire impaling Danvers of Wilts, Warwickshire, Northamptonshire and Oxfordshire. The arms are of Styleman, Sable (black), a unicorn passant or (gold), on a chief of the second (gold) three pallets of the first (black), impaling Danvers, gules (red) a chevron between three mullets of six points radiant or (gold), pierced azure (blue). John Styleman was a director of the East India Company 1716 - 18.

MOTHER $ PEARL

French Style

CODES: IR

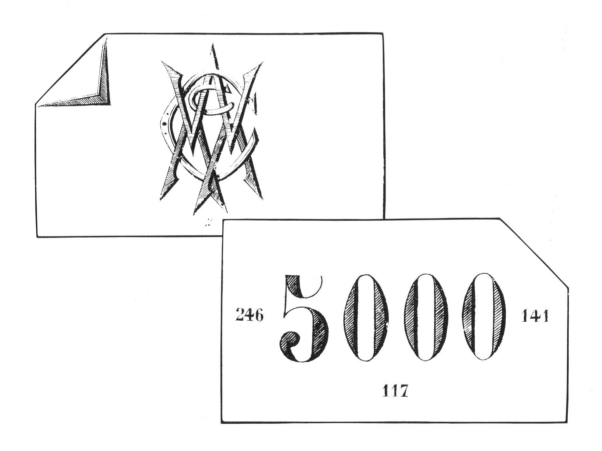

MOTHER-OF-PEARL
FRENCH STYLE

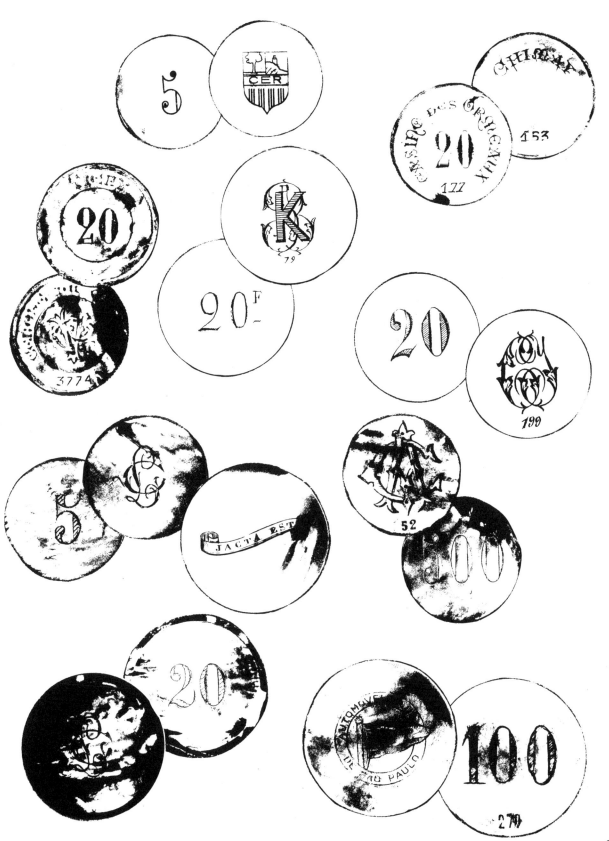

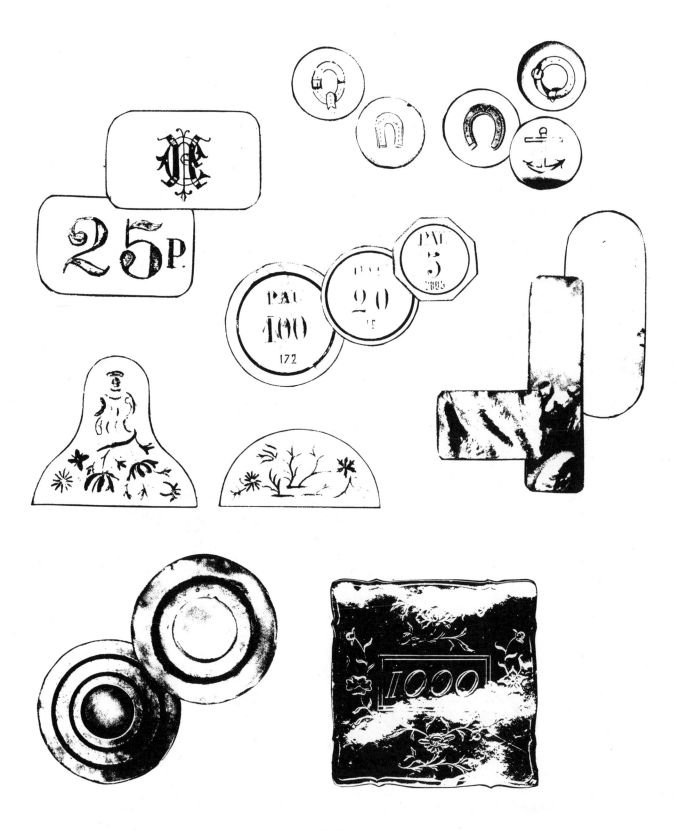

MOTHER-OF-PEARL
FRENCH STYLE

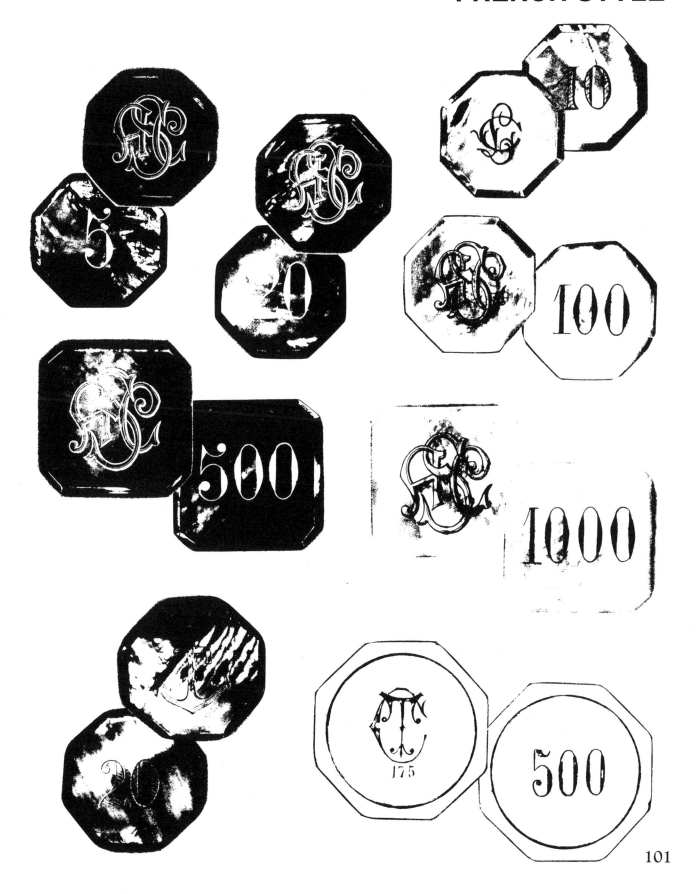

MOTHER-OF-PEARL
FRENCH STYLE

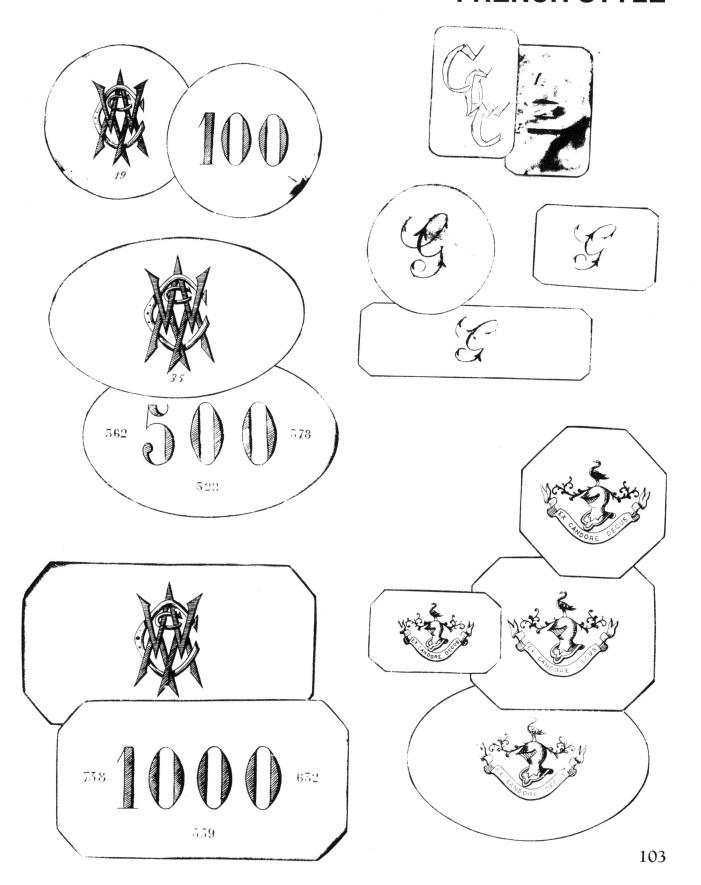

MOTHER-OF-PEARL
FRENCH STYLE

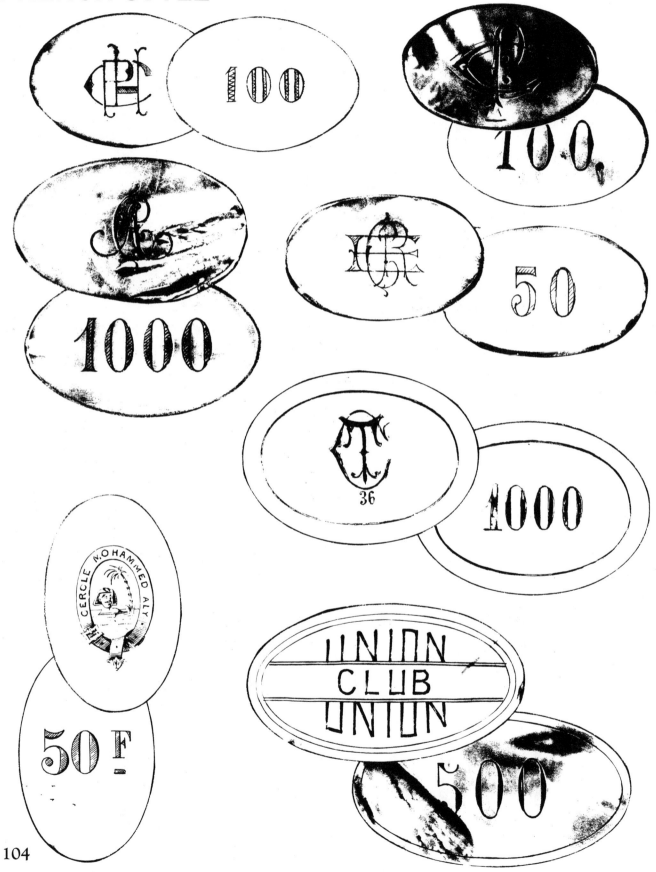

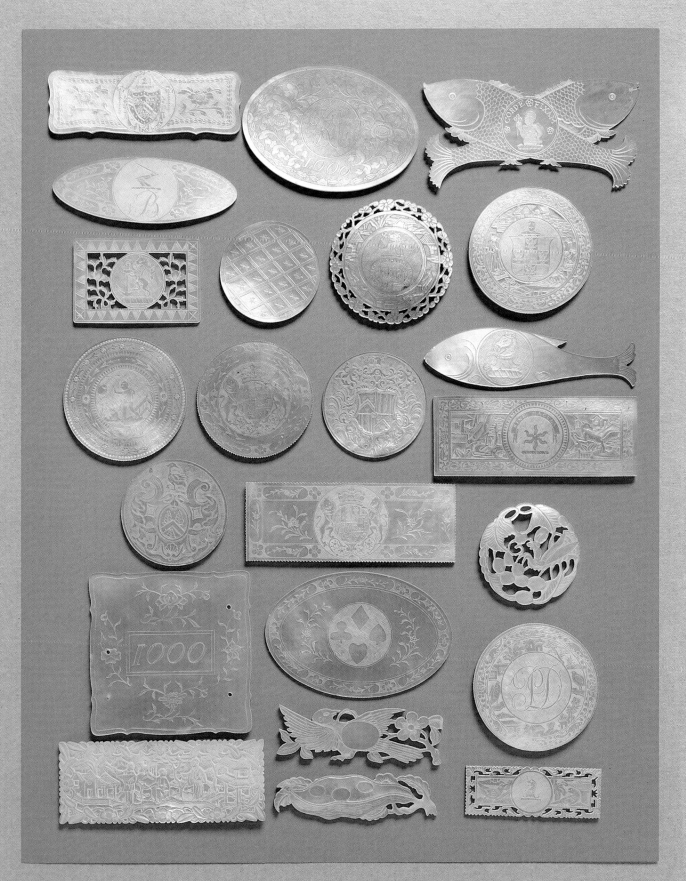

IVORY
Gambling Chips

IVORY GAMBLING CHIPS

During the last half of the 19th century in America the games of poker and faro provided the main gambling fare in saloons and gambling halls. Mississippi River steamboats were seldom without a "game." Although the stakes in these games were sometimes gold dust or coins, checks or chips were much easier to manage.

Poker is essentially an American game that evolved from the French game of pogue and the English game of brag. Poker started in the New Orleans area and moved up and down the Mississippi in the mid-1800s. The need for counters or chips to manage the banking in poker and faro, another popular game, coincided with the golden age of whaling (1820 – 1870), so ivory was a natural choice as a material for gambling chips. Chips were also made of African Elephant ivory.

Chips provided players with flexibility. Players themselves could determine the value of a given chip. The problem was that chips were like money, and they could be slipped in and out of a game. What was to keep a player from slipping out a chip worth a quarter in one game and slipping that chip into another game where it was worth five dollars? It was obvious that chips needed to be made so that they could not be copied. Because ivory was not easily obtainable and could be designed by specialists, it was seen as a logical resource for a game chip. The bone and mother-of-pearl chips had been the favorite of Europeans, but neither ever caught on in America.

Although some ivory gambling chips were made in England, more than 95% of chips and chip designs known to collectors are American. Most were manufactured in New York City between 1860 and 1910, and in general, ivory chips made in the 1860s through the 1880s were more intricately designed than those made between 1890 and 1910.

Ivory chips made for gambling were designed with fancy designs and/or numerals. Unlike their mother-of-pearl counterparts, ivory chips were all the same shape (circular) and nearly all the same size (1-1/2" to 1-5/8"). A twenty-five-dollar chip was occasionally slightly thicker and larger in diameter than the one- and five-dollar chips in the same set.

There were two types of chip sets: design and numeral. Design sets contained chips with the same design but different colored borders. In these sets, the design, as opposed to a specific numeral, allowed players to determine the value of each chip. Most commonly, chip values were set as follows: white rim = 1 unit; red rim = 5 units; and gold rim = 25, 50, or 100 units. If there were four colors, yellow usually represented the highest value. Values were determined by the house or by the players participating in the game, as in the case of home poker games today.

Other categories of design chips included concentric rings, monogrammed, and commemorative.

Numeral sets contained some chips with one design and others with numerals on them. In this set, one-unit chips usually had a geometric design. Each five-unit chip (often red) had the numeral 5, and each twenty-five-dollar chip (usually gold or green) had the numeral 25. Sometimes a set contained a few 50s or 100s. In general, numeral chips measured about 1¹/₂" in diameter, but in some sets the 25s, 50s, or 100s were larger. The higher denomination chips and larger chips are much rarer and, consequently, much more expensive to acquire. Chips with 1s, 10s, or 20s on them are also rare.

A set of ivories could range in size from 100 to 700 chips. Often the chips were sold in imaginatively-designed wooden boxes that represented a third to a fourth of the value of the set. Most commonly a set contained three or four different chip designs.

Today, ivory chip values range from $20 to $2000. The average price of an ivory chip is currently $50. Although ivory chips are often difficult to find, five or eight sets a year surface for collectors to buy and trade.

When this book was first published in 1984, collectors were aware of only about 250 different ivory designs. Thirteen years later we can identify 1400 different chip designs. We feel certain that at least a few hundred new finds still exist.

Ken Chopping, an ivory chip collector, has been researching the history and manufacture of ivory chips and has summarized his findings in the following pages.

THE GAME OF FARO

In the newly independent United States, the 1780s and 1790s were times of heavy drinking and gambling, and saw the rise of professional gamblers who brought the game of faro from the French Territories and towns.

With the annexation of the French Territories in 1803, gamblers in New Orleans and Mobile quickly spread northward along the Mississippi River and traveled between the major cities of the East Coast. Faro quickly became the most popular game and was reported to be widely played by 1813.

Asbury, in his *Sucker's Progress* (1938), wrote, "Faro was the rock upon which were reared the elaborate gambling houses of the early and mid-1800s." Faro was also the game that created tremendous demand for large quantities of ivory faro checks.

The best contemporary picture of the early gambling scene in the U.S. is from one of those early gamblers, Robert Bailey, of Berkeley Springs, VA. In his 1822 autobiography, Bailey wrote that he kept a faro table at Sweet Water Springs, and "I have been at faro tables at the different Springs, Philadelphia, New York, Boston, Baltimore, Richmond, Fredericksberg, Petersberg, and Charleston." He described Mann's Tavern in Annapolis in the 1790s: "Gamblers were in their zenith, some keeping Faro tables, some Rolet, some Black & Red, some a wheel, etc." He also described a visit in 1810 to New Orleans, where he played at the four or five faro banks there. Bailey followed the horse racing circuits in and near Virginia, setting up his faro table at social gatherings after the races.

Faro was a banking game, requiring a sizable bank with a large number of checks. According to James D. McCabe, Jr. in his book *Lights and Shadows of New York*, published in 1872, in a game of faro, "*the player buys ivory checks and never uses money openly."*

Jonathon Green, in his 1857 *Gambling Exposed*, quoted a gambler explaining faro in 1834: *"The man that plays this game, has to go to great expense; he has to produce, sir, a fine silver box, worth, perhaps, one hundred dollars; and then he has to supply himself with a number of ivory pieces, turned round like a dollar, some of them colored red, with various figures on them, and some of them white, without any coloring, except perhaps around the edge; and these checks, as they are called, will cost, probably, two hundred dollars."*

Green's gambler described the reactions of a young man watching the game of faro for the first time: *"He was very much delighted with the game, the box, the instrument itself, the beautiful checks."* He asked, *"Is not that game of faro a pretty one?"*

Green again described ivory checks in use in a faro game in Colombia, Arizona in 1839: *"These checks are of ivory, and are near the size of a dollar, and are made to represent money. The bankers will have some four or five hundred of these. About half are made white and plain, and are generally used to represent one dollar each. The balance are red, and have the figure 5 on each side, and each one represents five dollars. Sometimes they have ten dollar checks."*

Mason Long, another gambler, wrote: *"Fort Wayne in 1866–67 was noted as a gambling town. I opened a faro game in the Occidental Hotel."* He described a police raid: *"They allowed us to settle up the game, and then confiscated my tools and marched us to the lock-up. I . . . lost my kit of checks, valued at one hundred dollars."* He wrote of the confiscation of many valuable kits of tools, and in another raid, *"one of the police 'froze' to my check-rack, which I hated to part with."* Later, in New York City in the 1890s, *"The police confiscated a motley array of gambling equipment, including thousands of ivory chips."*

In 1873, in *Wanderings of a Vagabond*, John Morris (a pseudonym of the gambler John O'Connor) described a faro layout: *"A regular out-and-out faro game, with all its paraphernalia, consisted of an elegant mahogany box ornamented with a handsome picture of the royal 'tiger,' a fine silver dealing-box, six hundred ivory checks, on each of which was carved the head of a horse, their valuation at play being determined by their different colors: thus the colors being red, white and blue; the first represent one, the second five, and the third twenty-five. Over the table was spread a fine green cloth, and on it a lay-out composed of thirteen cards, ranging from the ace to the king."*

Morris later described another game: *"The stakes usually consist of counters or checks, made of ivory, representing different sums."* At a faro table in Long Branch, *"there was a third table, while at the man's elbow there were piles of ivory checks. This I knew to be the faro bank, and a silver box was situated upon it, the dealing box."* Morris also wrote that he followed the horse races, setting up faro banks after the races. He described one professional gambler's attire, which included a green velvet vest, festooned with highly polished horse-head buttons.

Morris went to great length to distinguish between gamblers and "sharpers." Sharpers operated "skinning houses" with rigged games. He stated that in a first-class skinning house *"the gaming paraphernalia consist of a faro-table of the finest design and workmanship ... the checks and other articles belonging to the games are of the most elaborate style possible."*

Gamblers and sharpers from New Orleans began moving to New York City and were reported to be numerous there by 1819. A public gambling house opened at Wall and Water Streets in 1825. Finely decorated private gambling clubs were opened in the 1820s in Washington, D.C. and Baltimore. *The Niles Register* in 1831 stated that New York City was "infested with gamblers." By the early 1830s gamblers were reported to be thick on the river ways north of New Orleans.

Citizen uprisings in some river towns motivated many of those gamblers to relocate to the major East Coast cities. By 1835 the *New York Sun* was reporting that there were 500 gamblers in Baltimore. In the 1830s and 1840s, New York City was the largest gambling city, reported to have had 200 faro banks in operation. Those would have had up to 100,000 ivory checks.

IVORY CHIP MANUFACTURERS

The need for game pieces provided some enterprising business types to manufacture chips. The earliest U.S. ad found for ivory chips is that of Charles Shipman in New York City in 1767, advertising that he *"has commenced business in wood and ivory turning, being trained in a large manufactory in Birmingham, England."* The ad listed Shipman's ivory products, including "ivory counters, engraved with alphabets and numerals, ideal for children's games." In his first year in New York, he was making ivory counters as he had learned to do in England. Listed in Stauffer's *American Engraver*, Shipman was an ivory turner and engraver as well as a seal manufacturer.

Many colonial towns in the 1700s had a wood and ivory turner who could provide game pieces for any game. In Charleston in 1738, turner George Bridge offered "ivory turning and billiard balls," and in 1796 E. Smith, "Turner from London," offered "ivory turning in toy or fancy way, billiard balls." In 1804 Peter Blancan, "Turner from Paris," provided "billiard balls, chess & backgammon, checker men." In Norfolk in 1772, Hardress Waller advertised "Will turn Billiard Balls of all sizes at ten shillings a pair and smooth old ones at five shillings." Several ivory turners created goods in Savannah and New Orleans in the 1810–1820 period.

Early ivory turners and other craftsmen could not yet be specialized, but had to make a wide variety of goods. Some who made scientific instruments and guns also offered billiard balls, dice, and backgammon materials. It was said that "silversmith and engraver Paul Revere also set teeth," and some ivory turners made false teeth. One ad for dental services also stated: "makes umbrellas and makes dice and chessmen."

The largest U.S. ivory turning firm in the early 1800s was James Ruthven & Son, founded in 1783 in New York City at 92 Partition Street, later renamed Fulton. (Fulton Street soon became a major location of ivory shops.) The Ruthvens, from Scotland, seem to have specialized in billiards and game goods, and probably were the first major source of ivory faro checks. The Ruthvens likely began making chips in the 1790s.

J. F. Remmey succeeded the Ruthvens in the 1840s (Figure 1, page 114). Remmey was an ivory turner as well as an engraver and seal manufacturer. The Remmeys operated the firm to 1918, when a news photograph showed William Remmey with ivory products made in his shop, including an ivory chip. The firm's ledgers list sales of ivory checks in the 1830s with whites and red 5s.

In the late 1790s, the ivory comb industry was developing in New York, Connecticut, and Massachusetts. Julius Pratt in 1798 invented a saw to speed up the cutting of fine teeth in ivory combs. Large ivory factories were founded in Ivoryton and Deep River, CT, including Pratt, Read & Co. and Comstock Cheney Co. During the days when ivory faro chips were being sold in large sets of up to 500 chips, small ivory shops and gambling dealers likely relied on the very specialized ivory cutters in Connecticut for unfinished chip blanks.

Pratt, Reed & Co.'s expertise was curing and cutting ivory. The company's blocking, facing, and slitting saws for ivory combs and keys were well suited to the cutting of ivory chip blanks in large quantities. The company made a wide assortment of round ivory inserts for use by other manufacturers and also made billiard balls and game pieces for other ivory and game dealers. From 1851 to 1869 Pratt, Read & Co. had an ivory shop in New York City at 146 Fulton Street, near the Ruthven shop, and the Ruthven ledgers record sales of ivory to Pratt, Read.

In the early 1800s the Ruthven shop at 92 Fulton was the center of the manufacture and sale of ivory billiards and faro good in the U.S. Billiards and faro were growing in popularity, and creating a tremendous demand for ivory billiard balls and ivory checks. Only one 1820 ad is known from the Ruthvens, but a son, Robert Ruthven, left and started his own ivory shop in Baltimore in 1816, advertising as shown, (Figure 3, page 114):

The young Ruthven saw the rising demand for ivory goods in Baltimore to meet the demand of the billiards and gambling houses. He was still using the English term *counter* as the "argot" of *faro* was not yet developed.

In 1818 John Phyfe, an apprentice from the New York Ruthven shop, left and opened his own ivory shop nearby. He advertised widely, emphasizing ivory game pieces and faro checks. In the 1830s and 1840s Phyfe frequently ran this ad (Figure 4, page 114), illustrated with his trademark elephant, in *The Shipping and Commercial List of New York City*.

That newspaper carried a complete listing of all arrivals and departures from East Coast, Gulf, and River ports, the Caribbean, Panama, and California. Phyfe surely was aiming at gamblers who traveled between East Coast ports and the Gulf and River ports. His ads would have been hard for a traveling gambler to miss.

Most of Phyfe's ads contained the item, "ivory faro checks in new and fancy patterns." Phyfe may have been responsible for many of the ivory chip designs that collectors have today. He was from Scotland and likely was related to Duncan Phyfe, whose cabinet shop was at 92 Fulton Street. Duncan Phyfe made card

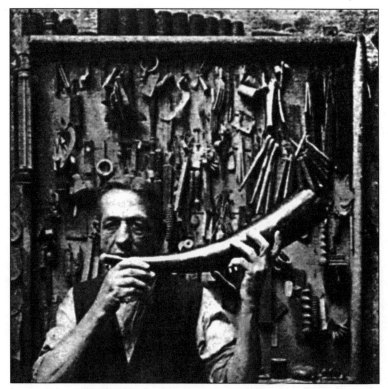

Figure 1: J.F. Remmey in his ivory shop, New York City 1918.

J. F. REMMEY,
(Successor to Vandenbergh & Ruthven,)
Turner in Ivory, Wood & Metal,
AND SEAL MANUFACTURER,
98 Fulton Street, (rear,) New York.
[Established 1788.]

Figure 2: Remmey newspaper advertismenrt

Robert E. Ruthven
FROM N. YORK
Gold, Ivory, Brass & Hardwood Turner,
Has commended business in the above line in this city,
IVORY—Billiard Balls . . . Counters of any size or colour.
Baltimore, Maryland 8 May 1816

Figure 3: Baltimore newspaper advertisemenrt circa 1816

tables—is favorite design motif was the acanthi leaf. That is the single most common design element on old ivory faro chips.

So it is apparent that beginning in 1815, as demand for faro checks was growing, skilled ivory turners and cutters were supplying them. The expertise for the making and engraving of those ivory chips had been developed in Europe and brought to the United States. Gamblers found skilled ivory turners ready to supply them with fancy ivory faro checks. The early faro checks seem to have been made and sold by ivory manufacturers and dealers in New York City. Check designs were probably well established by the 1830s and 1840s.

From the 1850s into the 1880s, faro goods and ivory checks were standard goods sold by a number of billiards dealers in San Francisco and New York City. In 1848 the F. Grote Co. opened as a billiards manufacturer at 78 Fulton Street and soon offered a full line of faro goods. No catalogs are known, but Grote's ads listed ivory checks (Figures 5 & 6):

The illustration used in Grote's ad was apparently from the cover of the Pratt, Read & Co. catalog.

Two other German ivory manufacturers had billiards shops on Fulton Street in the 1850s and 1860s—John Schreitmueller and Peter Totans. Both men listed ivory checks in their ads (Figures 7 & 8):

Beginning in 1855, another large billiards manufacturer, William Griffith, had a shop at 146 Fulton Street. His 1872 catalog had two pages of faro goods, including both ivory faro checks and ivory poker chips. The faro checks were offered in three sizes and two grades of engraving.

IVORY MANUFACTORY.

JOHN PHYFE, dealer in Ivory, and manufacturer of Ivory Goods, **19 Murray-street**, offers for sale:

Ivory Billiard Balls—Suited to this, the Southern, or Spanish markets—warranted of the first quality.

Ivory Pool, Bagatelle, and Roulette Balls.

Ivory Checks—In great variety, of new and fancy patterns.

Ivory Domino's—In rosewood and mahogan cases.

Ivory Backgammon Men and Dice Boxes—Richly carved and plain.

Fancy Wood Card Boxes—Highly ornamented and plain, with cards complete warranted of the best quality.

Ivory Martingale Rings & Miniature Sheets.

Ivory Tablets—assorted sizes.

Ivory Paper Folders and Page Markers.

Ivory Teething Rings and Whistles.

Piano Ivory—Well dried, and put up in setts of different qualities, for immediate use. This article has been well tested by the trade for years past, and has given general satisfaction.

Ebony Sharps—In setts.

ALSO,

Prime and Scrivella Ivory, Sea Horse and Whale Teeth, Boxwood, Ebony, Cocoa, Satin, and other hard Woods; all of which will be sold in quantities to suit purchasers, and on the most favorable terms.

Feb. 23.—c

Figure 4

F. GROTE,

TURNER & DEALER IN IVORY

78 FULTON, CORNER OF GOLD STREET, NEW YORK.

BILLIARD, BAGATELLE AND POOL BALLS,

TENPIN BALLS AND PINS,

CHECKS IN GREAT VARIETY,

Martingale & Napkin Rings, and all other kinds of Ivory Goods,

WHOLESALE AND RETAIL.

Piano and Melodeon Ivory

ALSO,

MANUFACTURER AND IMPORTER OF CUES,

Cue Leathers, Chalks, Brushes, new Improved Cue Cutters, Presses, &c.

F. GROTE.   A. Jos. KAPP.   A. H. GROTE.

Figure 5

The poker chips were smaller and without engraving (Figure 9):

In San Francisco, three German ivory turners were in the billiards business by 1855: Jellinek & Doerger, Jacob Strahle, and John G. H. Meyer. All sold faro goods and ivory checks. Doerger used the same ad as F. Grote Co. in 1868 and advertised "have constantly on hand and manufacture to order... checks." Strahle offered free catalogs. Two of Meyer's ivory turners, John Kewnig and Charles Eisel, opened their own shop in the 1870s and apparently made and sold ivory checks. Will & Finck, a major cutlery firm, was in business by 1852, and Julius Finck made and sold "advantage" faro goods from a locked room at the rear of the store. "Advantage goods" referted to cheating devices. Charles Eisel later worked for Will & Finck, from 1881 into the 1890s.

Figure 6

Figure 7

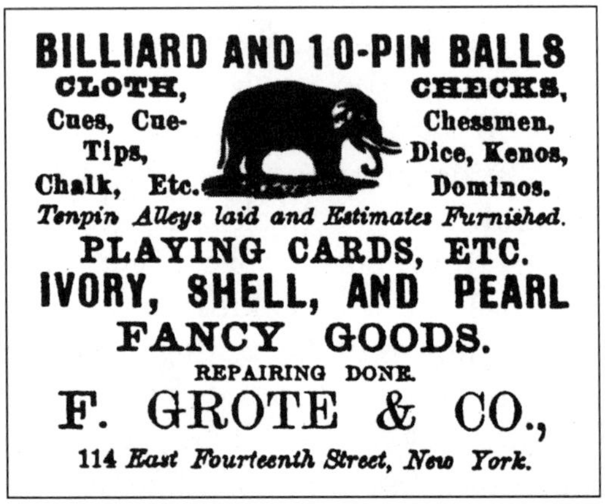

SPORTING HOUSES

There were several gambling dealers by the mid-1800s. E N. Grandine in New York City was a manufacturer of "advantage" playing cards and a major gambling dealer in the 1860s. He sold a full line of faro goods and ivory checks. Collectors have two of his catalogs, and one was published in 1872 by Morris in his *Wanderings of a Vagabond*. Grandine was followed much later by William Suydam Co.

Will & Finck, the cutlery and faro goods store in San Francisco, was also a major gambling dealer. Two gambling catalogs from that firm are known today, and one was published in 1894 by John Nevil Maskelyne

PETER TOTAN'S,

Turner, and Dealer in Ivory BILLIARD BALLS of every kind.

CHECKS IN GREAT VARIETY, MARTINGALE AND NAPKIN RINGS.

Importer of French Cue Tips, Chalk and Brushes, and Manufacturer of Plain and Fancy Cues.

No. 89 FULTON STREET, New York.

Factory, corner of Suydam St. and Myrtle Avenue, Brooklyn, E. D.

Figure 8

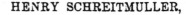

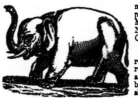

in his *Sharps and Flats*. The ivory checks were omitted, however, as Maskelyne was interested only in revealing crooked or rigged gambling goods sold by the "sporting houses." (Professional gamblers were referred to as sports or sporting gentlemen.) A Will & Finck ad from the *New York Clipper* of 1885 is shown on the next page (Figure 10):

Chicago and Cincinnati also had gambling and billiards. From the mid-1850s, Mason & Co. in Chicago was a major gambling supply house, and it continued to operate until recently. Mason & Co. advertised clubroom furniture and engraving of designs in the *New York Clipper* of 1885 (Figures 11 and 12):

W. H. GRIFFITH & CO'S ILLUSTRATED CATALOGUE. 45

Faro Checks.

FIRST QUALITY.

1½ in. plain, per hundred	$32 00
1 9-16 " "	35 00
1⅝ " "	38 00
1½ fancy, "	35 00
1 9-16 " "	38 00
1⅝ " "	40 00

SECOND QUALITY.

1 7-16 in. plain	$24 00
1½ "	25 50
1 9-16 "	28 00
1⅝ "	30 50
1½ in. fancy	28 00
1 9-16 "	30 50
1⅝ "	32 00

Coppers, splits and markers included.
Broken sets of checks filled up and re-colored, at short notice.

Poker Chips.

IVORY—Either Red, White or Blue.

1 in. per hundred	$10 00
1⅛ "	12 00
1¼ "	15 00
1⅜ "	18 00

BONE.

1 in. cut to measure, per hundred	$2 50
1⅛ " "	4 00
1¼ " "	6 00
1⅜ " "	8 00
1½ " "	10 00
Plain bone chips	$1, 1 25, 1 50, 1 75 per hundred.
Boston counters, per set	$3 and $4 00

Figure 9

Figure 10

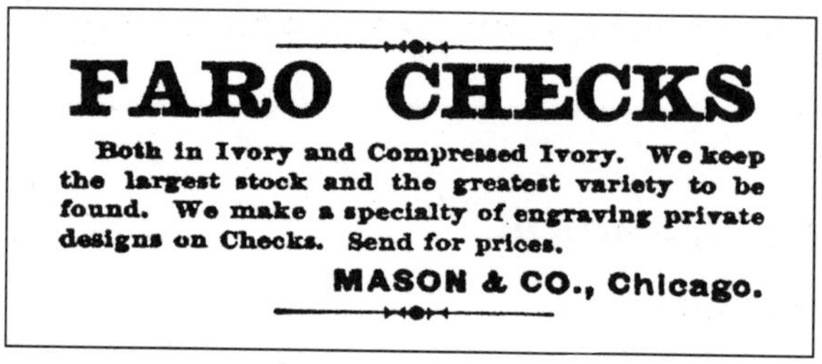

Figure 11

Figure 12

118

Early wood and ivory manufacturers made every type of game piece, and many were also engravers. In the first half of the 1800s only a few major ivory shops made and sold billiards and gambling goods. At the same time, there were several major ivory importing and cutting firms in Connecticut that made goods for other manufacturers. With the demand for faro checks increasing tremendously by the 1830s, it is likely that the New York City ivory dealers increasingly relied on firms in Connecticut, such as Pratt, Read & Co., for unfinished faro checks to supply many hundreds of faro banks.

The work of engraving was possibly done in finishing shops in the city. In 1897 the Probst & Rufil Mfg. Co. at 407 Broome Street were manufacturers of "Ivory Cutlery and Umbrella handles, Buttons & Ornaments, Checks & Dice, Billiard balls, Articles in Pearl, Ivory Tortoise Shell, for the Jewelry and Fancy Trade," and offered "CARVING & ENGRAVING, at popular prices." Earlier firms had specialized in finishing pearl buttons and other goods. Certainly the ivory dealers could have used such specialty firms for engraving and finishing checks, especially when demand was heavy. Ivory chips were sold primarily by ivory billiards and gambling dealers and by several gambling supply firms.

Judging from the numbers of ivory shops and the popularity of the game of faro, the peak years of ivory chip production were from the 1850s to the 1870s. By the 1880s faro was less popular. People were using chips while playing poker and craps, but by that time chips were being made much more cheaply of other materials. Specialty retail firms, such as Abercrombie & Fitch, offered pearl and ivory chip sets in the 1890s, but ivory chips became a luxury.

Composition chips became available for about one-tenth the cost of ivory chips. In 1880, a set of 100 ivory chips sold for $25–$35. In Suydams' 1881 catalog, "ivoroyed checks" were advertised for $5 to $10 per 1000 chips. There were most likely a "French ivory" celluloid, which might have contained some ivory scraps. This material was sometimes called "compressed ivory."

In 1896 Will & Finck advertised in their new catalog the service of "re-engraving (ivory chips), so that they will be equal to new." This service cost the customer 12 cents per chip.

Companies continued to make ivory chips on special order into the early 1900s, but most of the later sets did not have numerical values on them. They were cheaper this way and also allowed players the flexibility of determining their own chip values.

Makers & Sellers of Ivory Chips in the U.S.

Prior to 1783

New York City — Charles Shipman

1783–1849

New York City — James Ruthven & Son
J. F. Remmey
John Phyfe

1816–1820

Baltimore — Robert Ruthven

1849–1870s

New York City — J. M. Remmey
John Phyfe
F. Grote
John Schreitmueller,
E. N. Grandin
Edward Griffith
Peter Totans
Shardlow Bros.

Connecticut — Pratt, Read & Co.
Comstock Cheney

San Francisco — John G. H. Meyer
Jacob Strahle
Charles Doerger
Will & Finck

Chicago — Mason & Co.

1880s to 1900s

New York City — Wm. Suydam Co., W. Remmey

San Francisco — Will & Finck

Chicago — Mason & Co.

IVORY
Design
CODES: ID, IE, & IF

Antique Chips
Value Rating Code*

a: 50¢   b: $1   c: $2-$3   d: $4-$5   e: $6-$7

f: $8-$9   g: $10-$14   h: $15-$19   i: $20-$29

j: $30-$39   k: $40-$49   l: $50-$69   m: $70-$89

n: $90-$109   o: $110-$149   p: $150-$199

q: $200-$299   r: $300-$399   s: $400-$499

t: $500-$699   u: $700-$999   v: $1000-$1999

w: $2000-$2999   x: $3000-$3999

y: $4000-$499   z: $5000+

*It is important to remember that quantities
of one chip or a set of chips would have
a much lower unit value per chip.

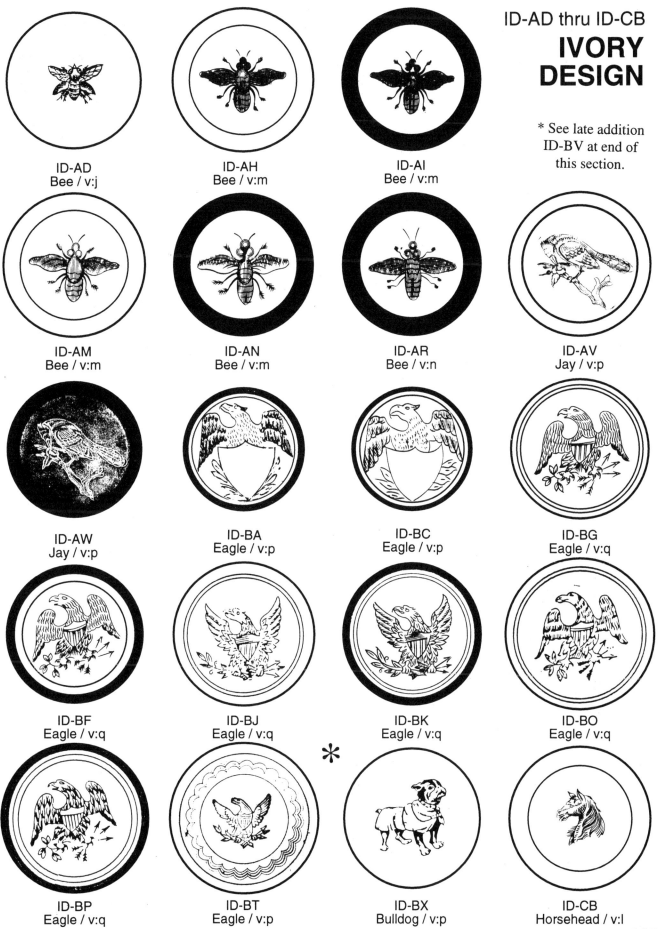

IVORY DESIGN

* See late addition
ID-BV at end of
this section.

ID-AD
Bee / v:j

ID-AH
Bee / v:m

ID-AI
Bee / v:m

ID-AM
Bee / v:m

ID-AN
Bee / v:m

ID-AR
Bee / v:n

ID-AV
Jay / v:p

ID-AW
Jay / v:p

ID-BA
Eagle / v:p

ID-BC
Eagle / v:p

ID-BG
Eagle / v:q

ID-BF
Eagle / v:q

ID-BJ
Eagle / v:q

ID-BK
Eagle / v:q

ID-BO
Eagle / v:q

ID-BP
Eagle / v:q

ID-BT
Eagle / v:p

ID-BX
Bulldog / v:p

ID-CB
Horsehead / v:l

123

IVORY DESIGN

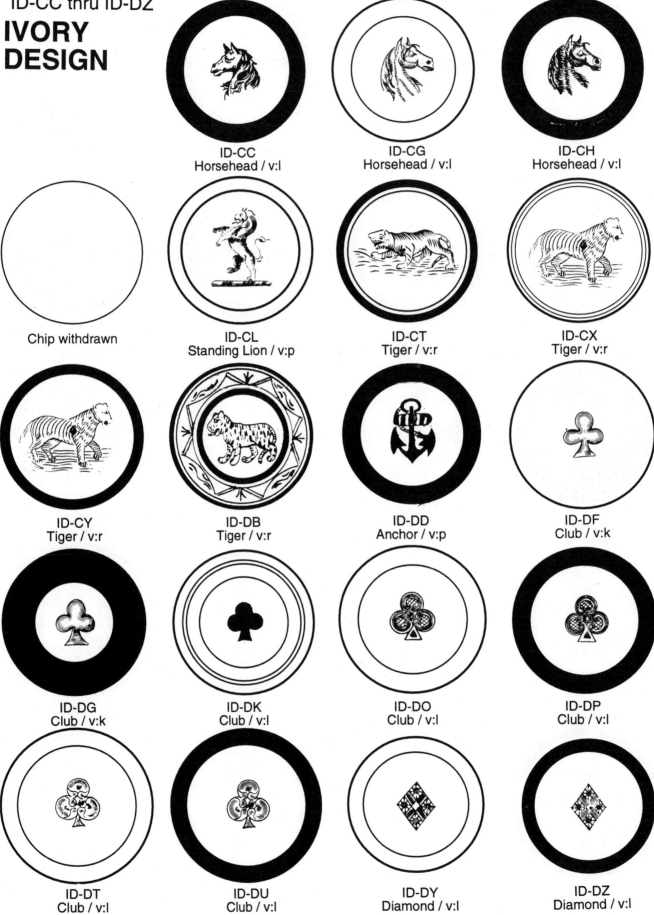

ID-CC
Horsehead / v:l

ID-CG
Horsehead / v:l

ID-CH
Horsehead / v:l

Chip withdrawn

ID-CL
Standing Lion / v:p

ID-CT
Tiger / v:r

ID-CX
Tiger / v:r

ID-CY
Tiger / v:r

ID-DB
Tiger / v:r

ID-DD
Anchor / v:p

ID-DF
Club / v:k

ID-DG
Club / v:k

ID-DK
Club / v:l

ID-DO
Club / v:l

ID-DP
Club / v:l

ID-DT
Club / v:l

ID-DU
Club / v:l

ID-DY
Diamond / v:l

ID-DZ
Diamond / v:l

124

IVORY
DESIGN

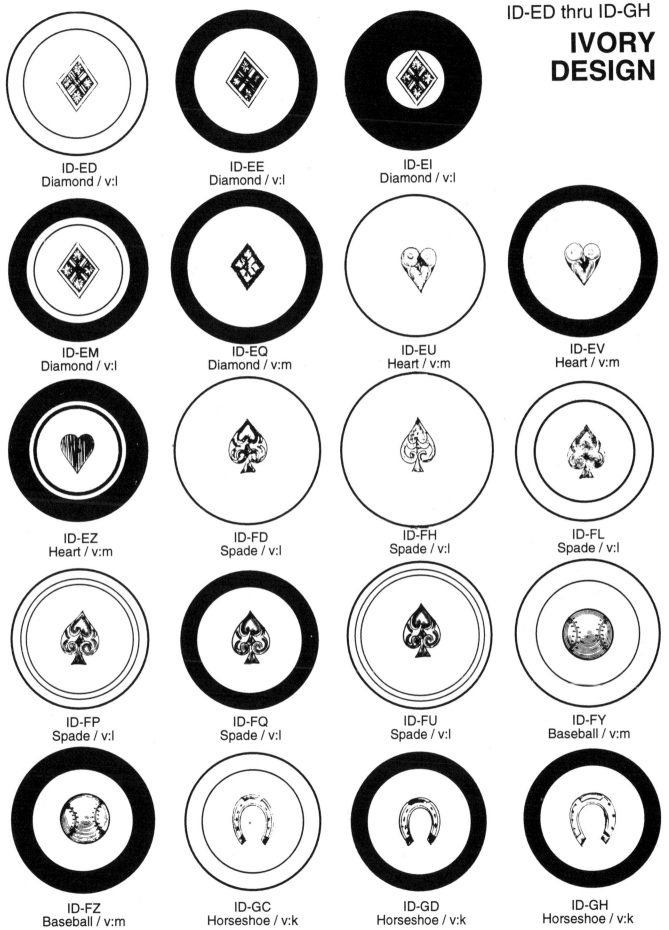

ID-ED
Diamond / v:l

ID-EE
Diamond / v:l

ID-EI
Diamond / v:l

ID-EM
Diamond / v:l

ID-EQ
Diamond / v:m

ID-EU
Heart / v:m

ID-EV
Heart / v:m

ID-EZ
Heart / v:m

ID-FD
Spade / v:l

ID-FH
Spade / v:l

ID-FL
Spade / v:l

ID-FP
Spade / v:l

ID-FQ
Spade / v:l

ID-FU
Spade / v:l

ID-FY
Baseball / v:m

ID-FZ
Baseball / v:m

ID-GC
Horseshoe / v:k

ID-GD
Horseshoe / v:k

ID-GH
Horseshoe / v:k

125

IVORY DESIGN

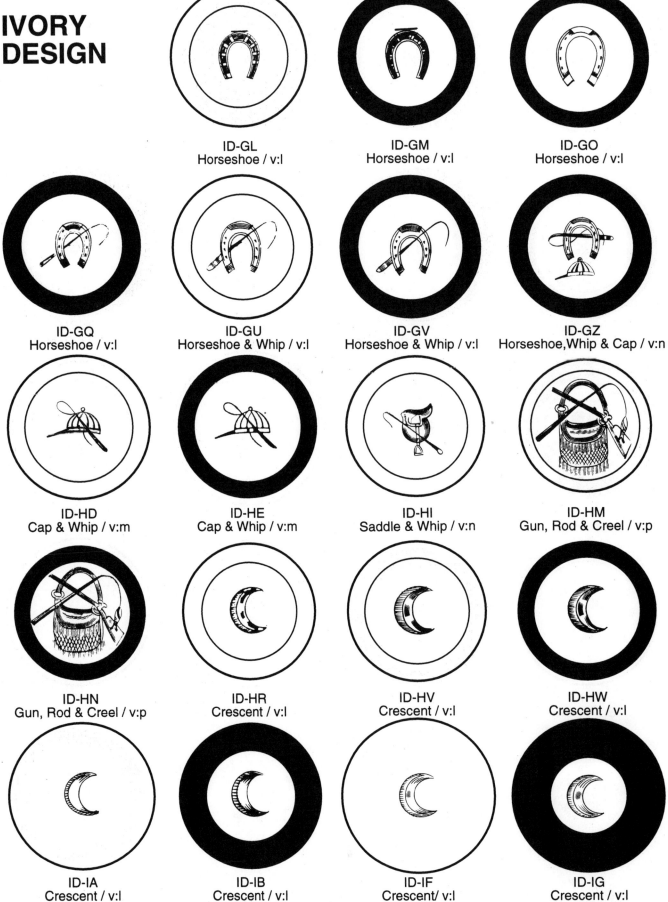

ID-GL
Horseshoe / v:l

ID-GM
Horseshoe / v:l

ID-GO
Horseshoe / v:l

ID-GQ
Horseshoe / v:l

ID-GU
Horseshoe & Whip / v:l

ID-GV
Horseshoe & Whip / v:l

ID-GZ
Horseshoe, Whip & Cap / v:n

ID-HD
Cap & Whip / v:m

ID-HE
Cap & Whip / v:m

ID-HI
Saddle & Whip / v:n

ID-HM
Gun, Rod & Creel / v:p

ID-HN
Gun, Rod & Creel / v:p

ID-HR
Crescent / v:l

ID-HV
Crescent / v:l

ID-HW
Crescent / v:l

ID-IA
Crescent / v:l

ID-IB
Crescent / v:l

ID-IF
Crescent/ v:l

ID-IG
Crescent / v:l

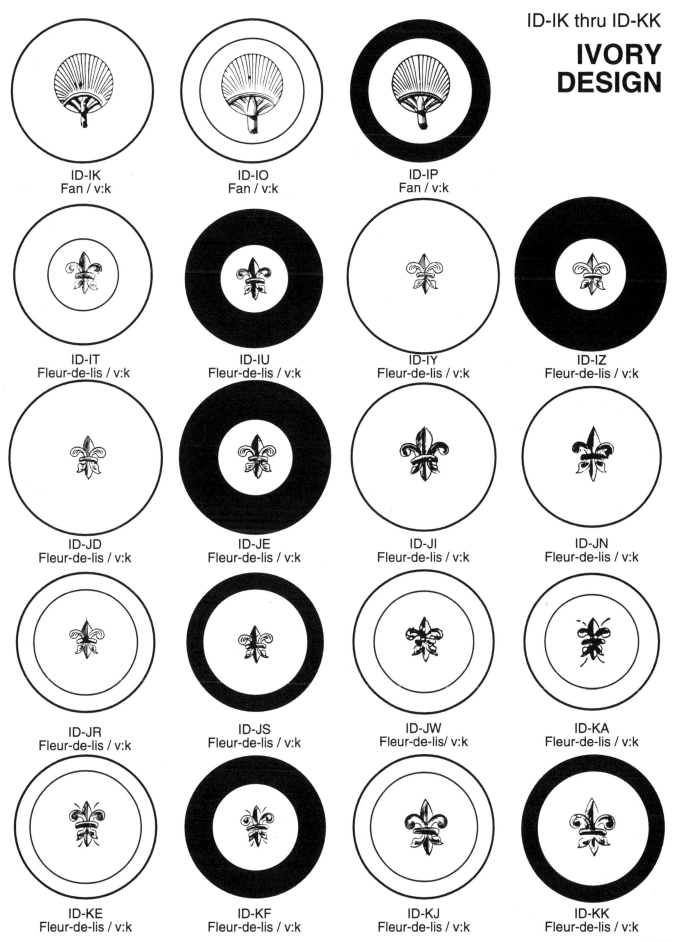

IVORY DESIGN

ID-IK
Fan / v:k

ID-IO
Fan / v:k

ID-IP
Fan / v:k

ID-IT
Fleur-de-lis / v:k

ID-IU
Fleur-de-lis / v:k

ID-IY
Fleur-de-lis / v:k

ID-IZ
Fleur-de-lis / v:k

ID-JD
Fleur-de-lis / v:k

ID-JE
Fleur-de-lis / v:k

ID-JI
Fleur-de-lis / v:k

ID-JN
Fleur-de-lis / v:k

ID-JR
Fleur-de-lis / v:k

ID-JS
Fleur-de-lis / v:k

ID-JW
Fleur-de-lis/ v:k

ID-KA
Fleur-de-lis / v:k

ID-KE
Fleur-de-lis / v:k

ID-KF
Fleur-de-lis / v:k

ID-KJ
Fleur-de-lis / v:k

ID-KK
Fleur-de-lis / v:k

IVORY DESIGN

ID-KO
Fleur-de-lis / v:k

ID-KS
Fleur-de-lis / v:k

ID-KT
Fleur-de-lis / v:k

ID-KX
Fleur-de-lis / v:k

ID-LB
Fleur-de-lis / v:k

ID-LF
Fleur-de-lis / v:k

ID-LJ
Fleur-de-lis / v:k

ID-LN
Fleur-de-lis / v:k

ID-LR
Fleur-de-lis / v:k

ID-LV
Fleur-de-lis / v:k

ID-LZ
Fleur-de-lis / v:k

ID-MD
Fleur-de-lis / v:k

ID-MH
Fleur-de-lis / v:k

ID-ML
Fleur-de-lis / v:k

ID-MM
Fleur-de-lis / v:k

ID-MQ
Fleur-de-lis / v:k

ID-MU
Fleur-de-lis / v:k

ID-MY
Fleur-de-lis / v:k

ID-NC
Fleur-de-lis / v:k

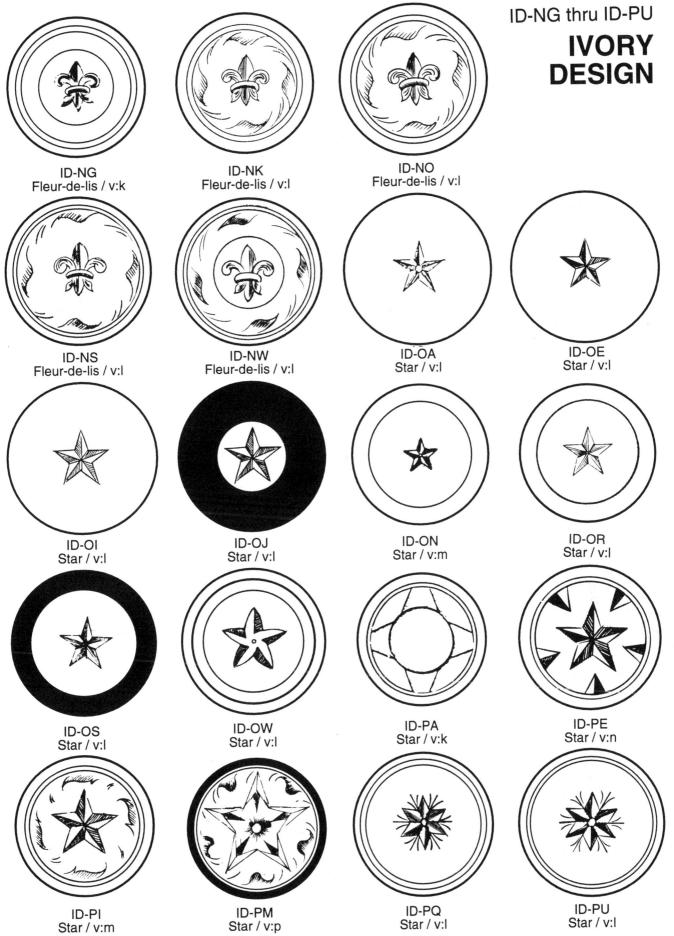

IVORY DESIGN

ID-NG
Fleur-de-lis / v:k

ID-NK
Fleur-de-lis / v:l

ID-NO
Fleur-de-lis / v:l

ID-NS
Fleur-de-lis / v:l

ID-NW
Fleur-de-lis / v:l

ID-OA
Star / v:l

ID-OE
Star / v:l

ID-OI
Star / v:l

ID-OJ
Star / v:l

ID-ON
Star / v:m

ID-OR
Star / v:l

ID-OS
Star / v:l

ID-OW
Star / v:l

ID-PA
Star / v:k

ID-PE
Star / v:n

ID-PI
Star / v:m

ID-PM
Star / v:p

ID-PQ
Star / v:l

ID-PU
Star / v:l

IVORY DESIGN

ID-PY
Star / v:l

ID-QC
Star / v:m

ID-QG
Star / v:m

ID-QK
Star / v:n

ID-QO
Shield on Stars

ID-QS
Coat-of-Arms / v:m

ID-QT
Coat-of-Arms / v:m

ID-QX
Coat-of-arms / v:m

ID-QY
Coat-of-arms / v:m

ID-RC
Coat-of-arms / v:k

ID-RD
Coat-of-arms / v:k

ID-RH
Lion on Crown / v:q

ID-RL
Crown / v:p

ID-RP
Justice / v:q

ID-RQ
Justice / v:q

ID-RR
Justice / v:r

ID-RS
Justice / v:r

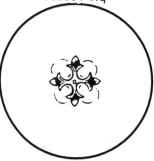

ID-RV
Cross / v:k

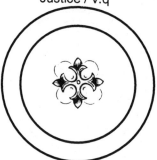

ID-RW
Cross / v:k

IVORY
DESIGN

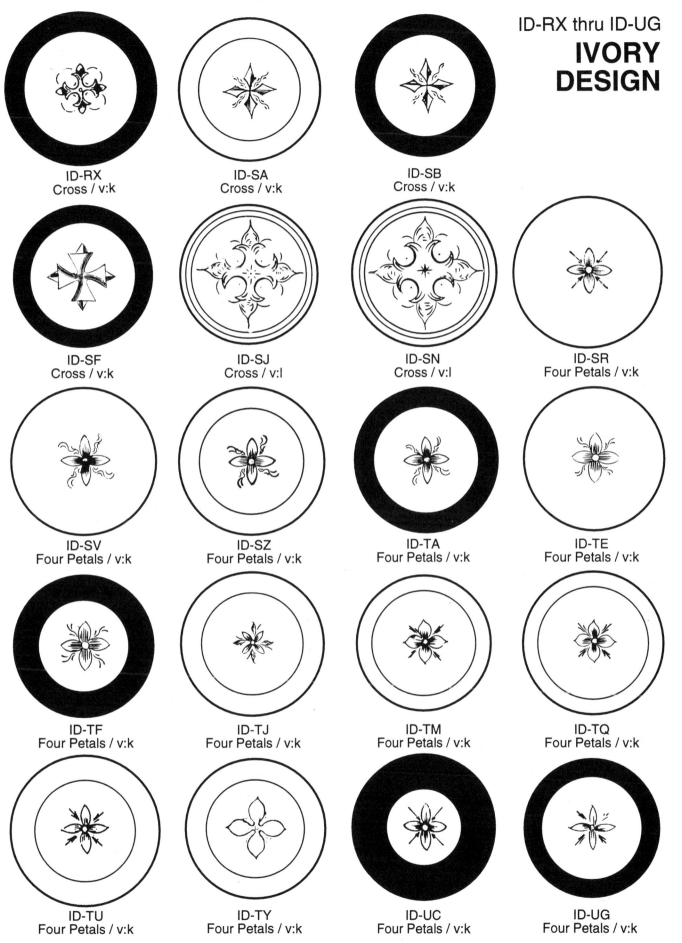

ID-RX
Cross / v:k

ID-SA
Cross / v:k

ID-SB
Cross / v:k

ID-SF
Cross / v:k

ID-SJ
Cross / v:l

ID-SN
Cross / v:l

ID-SR
Four Petals / v:k

ID-SV
Four Petals / v:k

ID-SZ
Four Petals / v:k

ID-TA
Four Petals / v:k

ID-TE
Four Petals / v:k

ID-TF
Four Petals / v:k

ID-TJ
Four Petals / v:k

ID-TM
Four Petals / v:k

ID-TQ
Four Petals / v:k

ID-TU
Four Petals / v:k

ID-TY
Four Petals / v:k

ID-UC
Four Petals / v:k

ID-UG
Four Petals / v:k

IVORY DESIGN

ID-UK
Four Petals / v:k

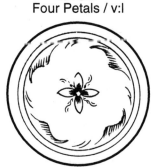

ID-UO
Four Petals / v:l

ID-UQ
Four Petals / v:k

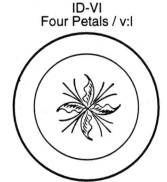

ID-US
Four Petals / v:k

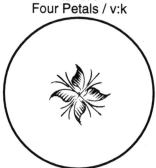

ID-UW
Four Petals / v:k

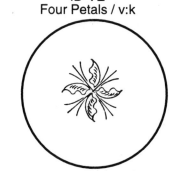

ID-VA
Four Petals / v:k

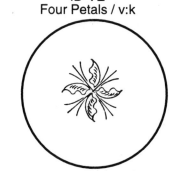

ID-VE
Four Petals / v:k

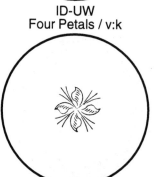

ID-VI
Four Petals / v:l

ID-VM
Four Leaves / v:k

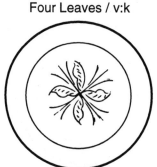

ID-VQ
Four Leaves / v:k

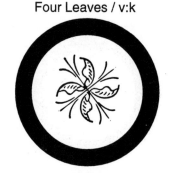

ID-VU
Four Leaves / v:k

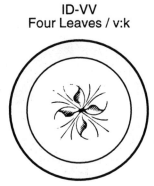

ID-VV
Four Leaves / v:k

ID-VW
Four Leaves / v:k

ID-WA
Four Leaves / v:k

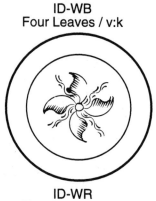

ID-WB
Four Leaves / v:k

ID-WF
Four Leaves / v:k

ID-WJ
Four Leaves / v:k

ID-WN
Four Leaves / v:k

ID-WR
Four Leaves / v:l

132

IVORY DESIGN

ID-WV
Four Leaves / v:k

ID-WZ
Four Leaves / v:l

ID-XD
Four Leaves / v:k

ID-XH
Four Leaves / v:k

ID-XI
Four Leaves / v:k

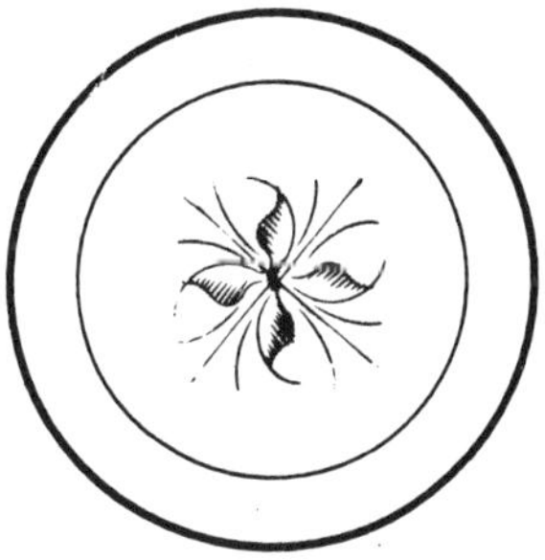

ID-XL
Four Leaves / v:k

ID-XM
Four Leaves / v:k

ID-XQ
Four Leaves / v:k

ID-XU
Four Leaves / v:k

ID-XY
Four Leaves / v:k

ID-YK
Four Leaves / v:k

ID-YS
Four Leaves / v:l

ID-YW
Four Leaves / v:m

ID-ZA
Four Leaves / v:m

ID-ZE
Four Leaves / v:m

ID-ZI
Four Leaves / v:k

ID-ZM
Four Leaves / v:l

ID-ZQ
Four Leaves / v:l

ID-ZU
Four Leaves / v:k

133

IVORY DESIGN

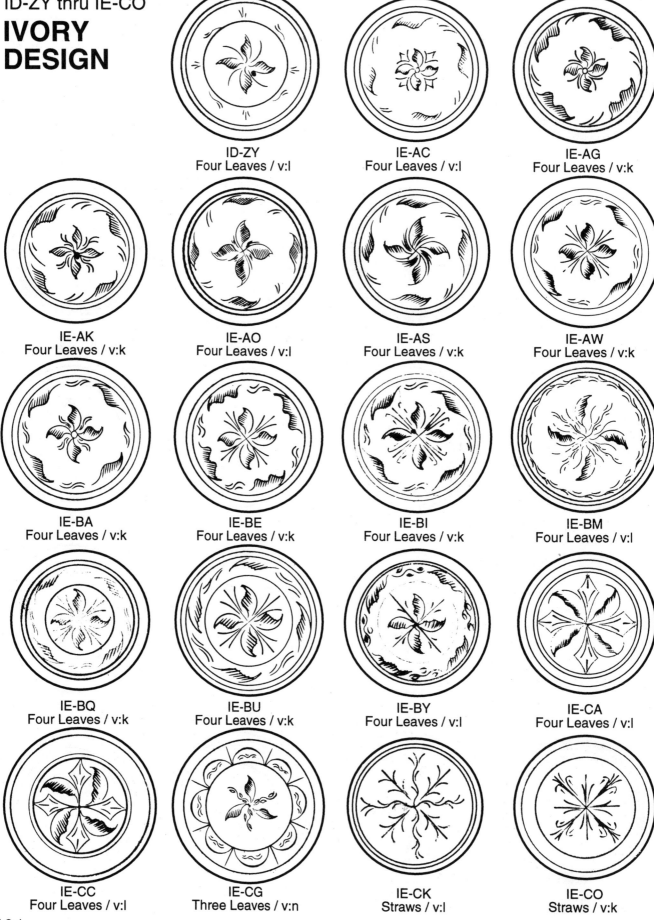

ID-ZY
Four Leaves / v:l

IE-AC
Four Leaves / v:l

IE-AG
Four Leaves / v:k

IE-AK
Four Leaves / v:k

IE-AO
Four Leaves / v:l

IE-AS
Four Leaves / v:k

IE-AW
Four Leaves / v:k

IE-BA
Four Leaves / v:k

IE-BE
Four Leaves / v:k

IE-BI
Four Leaves / v:k

IE-BM
Four Leaves / v:l

IE-BQ
Four Leaves / v:k

IE-BU
Four Leaves / v:k

IE-BY
Four Leaves / v:l

IE-CA
Four Leaves / v:l

IE-CC
Four Leaves / v:l

IE-CG
Three Leaves / v:n

IE-CK
Straws / v:l

IE-CO
Straws / v:k

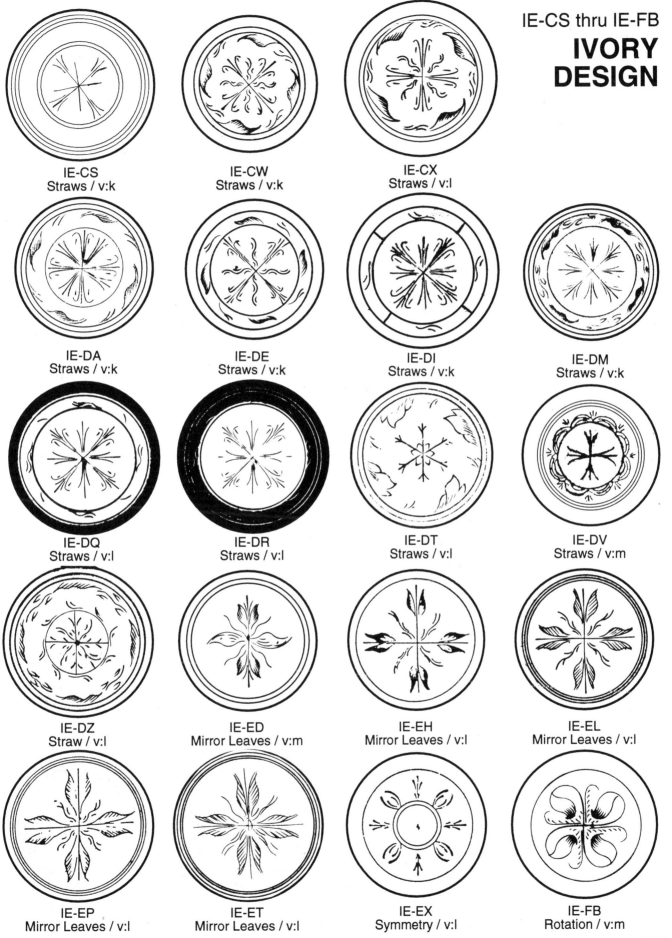

IVORY DESIGN

IE-CS
Straws / v:k

IE-CW
Straws / v:k

IE-CX
Straws / v:l

IE-DA
Straws / v:k

IE-DE
Straws / v:k

IE-DI
Straws / v:k

IE-DM
Straws / v:k

IE-DQ
Straws / v:l

IE-DR
Straws / v:l

IE-DT
Straws / v:l

IE-DV
Straws / v:m

IE-DZ
Straw / v:l

IE-ED
Mirror Leaves / v:m

IE-EH
Mirror Leaves / v:l

IE-EL
Mirror Leaves / v:l

IE-EP
Mirror Leaves / v:l

IE-ET
Mirror Leaves / v:l

IE-EX
Symmetry / v:l

IE-FB
Rotation / v:m

135

IVORY DESIGN

IE-FF
Rotation / v:m

IE-FJ
Reflection / v:l

IE-FN
Single Leaf / v:k

IE-FR
Single Leaf / v:l

IE-FV
Single Leaf / v:l

IE-FZ
Single Leaf / v:k

IE-GD
Single Leaf / v:k

IE-GF
Single Leaf / v:k

IE-GH
Single Leaf / v:k

IE-GL
Single Leaf / v:k

IE-GN
Single Leaf / v:l

IE-GP
Single Leaf / v:k

IE-GT
Single Leaf / v:k

IE-GX
Single Leaf / v:l

IE-HB
Single Leaf / v:k

IE-HF
Single Leaf / v:k

IE-HJ
Three Leaves / v:k

IE-HN
Three Leaves / v:k

IE-HR
Three Leaves / v:k

IVORY
DESIGN

IE-HV
Three Leaves / v:k

IE-HZ
Three Leaves / v:k

IE-ID
Three Leaves / v:k

IE-IH
Three Leaves / v:k

IE-IL
Three Leaves / v:k

IE-IP
Three Leaves / v:k

IE-IR
Three Leaves / v:k

IE-IT
Three Leaves / v:k

IE-IX
Three Leaves / v:k

IE-JB
Three Leaves / v:k

IE-JJ
Three Leaves / v:k

IE-JN
Three Leaves / v:k

IE-JR
Three Leaves / v:k

IE-JS
Three Leaves / v:k

IE-JU
Three Leaves / v:k

IE-JW
Three Leaves / v:k

IE-KA
Three Leaves / v:k

IE-KE
Three Leaves / v:k

IE-KI
Three Leaves / v:k

137

IVORY
DESIGN

IE-KN
Three Leaves / v:m

IE-KR
Three Leaves / v:l

IE-KV
Three Leaves / v:l

IE-KZ
Three Leaves / v:m

IE-LD
Three Leaves / v:l

IE-LH
Three Leavesf / v:l

IE-LL
Three Leaves / v:l

IE-LM
Three Leaves / v:l

IE-LQ
Three Leaves / v:l

IE-LU
Three Leaves / v:l

IE-LY
Three Leaves / v:l

IE-MC
Three Leaves / v:l

IE-MG
Three Leaves / v:l

IE-MK
Three Leaves / v:l

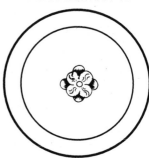

IE-MO
Blossom / v:k

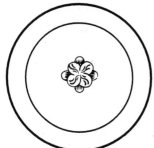

IE-MS
Blossom / v:k

IE-MT
Blossom / v:k

IE-MX
Blossom / v:k

IE-MY
Blossom / v:k

IVORY DESIGN

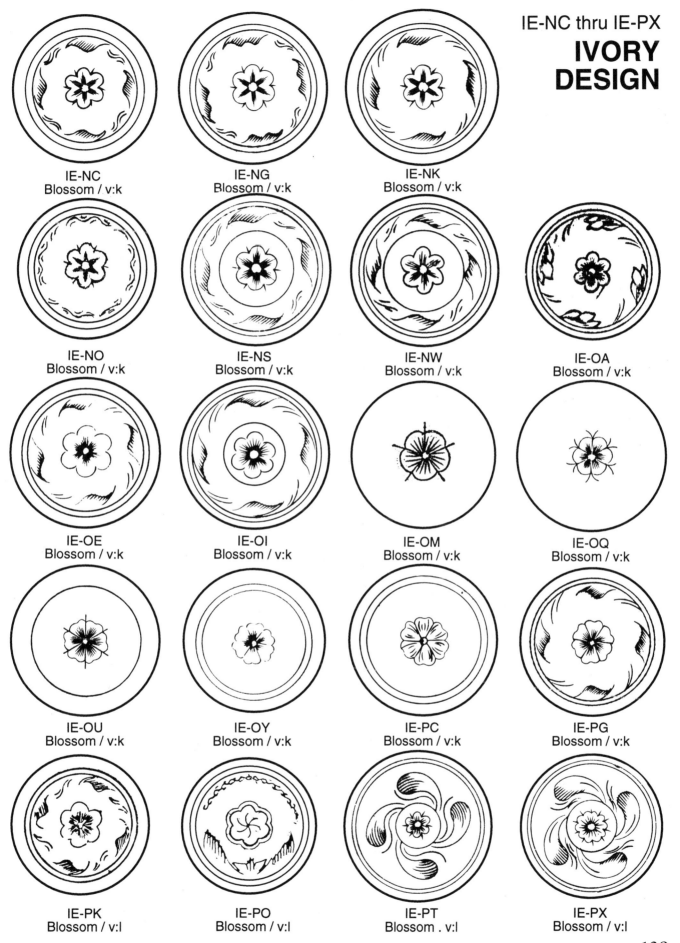

IE-NC
Blossom / v:k

IE-NG
Blossom / v:k

IE-NK
Blossom / v:k

IE-NO
Blossom / v:k

IE-NS
Blossom / v:k

IE-NW
Blossom / v:k

IE-OA
Blossom / v:k

IE-OE
Blossom / v:k

IE-OI
Blossom / v:k

IE-OM
Blossom / v:k

IE-OQ
Blossom / v:k

IE-OU
Blossom / v:k

IE-OY
Blossom / v:k

IE-PC
Blossom / v:k

IE-PG
Blossom / v:k

IE-PK
Blossom / v:l

IE-PO
Blossom / v:l

IE-PT
Blossom . v:l

IE-PX
Blossom / v:l

139

IVORY DESIGN

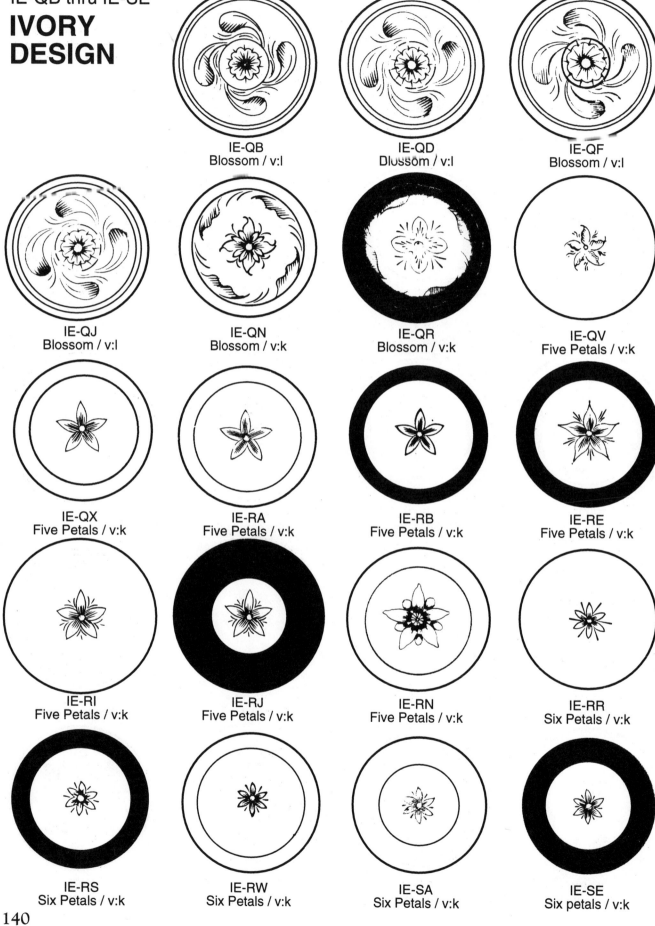

IE-QB
Blossom / v:l

IE-QD
Blossom / v:l

IE-QF
Blossom / v:l

IE-QJ
Blossom / v:l

IE-QN
Blossom / v:k

IE-QR
Blossom / v:k

IE-QV
Five Petals / v:k

IE-QX
Five Petals / v:k

IE-RA
Five Petals / v:k

IE-RB
Five Petals / v:k

IE-RE
Five Petals / v:k

IE-RI
Five Petals / v:k

IE-RJ
Five Petals / v:k

IE-RN
Five Petals / v:k

IE-RR
Six Petals / v:k

IE-RS
Six Petals / v:k

IE-RW
Six Petals / v:k

IE-SA
Six Petals / v:k

IE-SE
Six petals / v:k

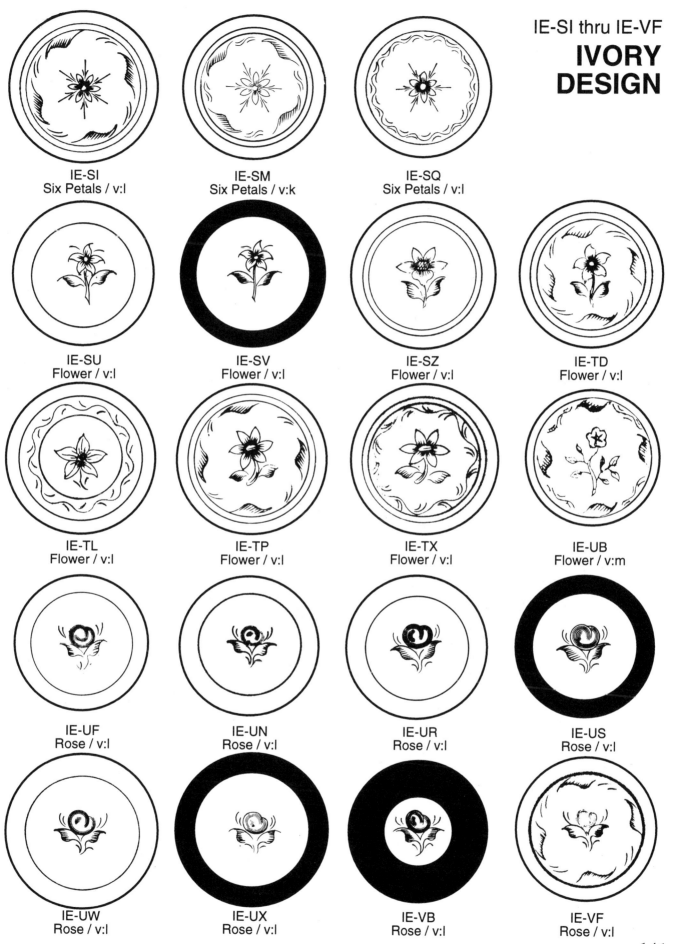

IVORY DESIGN

IE-SI
Six Petals / v:l

IE-SM
Six Petals / v:k

IE-SQ
Six Petals / v:l

IE-SU
Flower / v:l

IE-SV
Flower / v:l

IE-SZ
Flower / v:l

IE-TD
Flower / v:l

IE-TL
Flower / v:l

IE-TP
Flower / v:l

IE-TX
Flower / v:l

IE-UB
Flower / v:m

IE-UF
Rose / v:l

IE-UN
Rose / v:l

IE-UR
Rose / v:l

IE-US
Rose / v:l

IE-UW
Rose / v:l

IE-UX
Rose / v:l

IE-VB
Rose / v:l

IE-VF
Rose / v:l

141

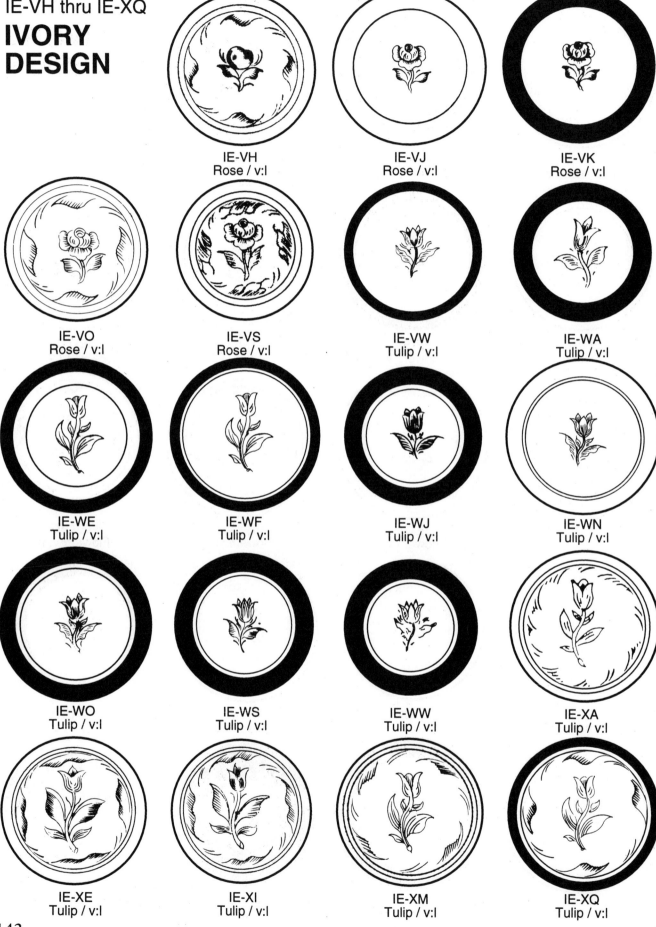

IVORY DESIGN

IE-VH
Rose / v:l

IE-VJ
Rose / v:l

IE-VK
Rose / v:l

IE-VO
Rose / v:l

IE-VS
Rose / v:l

IE-VW
Tulip / v:l

IE-WA
Tulip / v:l

IE-WE
Tulip / v:l

IE-WF
Tulip / v:l

IE-WJ
Tulip / v:l

IE-WN
Tulip / v:l

IE-WO
Tulip / v:l

IE-WS
Tulip / v:l

IE-WW
Tulip / v:l

IE-XA
Tulip / v:l

IE-XE
Tulip / v:l

IE-XI
Tulip / v:l

IE-XM
Tulip / v:l

IE-XQ
Tulip / v:l

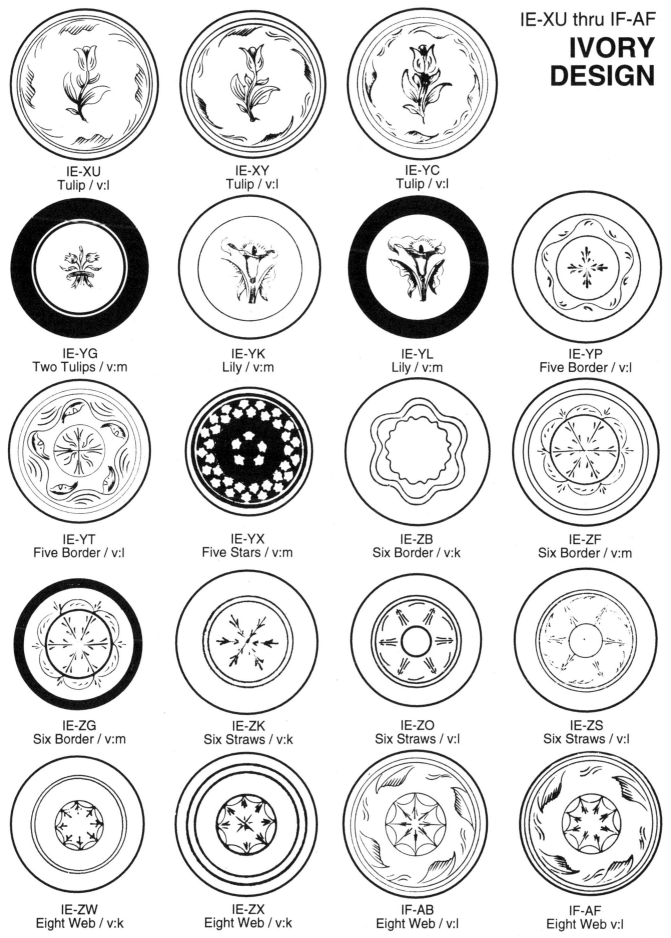

IVORY DESIGN

IE-XU
Tulip / v:l

IE-XY
Tulip / v:l

IE-YC
Tulip / v:l

IE-YG
Two Tulips / v:m

IE-YK
Lily / v:m

IE-YL
Lily / v:m

IE-YP
Five Border / v:l

IE-YT
Five Border / v:l

IE-YX
Five Stars / v:m

IE-ZB
Six Border / v:k

IE-ZF
Six Border / v:m

IE-ZG
Six Border / v:m

IE-ZK
Six Straws / v:k

IE-ZO
Six Straws / v:l

IE-ZS
Six Straws / v:l

IE-ZW
Eight Web / v:k

IE-ZX
Eight Web / v:k

IF-AB
Eight Web / v:l

IF-AF
Eight Web v:l

143

IVORY DESIGN

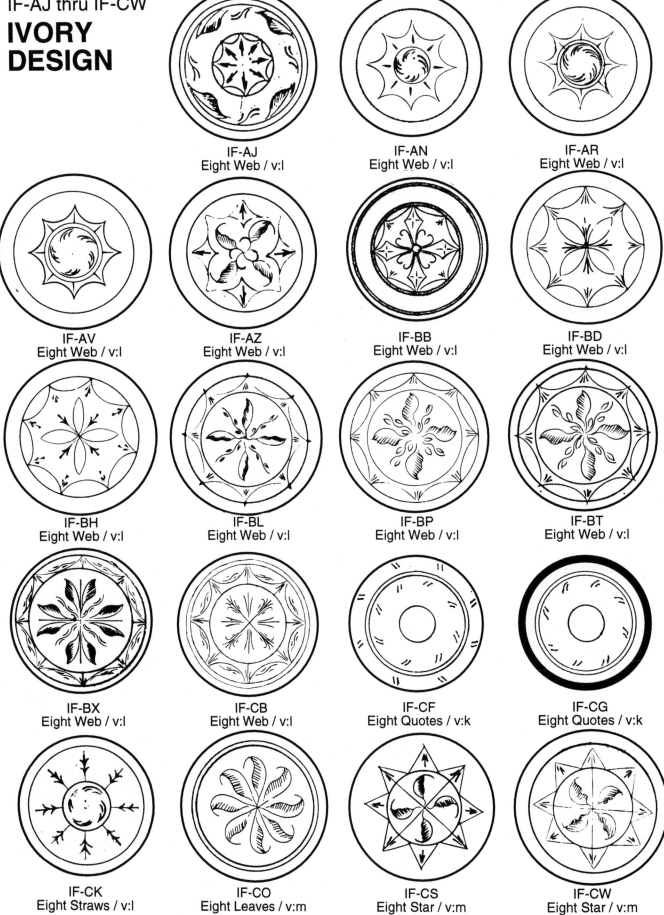

IF-AJ
Eight Web / v:l

IF-AN
Eight Web / v:l

IF-AR
Eight Web / v:l

IF-AV
Eight Web / v:l

IF-AZ
Eight Web / v:l

IF-BB
Eight Web / v:l

IF-BD
Eight Web / v:l

IF-BH
Eight Web / v:l

IF-BL
Eight Web / v:l

IF-BP
Eight Web / v:l

IF-BT
Eight Web / v:l

IF-BX
Eight Web / v:l

IF-CB
Eight Web / v:l

IF-CF
Eight Quotes / v:k

IF-CG
Eight Quotes / v:k

IF-CK
Eight Straws / v:l

IF-CO
Eight Leaves / v:m

IF-CS
Eight Star / v:m

IF-CW
Eight Star / v:m

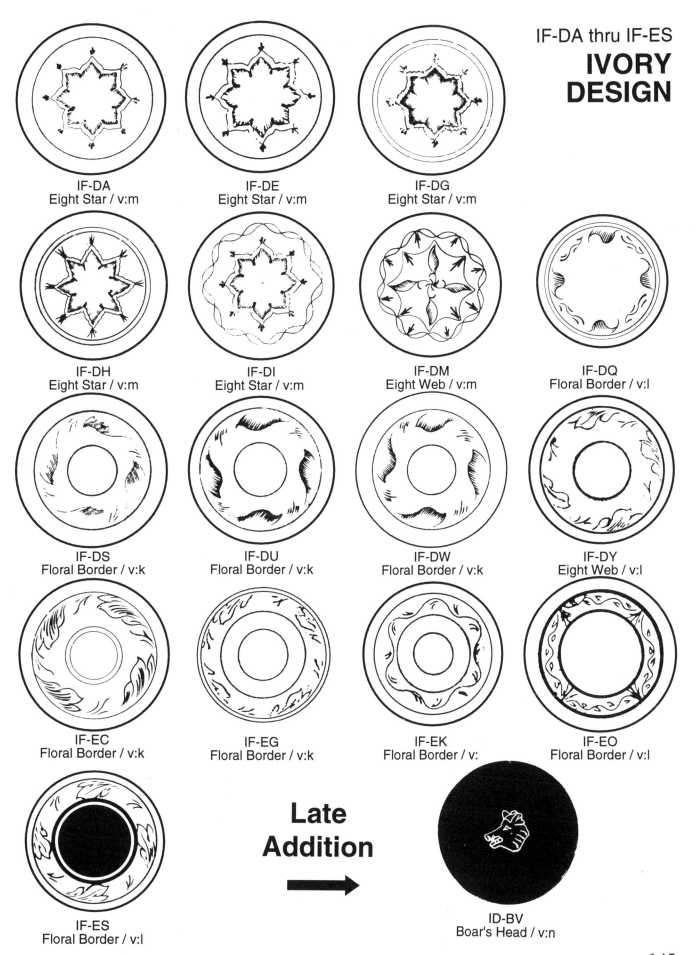

IVORY DESIGN

IF-DA
Eight Star / v:m

IF-DE
Eight Star / v:m

IF-DG
Eight Star / v:m

IF-DH
Eight Star / v:m

IF-DI
Eight Star / v:m

IF-DM
Eight Web / v:m

IF-DQ
Floral Border / v:l

IF-DS
Floral Border / v:k

IF-DU
Floral Border / v:k

IF-DW
Floral Border / v:k

IF-DY
Eight Web / v:l

IF-EC
Floral Border / v:k

IF-EG
Floral Border / v:k

IF-EK
Floral Border / v:

IF-EO
Floral Border / v:l

IF-ES
Floral Border / v:l

Late Addition

ID-BV
Boar's Head / v:n

IVORY

Monograms

CODES: IM

Antique Chips
Value Rating Code*

a: 50¢   b: $1   c: $2-$3   d: $4-$5   e: $6-$7

f: $8-$9   g: $10-$14   h: $15-$19   i: $20-$29

j: $30-$39   k: $40-$49   l: $50-$69   m: $70-$89

n: $90-$109   o: $110-$149   p: $150-$199

q: $200-$299   r: $300-$399   s: $400-$499

t: $500-$699   u: $700-$999   v: $1000-$1999

w: $2000-$2999   x: $3000-$3999

y: $4000-$499   z: $5000+

***It is important to remember that quantities
of one chip or a set of chips would have
a much lower unit value per chip.**

IVORY
MONOGRAMS

Some chips in this monogram section were made as "debt markers". V, X, D, C, and M represented Roman Numerals.

IM-AD
A / v:m

IM-AH
A / v:m

IM-AL
A / v:n

IM-AP
A / v:o

IM-AT
A / v:o

IM-AT
Reverse

IM-AX
A / v:o

IM-AX
Reverse

IM-AZ
A / v:q

IM-AZ
Reverse

IM-BB
Arecibo CC / v:m

IM-BB
Reverse

IM-BF
Arecibo CC / v:n

IM-BF
Reverse

IM-BJ
Arecibo CC / v:o

IM-BJ
Reverse

IM-BN
ADC / v:n

IM-BN
Reverse

IM-BR
BH / v:l

149

IVORY
MONOGRAMS

IM-BR
Reverse

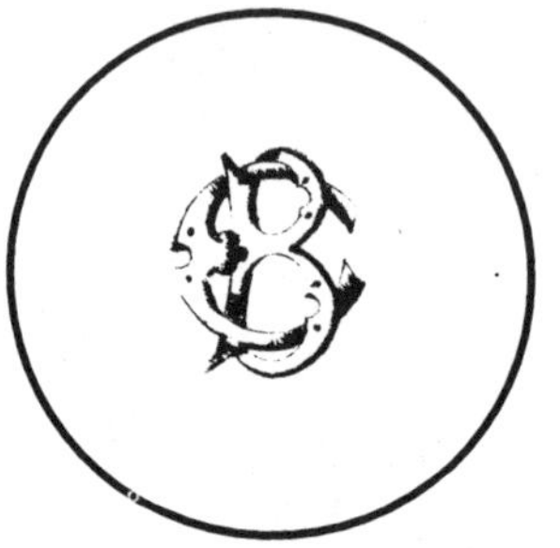

IM-BV
Edwin Booth / v:o

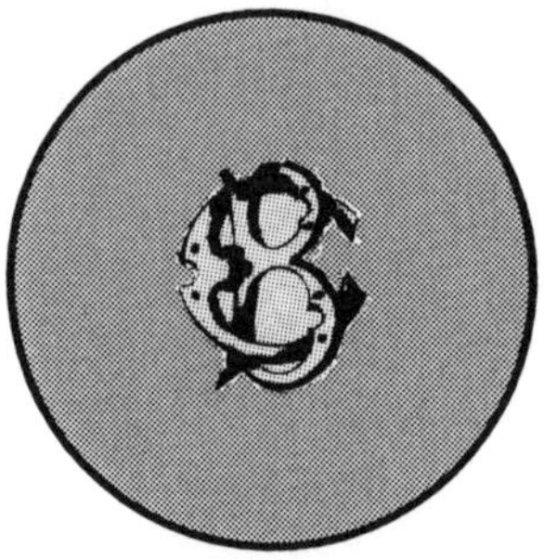

IIM-BW
Edwin Booth / v:o

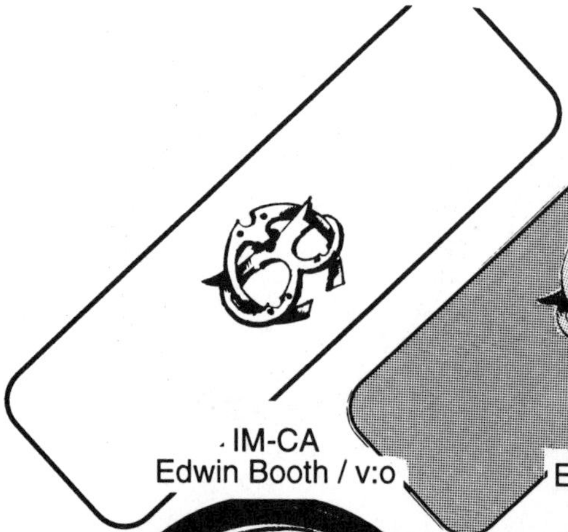

IM-CA
Edwin Booth / v:o

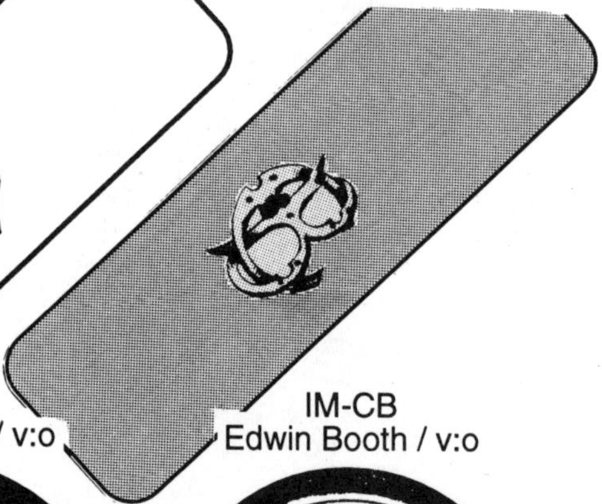

IM-CB
Edwin Booth / v:o

IM-CF
C (100) / v:l

IM-CJ
C / v:n

IM-CN
WC / v:q

IM-CR
C / v:p

IM-CR
Reverse

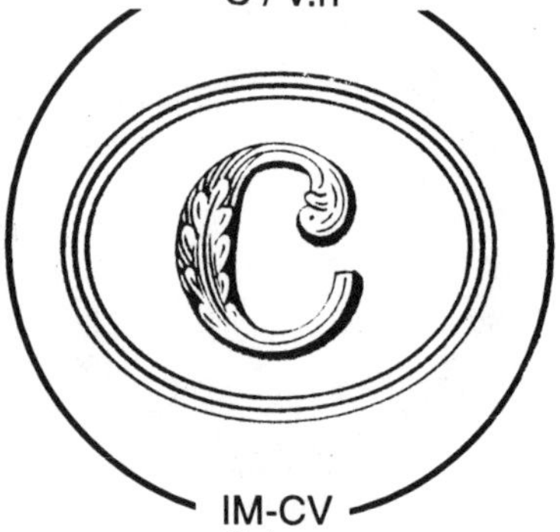

IM-CV
C / v:u

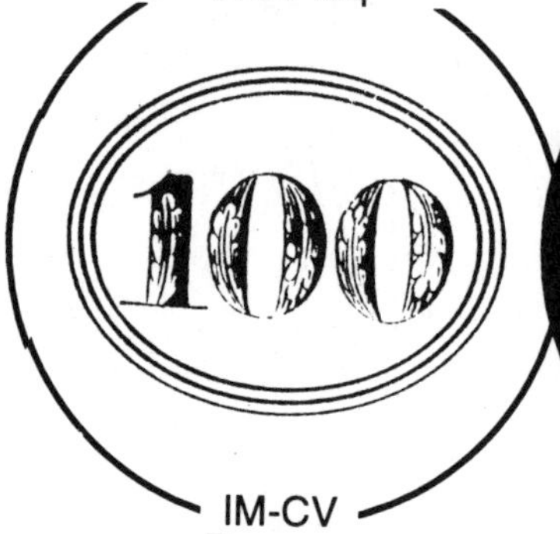

IM-CV
Reverse

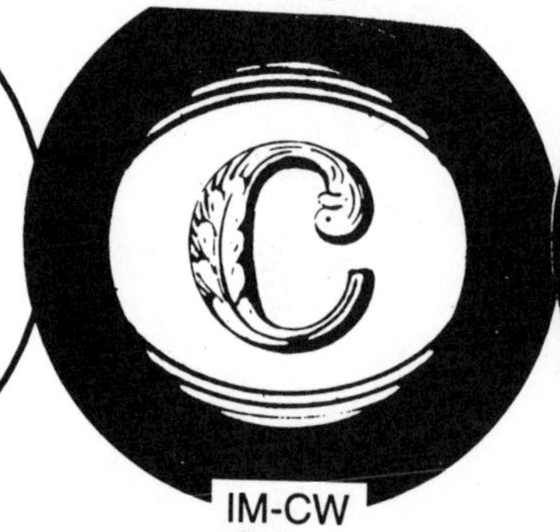

IM-CW
C / v:u

IM-CW
Reverse

IM-DA
D (500) / v:l

IM-DC
D / v:l

IM-DD
D / v:l

IM-DE
D / v:l

IM-DI
D / v:l

150

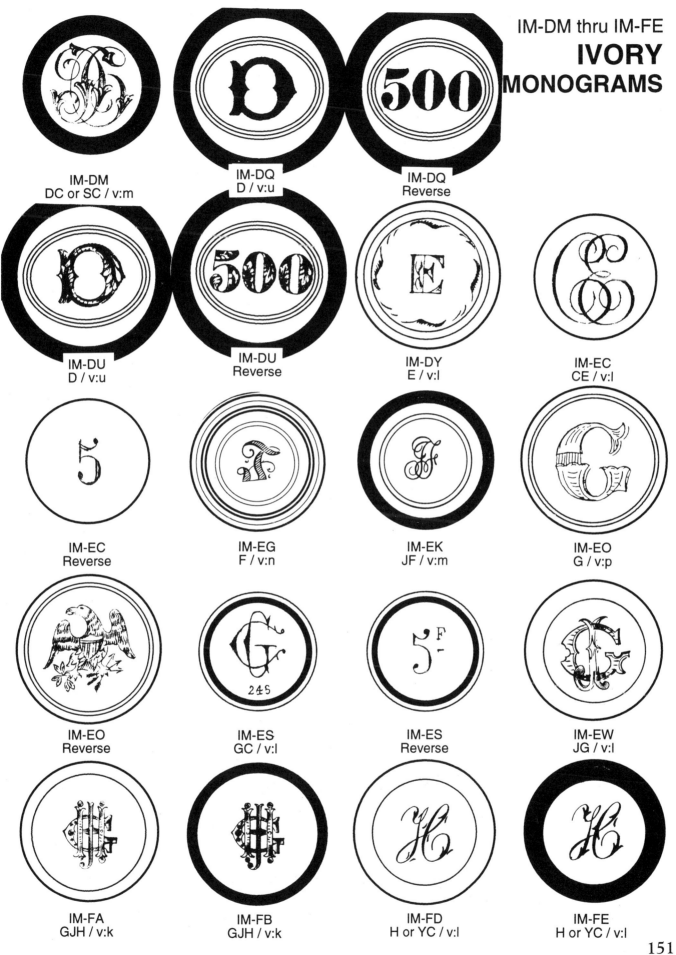

IM-DM
DC or SC / v:m

IM-DQ
D / v:u

IM-DQ
Reverse

IM-DU
D / v:u

IM-DU
Reverse

IM-DY
E / v:l

IM-EC
CE / v:l

IM-EC
Reverse

IM-EG
F / v:n

IM-EK
JF / v:m

IM-EO
G / v:p

IM-EO
Reverse

IM-ES
GC / v:l

IM-ES
Reverse

IM-EW
JG / v:l

IM-FA
GJH / v:k

IM-FB
GJH / v:k

IM-FD
H or YC / v:l

IM-FE
H or YC / v:l

151

IVORY MONOGRAMS

IM-FM
OI / v:m

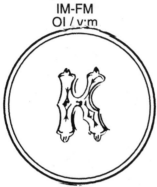

IM-FQ
HSI / v:l

IM-FS
HSI / v:l

IM-FU
K / v:q

IM-FY
K / v:u

IM-FY
Reverse

IM-GC
L (50) / v:l

IM-GG
L / v:k

IM-GK
LC or SC / v:l

IM-GK
Reverse

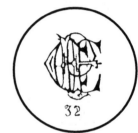

IM-GS
CPE / v:l

IM-GS
Reverse

IM-GT
CPE / v:l

IM-GT
Reverse

IM-HB
M / v:l

IM-HF
M / v:k

IM-HJ
M / v:w

IM-HJ
Reverse

IM-HN
MC / v:l

IVORY
MONOGRAMS

IM-HO
MC / v:l

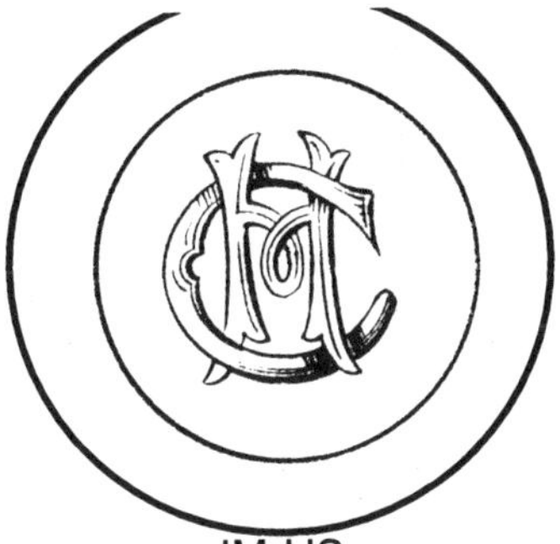

IM-HS
MC or HC / v:o

IM-HW
MBC / v:l

IM-HW
Reverse

IM-HZ
MPC / v:l

IM-IA
MPC / v:l

IM-IE
JP / v:p

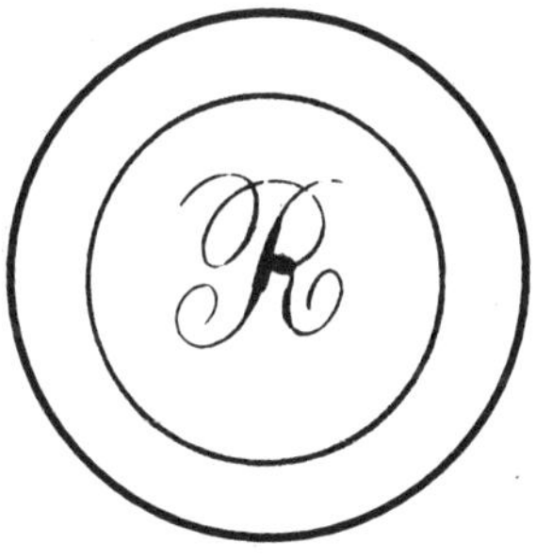

IM-IG
R / v:l

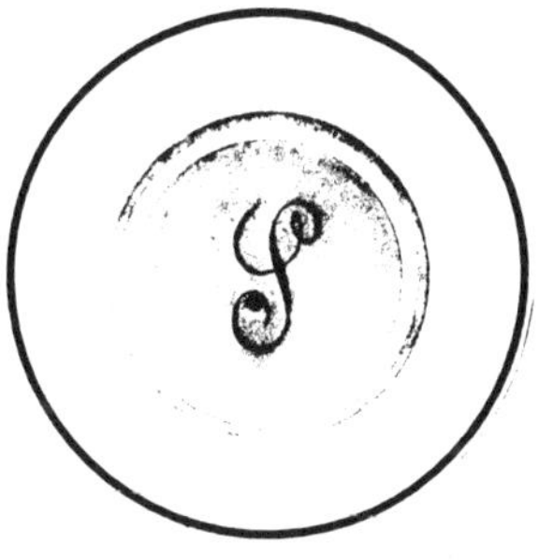

IM-IH
S / v:k

IM-II
S / v:m

IM-IM
S / v:p

IM-IO
WS / v:m

IM-IO
Reverse

IM-IQ
S & W / v:m

IM-IQ
Reverse

IM-IR
S & W / v:m

IM-IR
Reverse

IM-IV
US / v:l

IM-IZ
T / v:l

153

IVORY
MONOGRAMS

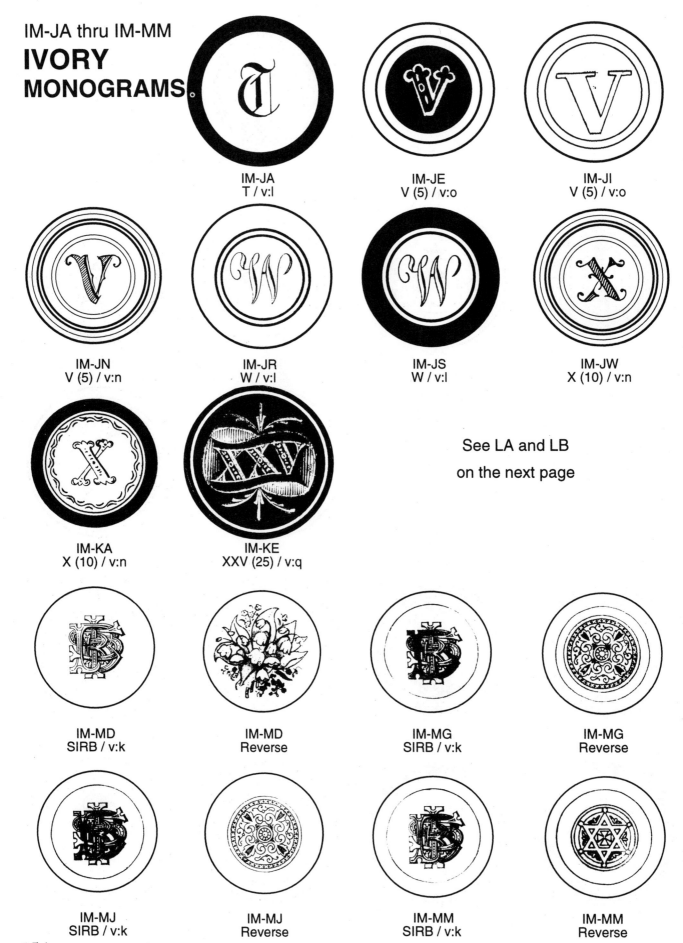

IM-JA
T / v:l

IM-JE
V (5) / v:o

IM-JI
V (5) / v:o

IM-JN
V (5) / v:n

IM-JR
W / v:l

IM-JS
W / v:l

IM-JW
X (10) / v:n

IM-KA
X (10) / v:n

IM-KE
XXV (25) / v:q

See LA and LB

on the next page

IM-MD
SIRB / v:k

IM-MD
Reverse

IM-MG
SIRB / v:k

IM-MG
Reverse

IM-MJ
SIRB / v:k

IM-MJ
Reverse

IM-MM
SIRB / v:k

IM-MM
Reverse

IVORY
MONOGRAMS

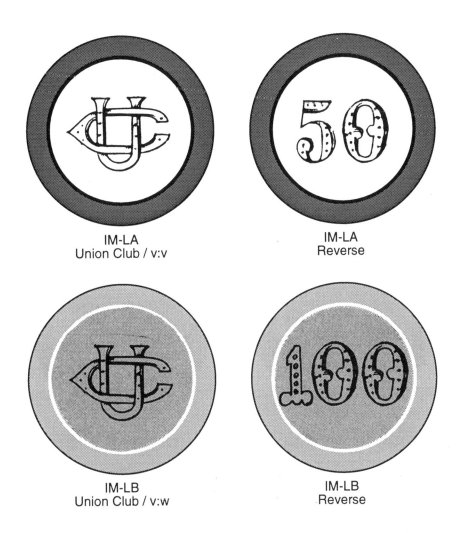

IM-LA
Union Club / v:v

IM-LA
Reverse

IM-LB
Union Club / v:w

IM-LB
Reverse

IVORY
Numerals
CODES: IN, IO, IP & IQ

Antique Chips
Value Rating Code*

a: 50¢   b: $1   c: $2-$3   d: $4-$5   e: $6-$7

f: $8-$9   g: $10-$14   h: $15-$19   i: $20-$29

j: $30-$39   k: $40-$49   l: $50-$69   m: $70-$89

n: $90-$109   o: $110-$149   p: $150-$199

q: $200-$299   r: $300-$399   s: $400-$499

t: $500-$699   u: $700-$999   v: $1000-$1999

w: $2000-$2999   x: $3000-$3999

y: $4000-$499   z: $5000+

*It is important to remember that quantities
of one chip or a set of chips would have
a much lower unit value per chip.

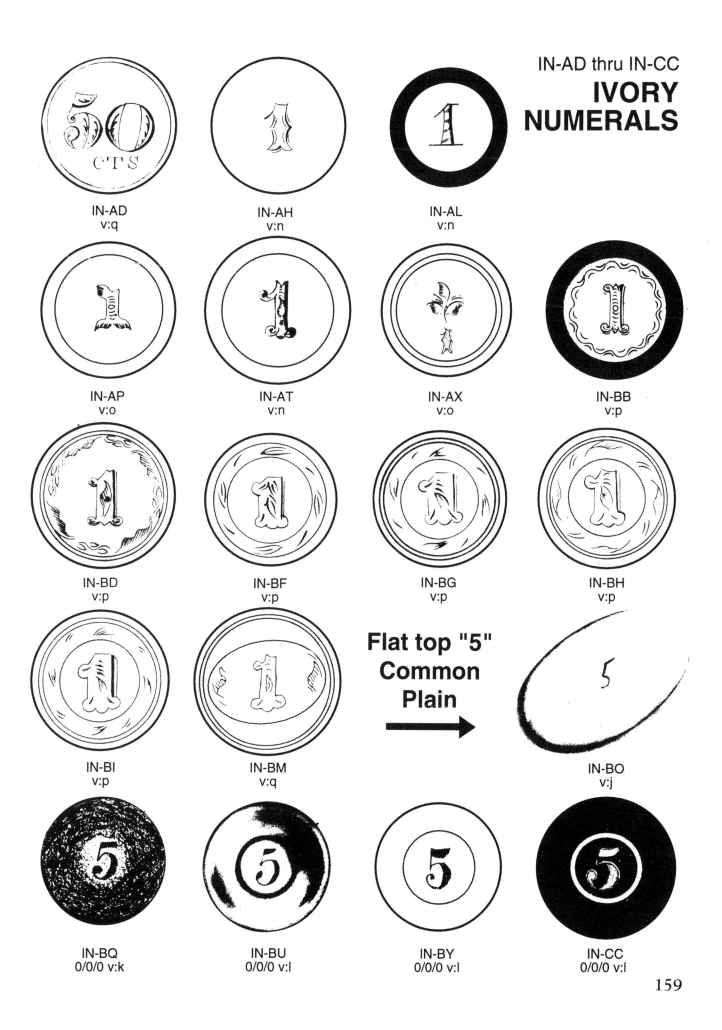

IVORY
NUMERALS

IN-AD
v:q

IN-AH
v:n

IN-AL
v:n

IN-AP
v:o

IN-AT
v:n

IN-AX
v:o

IN-BB
v:p

IN-BD
v:p

IN-BF
v:p

IN-BG
v:p

IN-BH
v:p

IN-BI
v:p

IN-BM
v:q

**Flat top "5"
Common
Plain**

IN-BO
v:j

IN-BQ
0/0/0 v:k

IN-BU
0/0/0 v:l

IN-BY
0/0/0 v:l

IN-CC
0/0/0 v:l

IVORY
NUMERALS

IN-CG
2/F/2 v:l

IN-CK
3/3/3 / v:l

IN-CO
3/3/3 / v:l

IN-CS
3/5/3 v:l

IN-CW
3/F/2 / v:l

IN-DA
3/F/2 / v:l

IN-DE
3/F/2 / v:l

IN-DI
3/F/3 / v:l

IN-DM
3/F/3 / v:l

IN-DQ
3/F/3 / v:l

IN-DU
3/F/3 / v:l

IN-DY
3/F/3 / v:l

IN-EC
3/F/3 / v:l

IN-EE
3/F/3 / v:l

IN-EG
3/F/3 / v:l

IN-EK
3/F/3 / v:l

IN-EO
3/F/3 / v:l

IN-ES
3/F/3 / v:l

IN-EW
3/U/3 / v:l

160

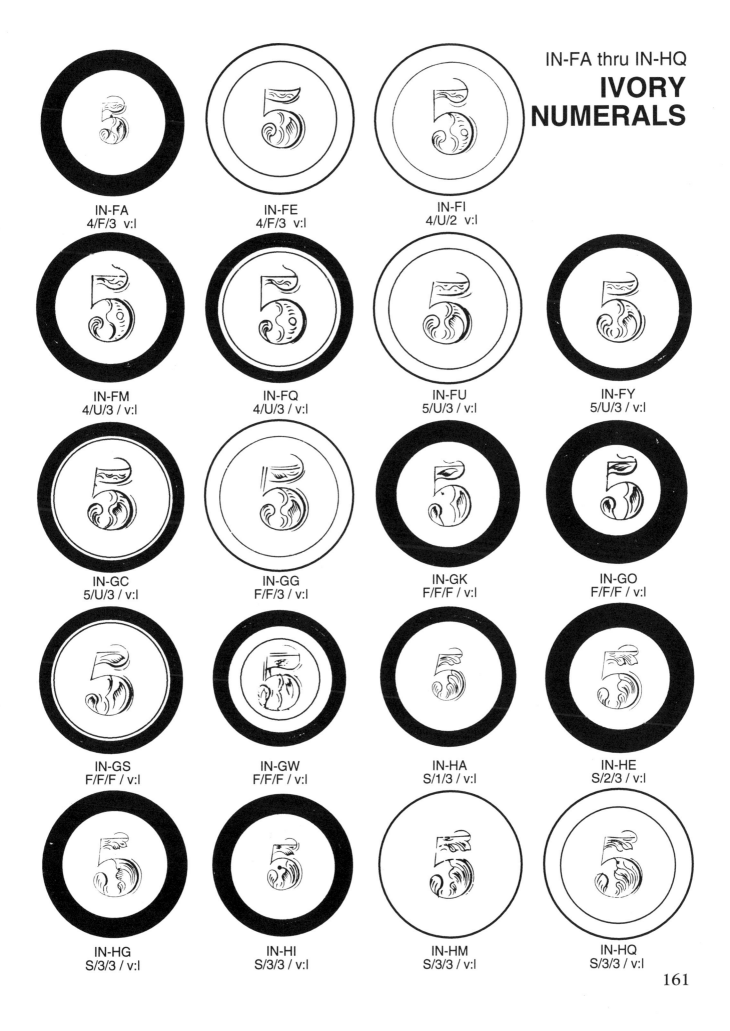

IVORY NUMERALS

IN-FA
4/F/3 v:l

IN-FE
4/F/3 v:l

IN-FI
4/U/2 v:l

IN-FM
4/U/3 / v:l

IN-FQ
4/U/3 / v:l

IN-FU
5/U/3 / v:l

IN-FY
5/U/3 / v:l

IN-GC
5/U/3 / v:l

IN-GG
F/F/3 / v:l

IN-GK
F/F/F / v:l

IN-GO
F/F/F / v:l

IN-GS
F/F/F / v:l

IN-GW
F/F/F / v:l

IN-HA
S/1/3 / v:l

IN-HE
S/2/3 / v:l

IN-HG
S/3/3 / v:l

IN-HI
S/3/3 / v:l

IN-HM
S/3/3 / v:l

IN-HQ
S/3/3 / v:l

IN-HU thru IN-KO
IVORY
NUMERALS

IN-HU
S/3/3 / v:l

IN-HY
U/U/U / v:l

IN-IC
U/U/U / v:l

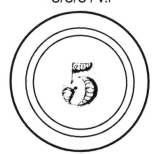

IN-IG
U/U/U v:k

IN-IK
U/U/U v:l

IN-IO
U/U/U v:l

IN-IS
U/U/U v:l

IN-IW
U/U/U v:l

IN-JA
U/U/U v:l

IN-JE
U/U/U v:l

IN-JI
U/U/U v:l

IN-JM
U/U/U v:l

IN-JQ
U/U/U v:l

IN-JU
U/U/U v:l

IN-JY
U/U/U v:l

IN-KC
U/U/U v:l

IN-KG
U/U/U v:l

IN-KK
U/U/U v:l

IN-KO
U/U/U v:l

162

IVORY
NUMERALS

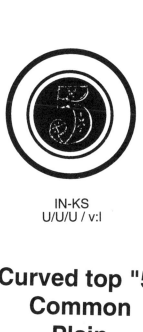

IN-KS
U/U/U / v:l

IN-KW
U/U/U / v:l

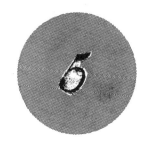

IN-LA
?/?/? / v:l

**Curved top "5"
Common
Plain**

→

IN-LE
0/0/0 / v:k

IN-LG
0/0/0 / v:k

IN-LI
0/0/0 / v:k

IN-LM
0/0/0 / v:l

IN-LQ
0/0/0 / v:l

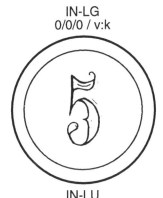

IN-LU
1/0/0 / v:l

IN-LY
3/0/4 / v:l

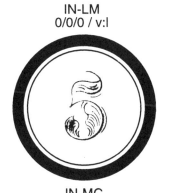

IN-MC
3/2/3 / v:l

IN-MG
3/3/S / v:l

IN-MK
3/5/3 / v:l

IN-MM
3/F/3 / v:l

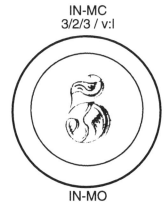

IN-MO
3/F/U / v:l

IN-MS
3/F/U / v:l

IN-MW
4/3/4 / v:l

IN-NA
4/F/3 / v:l

163

IVORY NUMERALS

IN-NE
5/U/3 / v:l

IN-NI
5/5/4 / v:l

IN-NM
S/4/2 / v:l

IN-NQ
8/3/S / v:l

IN-NU
9/3/S / v:m

IN-NY
11/3/S / v:m

IN-OC
U/U/3 / v:m

IN-OG
U/U/3 / v:m

IN-OH
U/U/3 / v:m

IN-OI
U/U/3 / v:m

IN-OK
U/U/3 / v:m

IN-OO
U/U/S / v:m

IN-OS
U/U/U / v:m

IN-OW
U/U/U / v:l

IN-PA
U/U/U / v:l

IN-PE
U/U/U / v:l

IN-PI
U/U/U / v:m

IN-PM
U/U/U / v:p

IN-PQ
U/U/U / v:p

164

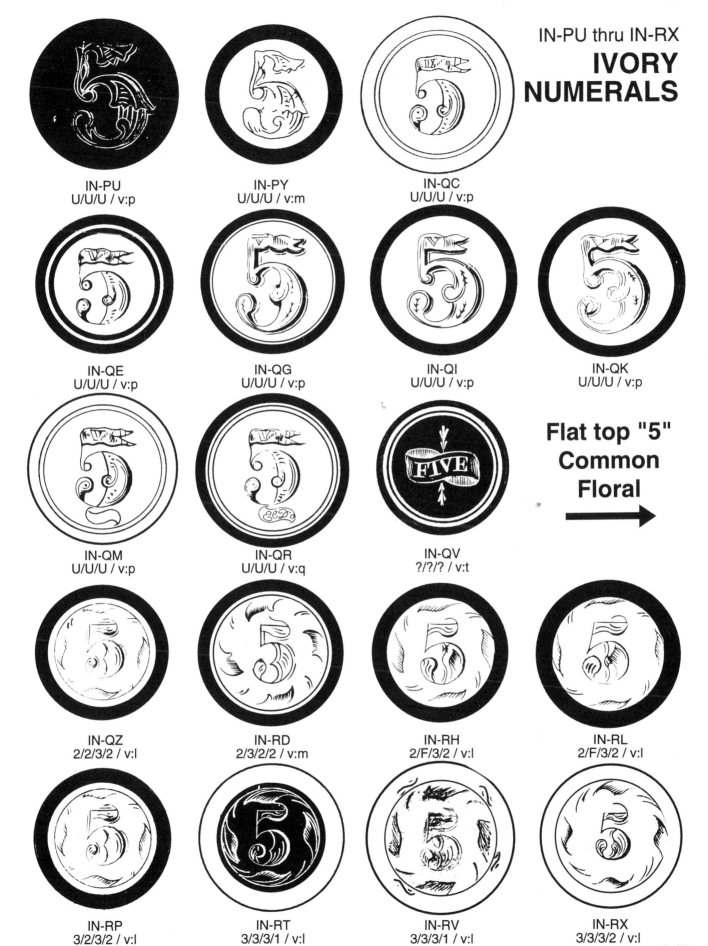

IVORY NUMERALS

IN-PU
U/U/U / v:p

IN-PY
U/U/U / v:m

IN-QC
U/U/U / v:p

IN-QE
U/U/U / v:p

IN-QG
U/U/U / v:p

IN-QI
U/U/U / v:p

IN-QK
U/U/U / v:p

IN-QM
U/U/U / v:p

IN-QR
U/U/U / v:q

IN-QV
?/?/? / v:t

**Flat top "5"
Common
Floral**
→

IN-QZ
2/2/3/2 / v:l

IN-RD
2/3/2/2 / v:m

IN-RH
2/F/3/2 / v:l

IN-RL
2/F/3/2 / v:l

IN-RP
3/2/3/2 / v:l

IN-RT
3/3/3/1 / v:l

IN-RV
3/3/3/1 / v:l

IN-RX
3/3/3/2 / v:l

165

IVORY
NUMERALS

IN-SB
3/3/3/2 / v:l

IN-SF
3/3/3/2 / v:l

IN-SJ
3/3/3/3 / v:l

IN-SN
3/3/3/3 / v:l

IN-SR
3/3/3/4 / v:l

IN-SV
3/3/3/4 / v:l

IN-SZ
3/4/3/2 / v:l

IN-TD
3/4/3/2 / v:l

IN-TF
3/6/3/1 / v:l

IN-TH
3/F/2/2 / v:m

IN-TL
3/F/3/2 / v:l

IN-TP
3/F/3/2 / v:l

IN-TT
3/F/3/2 / v:l

IN-TX
3/F/3/2 / v:l

IN-UB
3/F/3/2 / v:l

IN-UF
3/F/3/2 / v:l

IN-UJ
3/F/3/2 / v:l

IN-UN
3/F/3/2 / v:l

IN-UP
3/F/3/2 / v:l

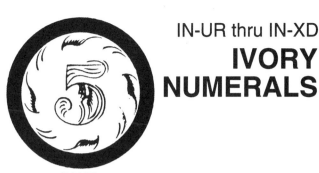

IVORY NUMERALS

IN-UR
3/F/3/2 / v:l

IN-UV
3/F/3/2 / v:l

IN-UZ
3/F/3/2 / v:l

IN-VD
3/F/3/2 / v:l

IN-VH
3/F/3/2 / v:l

IN-VL
3/F/3/2 / v:l

IN-VP
3/F/3/3 / v:l

IN-VR
3/F/3/3 / v:l

IN-VT
3/F/3/3 / v:l

IN-VX
3/F/3/3 / v:l

IN-WB
3/F/4/2 / v:l

IN-WF
3/F/4/2 / v:l

IN-WJ
4/F/3/2 / v:l

IN-WN
4/F/3/2 / v:l

IN-WP
4/F/3/3 / v:l

IN-WR
4/F/3/3 / v:l

IN-WV
4/U/2/2 / v:m

IN-WZ
4/U/2/2 / v:m

IN-XD
4/U/3/2 / v:m

IVORY
NUMERALS

IN-XH
5/F/3/2 / v:l

IN-XL
5/F/3/2 / v:l

IN-XP
7/U/4/2 / v:m

IN-XT
7/U/U/2 / v:m

IN-XV
9/7/7/2 / v:m

IN-XX
F/4/3/2 / v:l

IN-YB
F/F/F/3 / v:l

IN-YF
F/F/F/3 / v:l

IN-YH
F/F/F/3 / v:l

IN-YJ
F/F/F/3 / v:m

IN-YN
F/F/F/5 / v:l

IN-YR
S/1/3/2 / v:l

IN-YV
S/2/2/2 / v:l

IN-YZ
S/3/2/4 / v:l

IN-ZD
S/3/3/2 / v:l

IN-ZH
S/3/3/2 / v:l

IN-ZL
S/4/3/2 / v:l

IN-ZP
S/6/3/2 / v:l

IN-ZT
U/2/U/2 / v:m

168

IVORY NUMERALS

IN-ZX
U/3/2/4 / v:l

IO-AB
U/3/3/4 / v:m

IO-AF
U/4/3/2 / v:l

IO-AJ
U/F/F/5 / v:m

Curved top "5"
Common
Floral

IO-AN
2/2/2/2 / v:n

IO-AR
2/F/3/2 / v:l

IO-AV
3/2/S/2 / v:l

IO-AZ
3/2/S/2 / v:l

IO-BD
3/3/3/2 / v:l

IO-BH
3/4/3/U / v:n

IO-BL
3/4/4/U / v:n

IO-BP
3/F/3/2 / v:l

IO-BT
3/F/3/2 / v:m

IO-BX
3/U/S/2 / v:m

IO-CB
4/F/3/3 / v:m

IO-CF
4/U/2/2 / v:l

IO-CJ
9/3/5/3 / v:n

IO-CN
10/3/S/2 / v:m

169

IO-CR thru IO-FD
IVORY NUMERALS

IO-CR
10/3/S/3 / v:m

IO-CV
F/U/4/2 / v:n

IO-CZ
S/S/S/2 / v:m

IO-DD
S/S/S/2 / v:m

IO-DH
S/S/S/2 / v:m

IO-DL
S/S/S/2 / v:m

IO-DP
U/U/3/2 / v:n

IO-DT
U/U/3/2 / v:n

IO-DX
U/U/3/2 / v:n

IO-EB
U/U/3/4 / v:n

IO-EF
U/U/3/4 / v:o

IO-EJ
U/U/3/U / v:n

IO-EL
U/U/U/2 / v:m

Unusual 5's Grouped by Commonality of Design

→

IO-EN
v:n

IO-ER
v:o

IO-EV
v:o

IO-EZ
v:o

IO-FD
v:o

170

IVORY
NUMERALS

IO-FH
v:o

IO-FL
v:o

IO-FP
v:m

IO-FR
v:m

IO-FT
v:m

IO-FX
v:m

IO-GB
v:n

IO-GF
v:n

IO-GJ
v:n

IO-GN
v:n

IO-GR
v:n

IO-GV
v:o

IO-GZ
v:o

IO-HD
v:o

IO-HH
v:n

IO-HL
v:n

IO-HP
v:m

IO-HT
v:m

IO-HX
v:m

IVORY
NUMERALS

IO-IB
v:m

IO-IF
v:m

IO-IJ
v:o

IO-IL
v:p

IO-IN
v:o

IO-IR
v:n

IO-IV
v:m

IO-IZ
v:l

IO-JD
v:l

IO-JF
v:m

IO-JH
v:l

IO-JL
v:m

IO-JP
v:l

IO-JT
v:l

IO-JX
v:l

IO-JZ
v:m

IO-KB
v:l

IO-KF
v:l

IO-KJ
v:m

172

IVORY NUMERALS

IO-KL
v:m

IO-KN
v:m

IO-KO
v:m

IO-KR
v:m

IO-KV
v:m

IO-KZ
v:m

IO-LB
v:m

IO-LD
v:m

IO-LH
v:n

IO-LL
v:m

IO-LP
v:m

IO-LT
v:m

IO-LX
v:m

IO-MB
v:m

IO-MF
v:m

IO-MJ
v:m

IO-MN
v:m

IO-MR
v:m

IO-MV
v:m

IO-MZ thru IO-PP
IVORY
NUMERALS

IO-MZ
v:m

IO-ND
v:m

IO-NH
v:n

IO-NL
v:m

IO-NP
v:m

IO-NT
v:m

IO-NX
v:m

IO-OB
v:m

IO-OD
v:m

IO-OF
v:m

IO-OJ
v:m

IO-ON
v:m

IO-OR
v:n

IO-OV
v:m

IO-OZ
v:m

IO-PD
v:m

IO-PH
v:n

IO-PL
v:n

IO-PP
v:n

174

IVORY NUMERALS

IO-PR
v:n

IO-PT
v:p

IO-PX
v:k

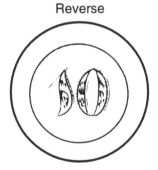

IO-PX
Reverse

IO-QB
v:n

IO-QF
v:m

IO-QJ
v:m

IO-QN
v:m

IO-QR
v:o

IO-QV
v:o

IO-QZ
v:k

IO-RD
v:k

**Flat top "5"
Common
Plain**

→

IO-RH
2/F/? / v:n

IO-RL
3/3/2 / v:m

IO-RN
3/3/3 / v:m

IO-RP
3/4/2 / v:m

IO-RT
3/F/2 / v:m

IO-RX
3/F/2 / v:m

IVORY
NUMERALS

IO-SB
3/F/2 / v:m

IO-SF
3/F/2 / v:n

IO-SJ
3/F/3 / v:m

IO-SL
3/F/3 / v:m

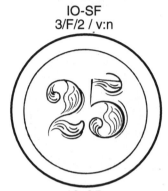

IO-SN
3/F/3 / v:m

IO-SP
3/F/3 / v:m

IO-SR
3/F/3 / v:m

IO-SL
3/F/3 / v:m

IO-SV
3/F/3 / v:m

IO-SZ
3/F/3 / v:m

IO-TD
3/F/F / v:m

IO-ST
3/F/3 / v:m

IO-SV
3/F/3 / v:m

IO-SZ
3/F/3 / v:m

IO-TD
3/F/F / v:m

IO-TH
3/F/? / v:m

IO-TL
3/U/S / v:m

IO-TP
4/6/3 / v:m

IO-TT
4/6/4 / v:m

IO-TX
4/F/2 / v:m

IO-TZ
4/F/3-4 / v:m

IO-UB
4/F/S / v:m

IO-UF
4/F/S / v:m

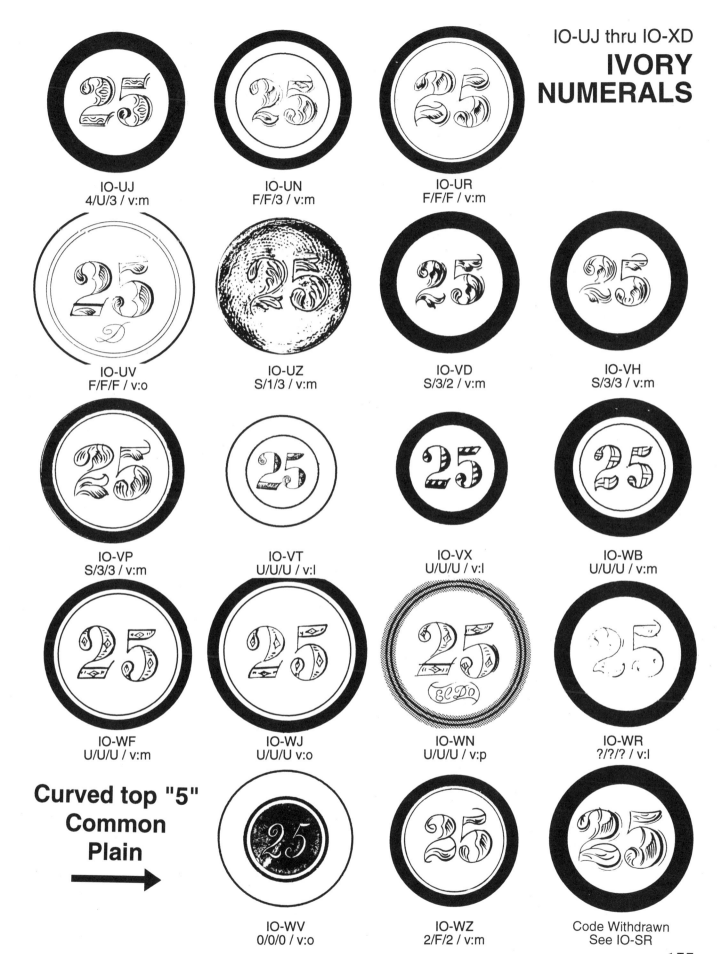

IVORY NUMERALS

IO-UJ
4/U/3 / v:m

IO-UN
F/F/3 / v:m

IO-UR
F/F/F / v:m

IO-UV
F/F/F / v:o

IO-UZ
S/1/3 / v:m

IO-VD
S/3/2 / v:m

IO-VH
S/3/3 / v:m

IO-VP
S/3/3 / v:m

IO-VT
U/U/U / v:l

IO-VX
U/U/U / v:l

IO-WB
U/U/U / v:m

IO-WF
U/U/U / v:m

IO-WJ
U/U/U v:o

IO-WN
U/U/U / v:p

IO-WR
?/?/? / v:l

**Curved top "5"
Common
Plain**

IO-WV
0/0/0 / v:o

IO-WZ
2/F/2 / v:m

Code Withdrawn
See IO-SR

IO-XH thru IO-ZT

IVORY
NUMERALS

** See late addition
IO-ZV at end of
this section.*

IO-XH
3/2/4 / v:m

IO-XL
3/3/S / v:n

IO-XP
3/6/0 / v:m

IO-XR
3/F/2-3 / v:m

IO-XT
3/F/3 / v:m

IO-XV
3/F/3 / v:m

IO-XX
3/F/3 / v:m

IO-YB
3/F/S / v:m

IO-YF
3/F/3 / v:m

IO-YJ
3/F/3 / v:m

IO-YN
3/U/4 / v:m

IO-YR
4/2/3 / v:m

IO-YV
4/F/3 / v:m

IO-YZ
4/F/3 / v:m

IO-ZD
4/U/3 / v:o

*

IO-ZH
F/F/F / v:m

IO-ZL
S/4/3 / v:m

IO-ZP
U/F/S / v:m

IO-ZT
U/U/4 / v:m

178

IO-ZX
U/U/U / v:m

**Flat top "5"
Common
Floral**

→

IP-AB
0/5/0/2 / v:m

IVORY NUMERALS

IP-AF
2/3/2/2 / v:m

IP-AJ
3/3/3/2 / v:m

IP-AP
3/3/3/2 / v:m

IP-AR
3/3/3/2 / v:m

IP-AV
3/3/3/2 / v:m

IP-AZ
3/3/3/3 / v:m

IP-BD
3/3/3/3 / v:m

IP-BH
3/3/3/3 / v:m

IP-BL
3/3/3/3 / v:m

IP-BP
3/4/3/2 / v:m

IP-BR
3/6/3/1 / v:m

IP-BT
3/F/1/2 / v:m

IP-BX
3/F/2/2 / v:m

IP-CB
3/F/2/2 / v:m

IP-CF
3/F/2/2 / v:m

IP-CJ
3/F/3/2 / v:m

IVORY NUMERALS

IP-CN
3/F/3/2 / v:m

IP-CR
3/F/3/2 / v:m

IP-CV
3/F/3/2 / v:m

IP-CZ
3/F/3/2 / v:m

IP-DD
3/F/3/2 / v:m

IP-DH
3/F/3/2 / v:m

IP-DL
3/F/3/2 / v:m

IP-DN
3/F/3-2/2 / v:m

IP-DP
3/F/3/2 / v:m

IP-DT
3/F/3/2 / v:m

IP-DV
3/F/3/2 / v:m

IP-DX
3/F/3/3 / v:m

IP-EB
3/F/4/2 / v:m

IP-ED
3/F/?/2 / v:m

IP-EE
3/F/3/3 / v:m

IP-EF
4/F/3/3 / v:m

IP-EJ
4/F/3/5 / v:m

IP-EN
4/U/2/2 / v:m

IP-ER
4/U/3/2 / v:m

IVORY NUMERALS

IP-EZ
5/U/3/2 / v:m

IP-FD
F/F/F/2 / v:m

IP-FH
F/F/F/2 / v:m

IP-FN
F/F/F/3 / v:m

IP-FP
S/2/3/2 / v:m

IP-FT
S/2/2/2 / v:m

IP-FX
S/3/3/2 / v:m

IP-GB
U/U/U/2 / v:m

Curved top "5"
Common
Floral
→

IP-GF
1/2/S/2 / v:n

IP-GH
2/F/2/2 / v:m

IP-GJ
3/3/3/2 / v:l

IP-GN
3/3/3/2 / v:m

IP-GR
3/3/3/U / v:m

IP-GV
3/3/4/2 / v:m

IP-GZ
3/3/4/2 / v:m

IP-HD
3/3/S/2 / v:n

IP-HH
3/4/3/2 / v:m

IP-HL
3/4/S/2 / v:m

IP-HP thru IP-KZ
IVORY
NUMERALS

IP-HP
3/F/2/2 / v:m

IP-HT
3/F/3/2 / v:m

IP-IF
3/F/3/2 / v:m

IP-IJ
3/F/3/2 / v:m

IP-IN
3/F/3/2 / v:m

IP-IR
3/F/3/2 / v:m

IP-IV
3/F/3/2 / v:m

IP-IZ
3/F/3/4 / v:n

IP-JD
3/U/0/2 / v:l

IP-JH
4/4/2/2 / v:m

IP-JL
4/4/U/2 / v:o

IP-JP
4/4/U/2 / v:o

IP-JX
10/3/S/3 / v:n

IP-KB
F/F/U/U / v:m

IP-KF
S/3/2/2 / v:m

IP-KJ
S/3/2/2 / v:m

IP-KN
S/S/S/5 / v:o

IP-KR
U/U/2/U / v:n

IP-KZ
U/U/3/U v:o

182

IVORY NUMERALS

IP-LD
U/F/3/1 / v:q

IP-LH
U/U/U/1 / v:q

IP-LL
U/U/U/1 / v:q

Uncommon
(Grouped by Design Similarity)

IP-LP
U/U/U/U / v:m

IP-LT
U/U/U/U / v:r

IP-LX
v:n

IP-LZ
v:m

IP-MB
v:n

IP-MF
v:m

IP-MJ

IP-MN
v:o

IP-MR
v:o

IP-MV
v:o

IP-MZ
v:n

IP-ND
v:n

IP-NH
v:o

IP-NL
v:o

IP-NP
v:q

IP-NT thru IP-QN

IVORY NUMERALS

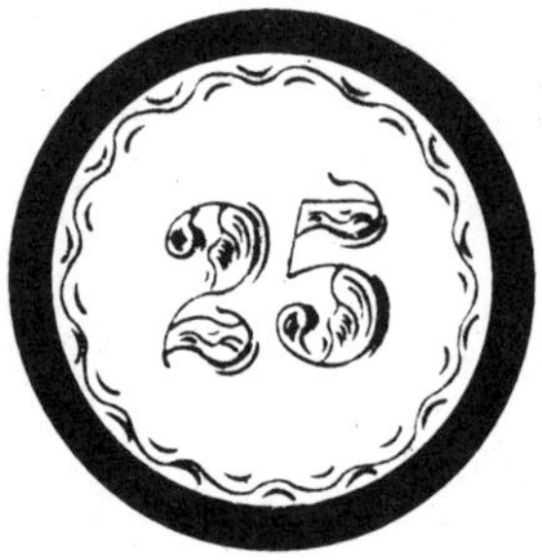

IP-NT
v:n

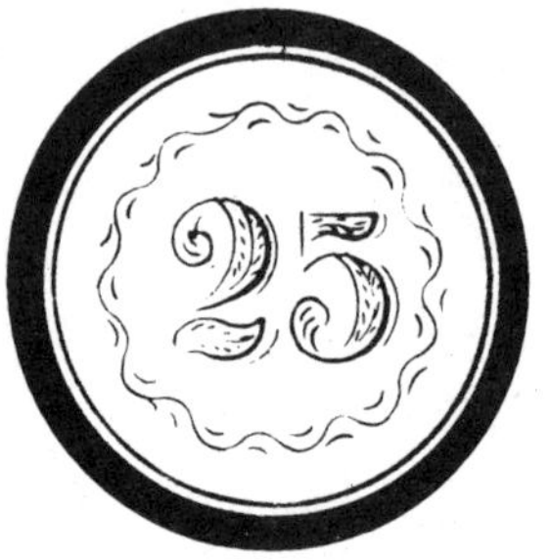

IP-NV
v:n

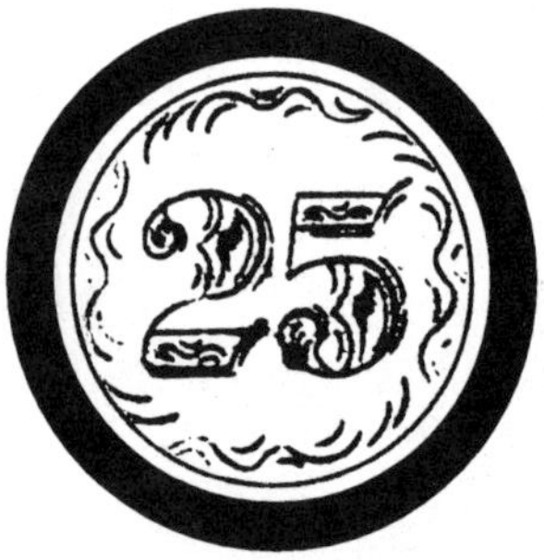

IP-NX
v:n

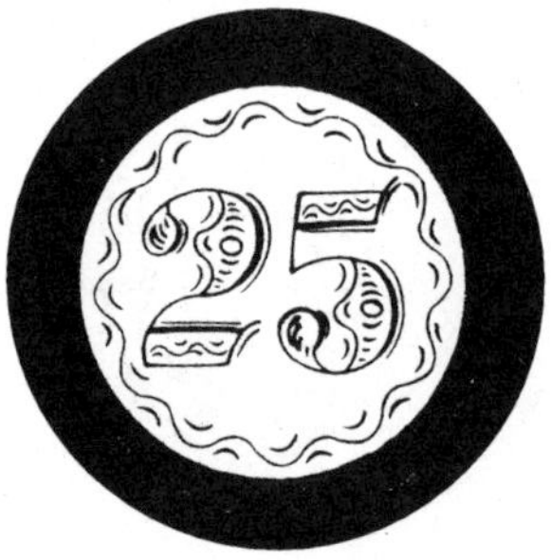

IP-OB
v:n

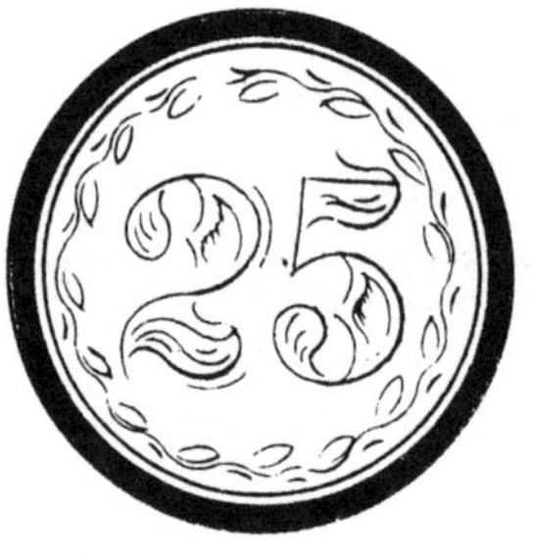

IP-OF
v:n

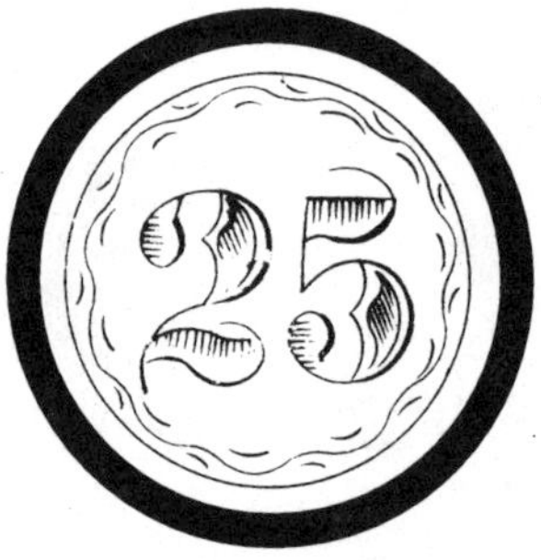

IP-OJ
v:n

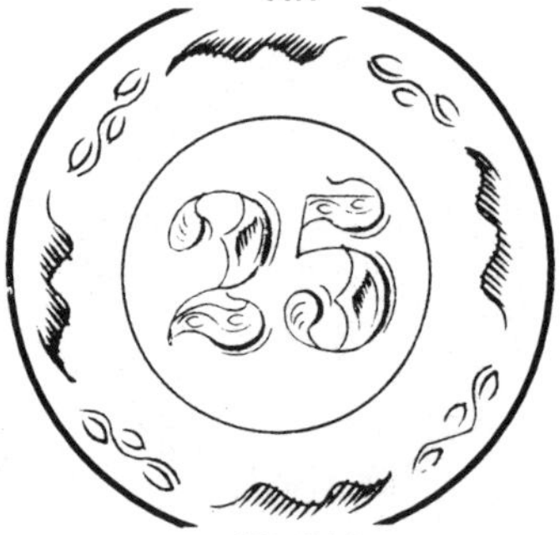

IP-ON
v:q

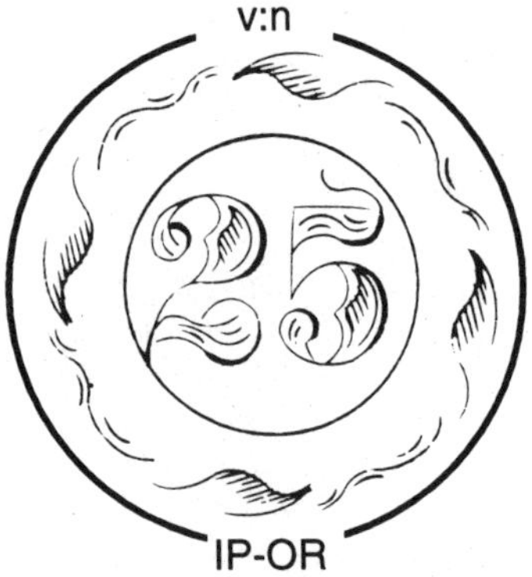

IP-OR
v:q

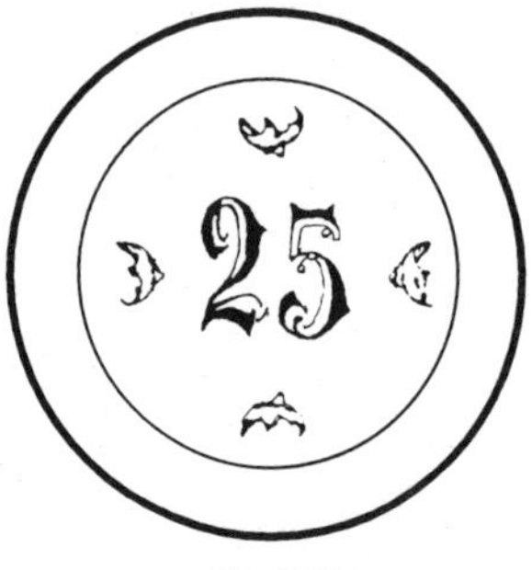

IP-OV
v:n

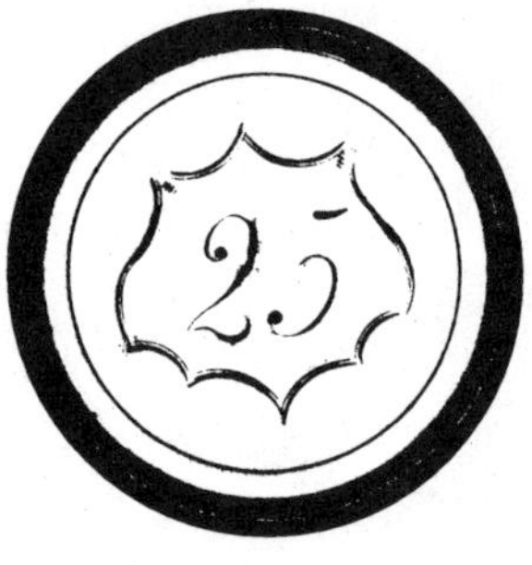

IP-OZ
v:n

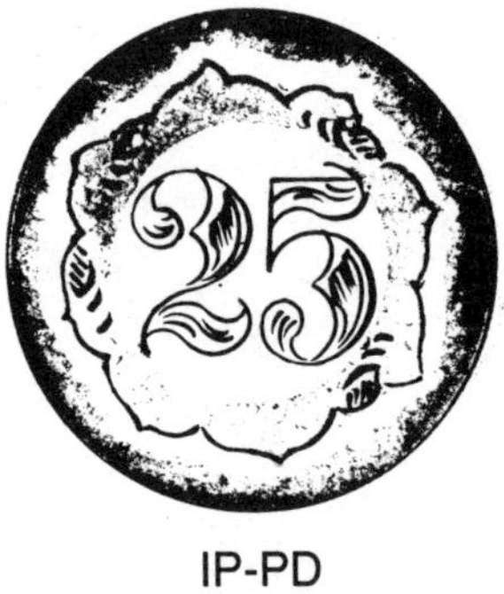

IP-PD
v:p

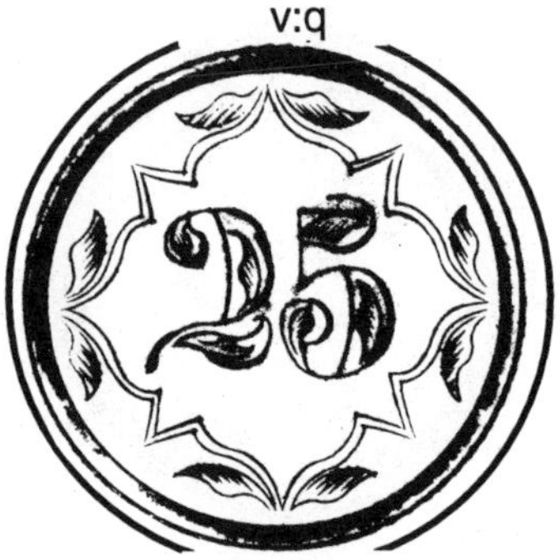

IP-PH
v:q

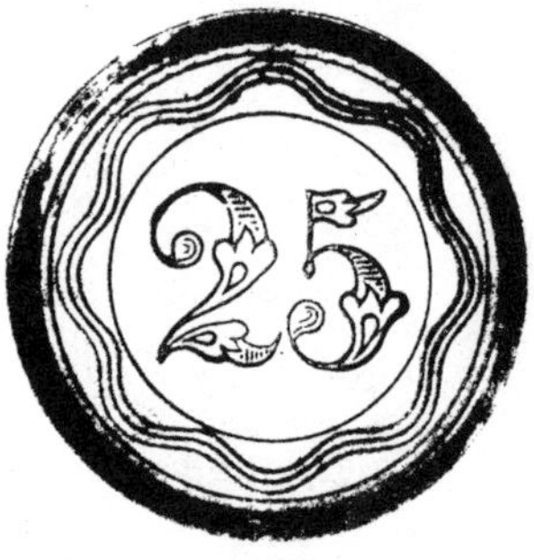

IP-PL
v:o

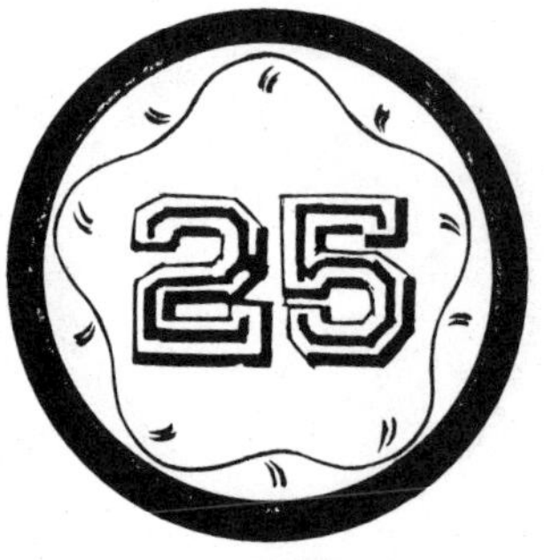

IP-PP
v:o

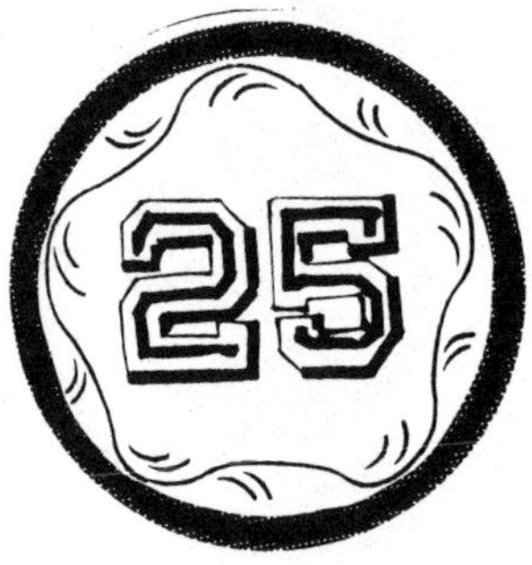

IP-PT
v:o

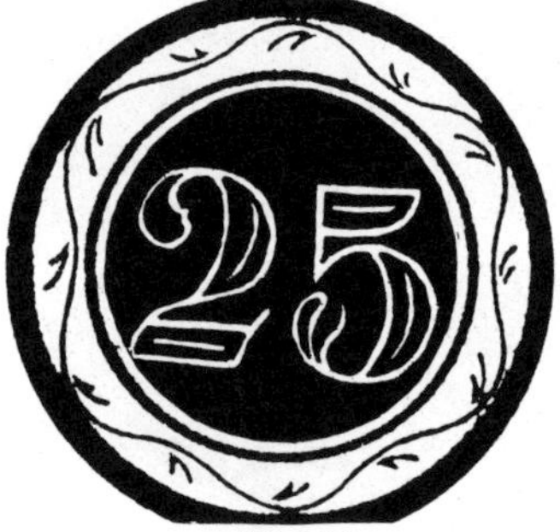

IP-PX
v:q

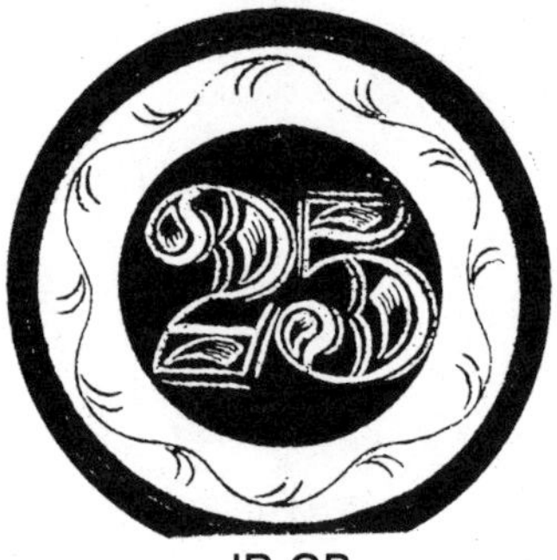

IP-QB
v:q

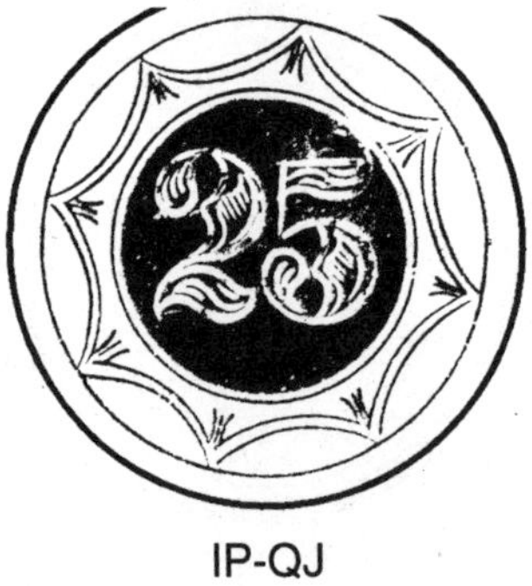

IP-QJ
v:n

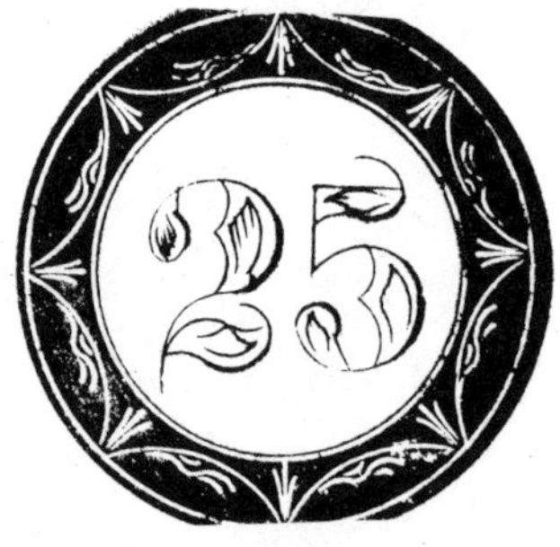

IP-QN
v:o

IVORY NUMERALS

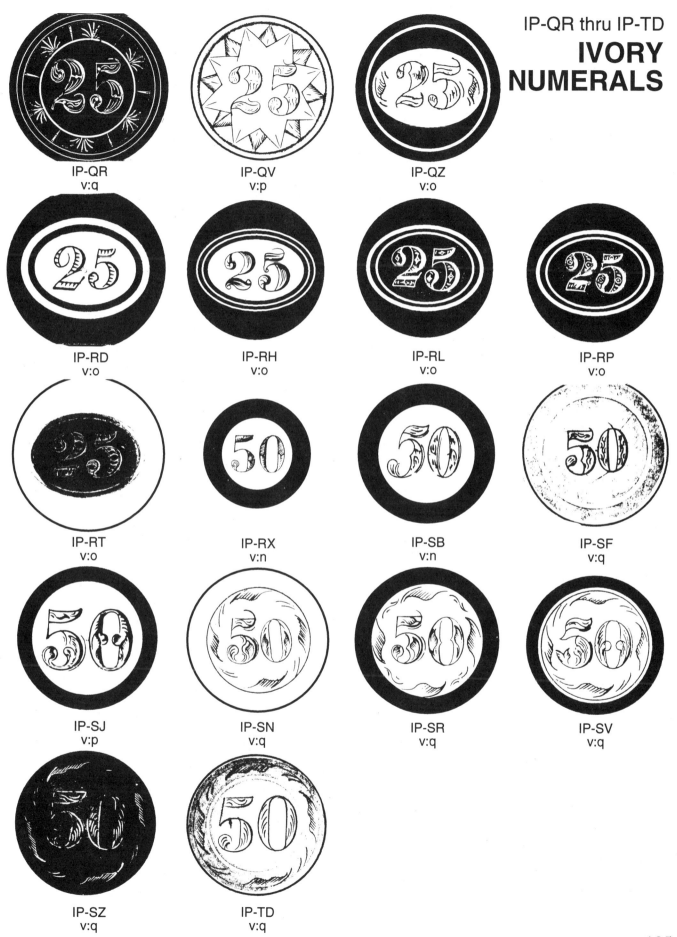

IP-QR
v:q

IP-QV
v:p

IP-QZ
v:o

IP-RD
v:o

IP-RH
v:o

IP-RL
v:o

IP-RP
v:o

IP-RT
v:o

IP-RX
v:n

IP-SB
v:n

IP-SF
v:q

IP-SJ
v:p

IP-SN
v:q

IP-SR
v:q

IP-SV
v:q

IP-SZ
v:q

IP-TD
v:q

IVORY
NUMERALS

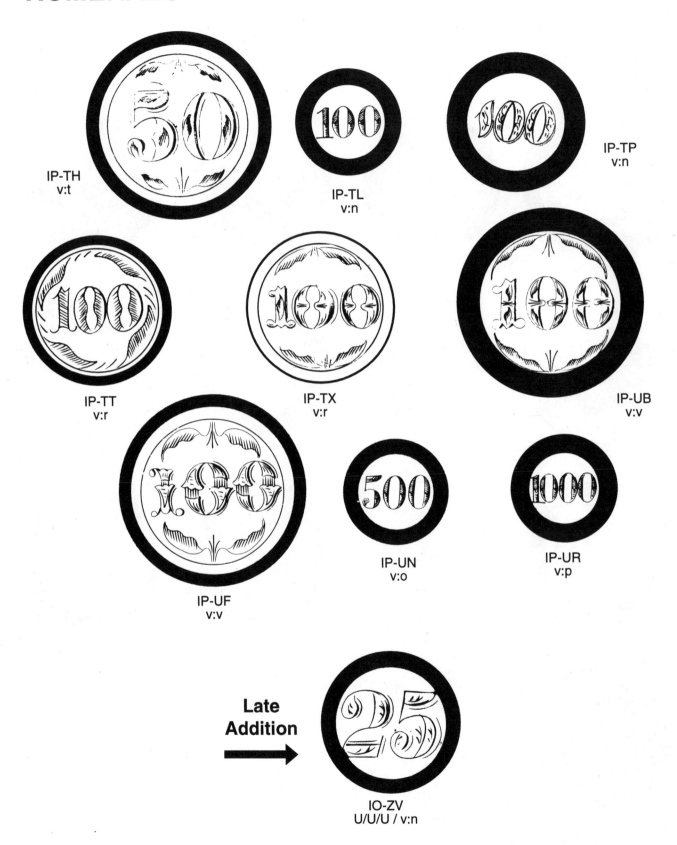

IP-TH
v:t

IP-TL
v:n

IP-TP
v:n

IP-TT
v:r

IP-TX
v:r

IP-UB
v:v

IP-UF
v:v

IP-UN
v:o

IP-UR
v:p

**Late
Addition**

IO-ZV
U/U/U / v:n

186

IVORY
FOREIGN
NUMERALS

IQ-AE
v:k

IQ-AK
v:m

IQ-AQ
v:l

IQ-AW
v:m

IQ-BC
v:m

IQ-BI
v:m

IQ-BO
v:m

IQ-BU
v:k

IQ-CA
v:l

IQ-CG
v:k

IQ-CM
v:k

IQ-CS
v:k

IQ-CY
v:k

IQ-DE
v:k

IQ-DK
v:l

IQ-DQ
v:l

IQ-DW
v:l

IQ-EC
v:n

IQ-EI
v:p

187

IVORY
FOREIGN
NUMERALS

IQ-EO
v:k

IQ-EU
v:k

IQ-FA
v:k

IQ-FG
v:k

IQ-FM
v:k

iIQ-FS
v:l

IQ-FY
v:l

IQ-GE
v:o

IQ-GN
v:m

IQ-GT
v:n

IQ-GZ
v:q

IQ-HF
v:l

IQ-HL
v:m

IQ-HR
v:k

IQ-HX
v:k

IQ-ID
v:k

IQ-IJ
v:k

IQ-JA
v:l

IVORY

Commemoratives
& Place Names

CODES: IR

Antique Chips
Value Rating Code*

a: 50¢   b: $1   c: $2-$3   d: $4-$5   e: $6-$7

f: $8-$9   g: $10-$14   h: $15-$19   i: $20-$29

j: $30-$39 k: $40-$49 l: $50-$69 m: $70-$89

n: $90-$109   o: $110-$149   p: $150-$199

q: $200-$299   r: $300-$399   s: $400-$499

t: $500-$699 u: $700-$999   v: $1000-$1999

w: $2000-$2999   x: $3000-$3999

y: $4000-$499   z: $5000+

*It is important to remember that quantities
of one chip or a set of chips would have
a much lower unit value per chip.

IVORY
COMMEMORATIVES
AND PLACE NAMES

* See late additions IR-ET and
IR-FQ at the end of this section.

IR-AD
Alamo / v:s

IR-AD
Reverse

IR-AL
Anchor / v:s

IR-AL
Reverse

IR-AT
Anchor / v:s

IR-AT
Reverse

IR-BB
Big Horn / v:t

IR-BB
Reverse

IR-BJ
Bonnefield's / v:t

IR-BJ
Reverse

IR-BR
Bonnefield's / v:t

IR-BR
Reverse

IR-BZ
Brooks's / v:r

IR-BZ
Reverse

IR-CH
Cottage / v:t

IR-CP
Hanover / v:s

IR-CX
Honest / v:s

Reverse is
different.

Graphic
Unavailable

IR-CX
Reverse

IVORY

COMMEMORATIVES

AND PLACE NAMES

IR-DG
Lee / v:s

IR-DF
Lee / v:s

IR-DG & DF
Common Reverse

IR-DJ
Lee / v:s

IR-DJ
Reverse

IR-DR
Middle / v:tl

IR-DR
Reverse

IR-DZ
Mississippi / v:t

IR-DZ
Reverse

IR-EH
Mississippi / v:r

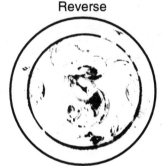

IR-EH
Reverse

IR-EP
Mohammed / v:q

IR-EP
Reverse

*

IR-EX
Natchez / v:s

IR-EX
Reverse

IR-FF
Palace / v:q

IR-FF
Reverse

IR-FN
Queen / v:t

IR-FN
Reverse

192

IVORY
COMMEMORATIVES
AND PLACE NAMES

*

IR-FV
Star of Texas / v:s

IR-FV
Reverse

IR-GD
Star of Texas / v:s

IR-GD
Reverse

IR-GL
Texas Belle / v:s

IR-GL
Reverse

IR-GT
Texas Belle / v:t

IR-GT
Reverse

IR-GV
Texas Belle / v:t

IR-GV
Reverse

IR-HB
Vicksburg / v:t

IR-HB
Reverse

*

IR-ET
Natchez / v:t

IR-ET
Reverse

*

IR-FQ
Tererano / v:l

193

Concentrics

CODES: IX & IY

Antique Chips
Value Rating Code*

a: 50¢   b: $1   c: $2-$3   d: $4-$5   e: $6-$7

f: $8-$9   g: $10-$14   h: $15-$19   i: $20-$29

j: $30-$39   k: $40-$49   l: $50-$69   m: $70-$89

n: $90-$109   o: $110-$149   p: $150-$199

q: $200-$299   r: $300-$399   s: $400-$499

t: $500-$699   u: $700-$999   v: $1000-$1999

w: $2000-$2999   x: $3000-$3999

y: $4000-$499   z: $5000+

***It is important to remember that quantities
of one chip or a set of chips would have
a much lower unit value per chip.**

IVORY
CONCENTRIC

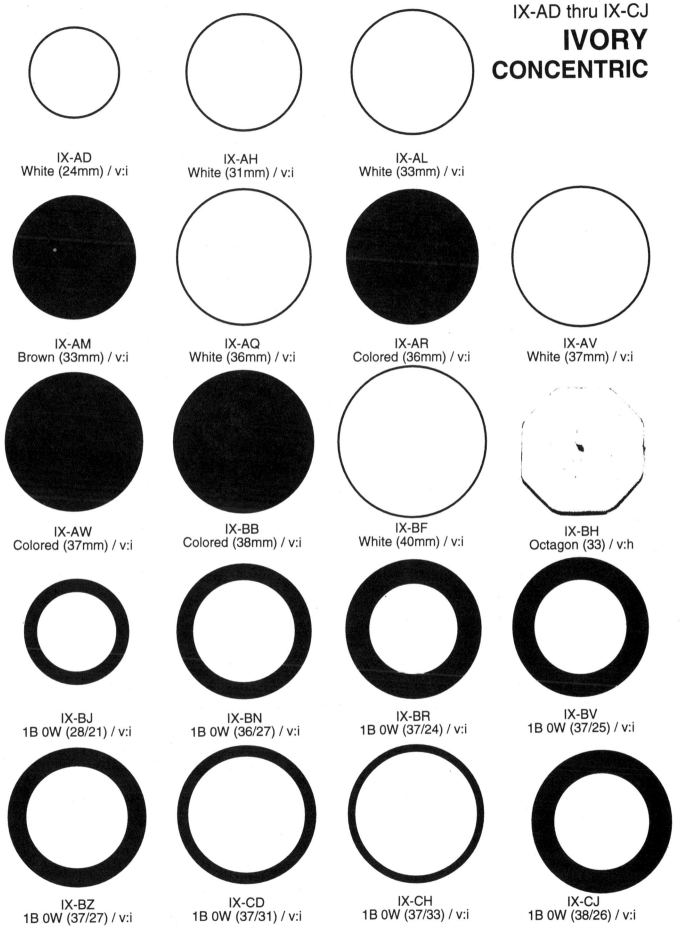

IX-AD
White (24mm) / v:i

IX-AH
White (31mm) / v:i

IX-AL
White (33mm) / v:i

IX-AM
Brown (33mm) / v:i

IX-AQ
White (36mm) / v:i

IX-AR
Colored (36mm) / v:i

IX-AV
White (37mm) / v:i

IX-AW
Colored (37mm) / v:i

IX-BB
Colored (38mm) / v:i

IX-BF
White (40mm) / v:i

IX-BH
Octagon (33) / v:h

IX-BJ
1B 0W (28/21) / v:i

IX-BN
1B 0W (36/27) / v:i

IX-BR
1B 0W (37/24) / v:i

IX-BV
1B 0W (37/25) / v:i

IX-BZ
1B 0W (37/27) / v:i

IX-CD
1B 0W (37/31) / v:i

IX-CH
1B 0W (37/33) / v:i

IX-CJ
1B 0W (38/26) / v:i

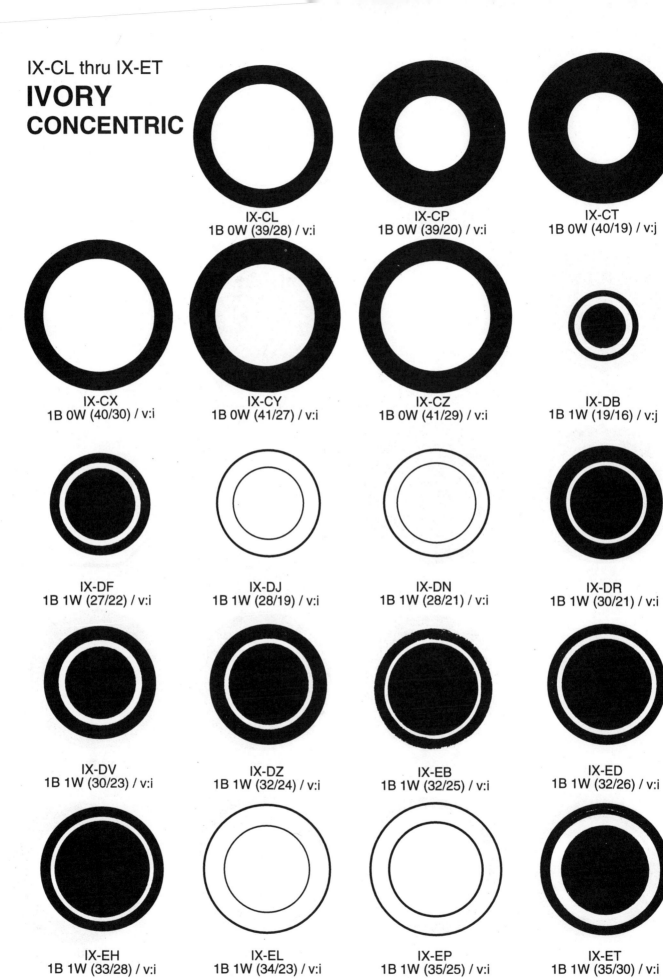

IVORY
CONCENTRIC

IX-CL
1B 0W (39/28) / v:i

IX-CP
1B 0W (39/20) / v:i

IX-CT
1B 0W (40/19) / v:j

IX-CX
1B 0W (40/30) / v:i

IX-CY
1B 0W (41/27) / v:i

IX-CZ
1B 0W (41/29) / v:i

IX-DB
1B 1W (19/16) / v:j

IX-DF
1B 1W (27/22) / v:i

IX-DJ
1B 1W (28/19) / v:i

IX-DN
1B 1W (28/21) / v:i

IX-DR
1B 1W (30/21) / v:i

IX-DV
1B 1W (30/23) / v:i

IX-DZ
1B 1W (32/24) / v:i

IX-EB
1B 1W (32/25) / v:i

IX-ED
1B 1W (32/26) / v:i

IX-EH
1B 1W (33/28) / v:i

IX-EL
1B 1W (34/23) / v:i

IX-EP
1B 1W (35/25) / v:i

IX-ET
1B 1W (35/30) / v:i

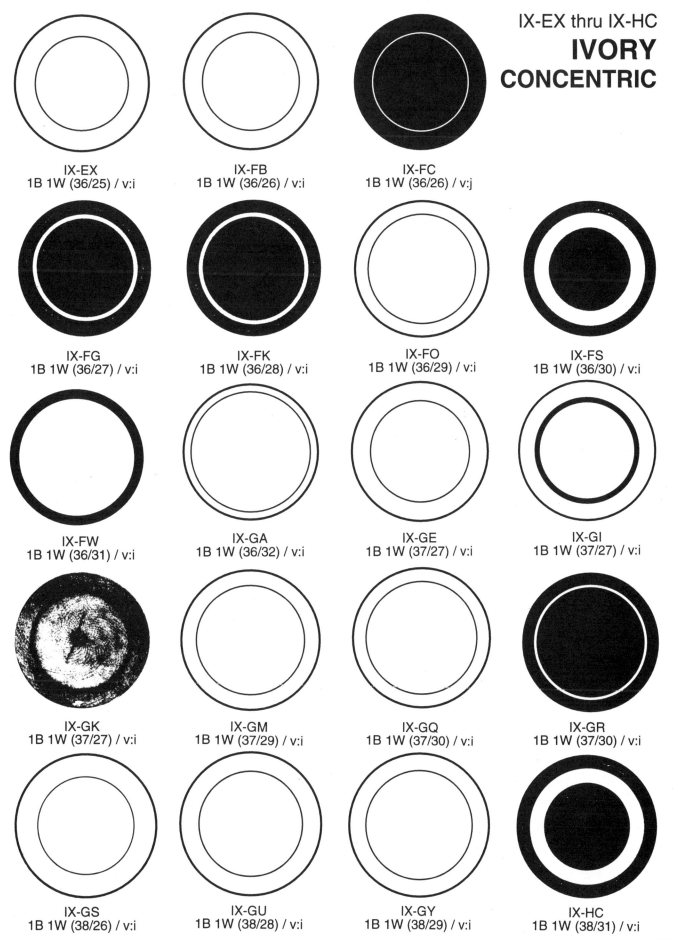

IVORY
CONCENTRIC

IX-EX
1B 1W (36/25) / v:i

IX-FB
1B 1W (36/26) / v:i

IX-FC
1B 1W (36/26) / v:j

IX-FG
1B 1W (36/27) / v:i

IX-FK
1B 1W (36/28) / v:i

IX-FO
1B 1W (36/29) / v:i

IX-FS
1B 1W (36/30) / v:i

IX-FW
1B 1W (36/31) / v:i

IX-GA
1B 1W (36/32) / v:i

IX-GE
1B 1W (37/27) / v:i

IX-GI
1B 1W (37/27) / v:i

IX-GK
1B 1W (37/27) / v:i

IX-GM
1B 1W (37/29) / v:i

IX-GQ
1B 1W (37/30) / v:i

IX-GR
1B 1W (37/30) / v:i

IX-GS
1B 1W (38/26) / v:i

IX-GU
1B 1W (38/28) / v:i

IX-GY
1B 1W (38/29) / v:i

IX-HC
1B 1W (38/31) / v:i

IVORY
CONCENTRIC

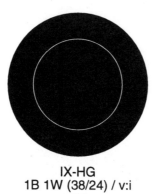

IX-HG
1B 1W (38/24) / v:i

IX-HK
1B 1W (39/24) / v:i

IX-HO
1B 1W (39/34) / v:i

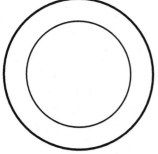

IX-HS
1B 1W (40/28) / v:i

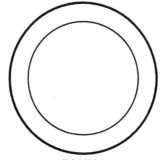

IX-HU
1B 1W (40/30) / v:i

IX-HW
1B 2W (25/16) / v:i

IX-IA
1B 2W (28/20) / v:i

IX-IE
1B 2W (32/24) / v:i

IX-II
1B 2W (36/28) / v:i

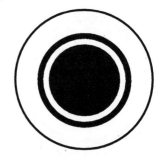

IX-IM
1B 2W (37/24) / v:i

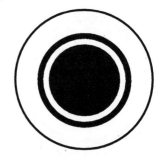

IX-IQ
1B 2W (37/25) / v:i

IX-IU
1B 2W (37/29) / v:i

IX-IY
2B 1W (32/22) / v:i

IX-JC
2B 1W (33/22) / v:i

IX-JG
2B 1W (33/23) / v:j

IX-JK
2B 1W (35/25) / v:i

IX-JO
2B 1W (35/29) / v:i

IX-JS
2B 1W (36/25) / v:i

IX-JW
2B 1W (36/29) / v:i

IVORY
CONCENTRIC

IX-JY
2B 1W (37/26) / v:i

IX-KA
2B 1W (37/28) / v:i

IX-KE
2B 1W (37/29) / v:i

IX-KI
2B 1W (37/30) / v:i

IX-KK
2B 1W (37/31) / v:i

IX-KM
2B 2W (25/19) / v:i

IX-KQ
2B 2W (25/21) / v:i

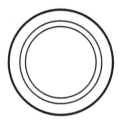

IX-KU
2B 2W (25/22) / v:i

IX-KY
2B 2W (26/21) / v:i

IX-LC
2B 2W (27/21) / v:i

IX-LG
2B 2W (28/22) / v:i

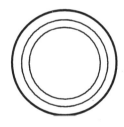

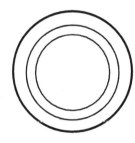

IX-LK
2B 2W (28/25) / v:i

IX-LO
2B 2W (28/23) / v:i

IX-LS
2B 2W (31/24) / v:i

IX-LW
2B 2W (32/25) / v:i

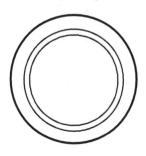
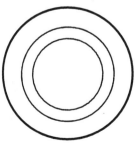

IX-MA
2B 2W (32/28) / v:i

IX-ME
2B 2W (32/28) / V:I

IX-MI
2B 2W (34/27) / v:i

IX-MM
2B 2W (35/25) / v:i

IX-MQ thru IX-PC
IVORY
CONCENTRIC

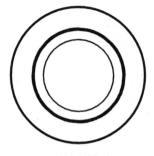

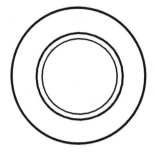

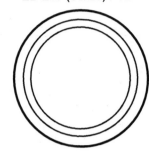

IX-MQ
2B 2W (35/29) / v:i

IX-MU
2B 2W (36/23) / v:i

IX-MY
2B 2W (36/25) / v:i

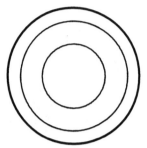

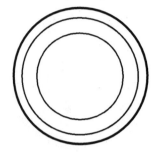

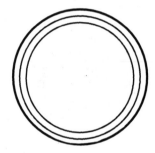

IX-NC
2B 2W (36/26) / v:i

IX-NG
2B 2W (36/29) / v:i

IX-NK
2B 2W (36/31) / v:i

IX-NO
2B 2W (36/31) / v:i

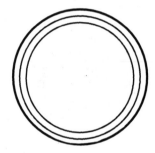

IX-NS
2B 2W (36/32) / v:i

IX-NW
2B 2W (36/32) / v:i

IX-OA
2B 2W (36/33) / v:i

IX-OE
2B 2W (36/33) / v:i

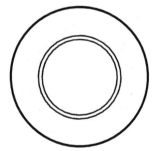

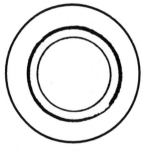

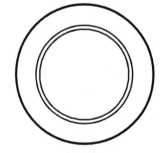

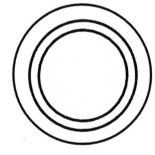

IX-OI
2B 2W (37/22) / v:i

IX-OK
2B 2W (37/25) / v:i

IX-OM
2B 2W (37/26) / v:i

IX-OQ
2B 2W (37/29) / v:i

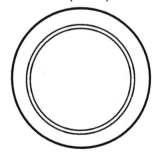

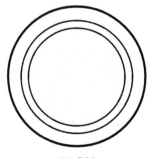

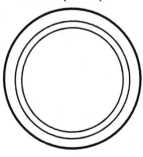

IX-OU
2B 2W (37/29) / v:i

IX-OW
2B 2W (37/29) / v:i

IX-OY
2B 2W (37/30) / v:i

IX-PC
2B 2W (37/31) / v:i

202

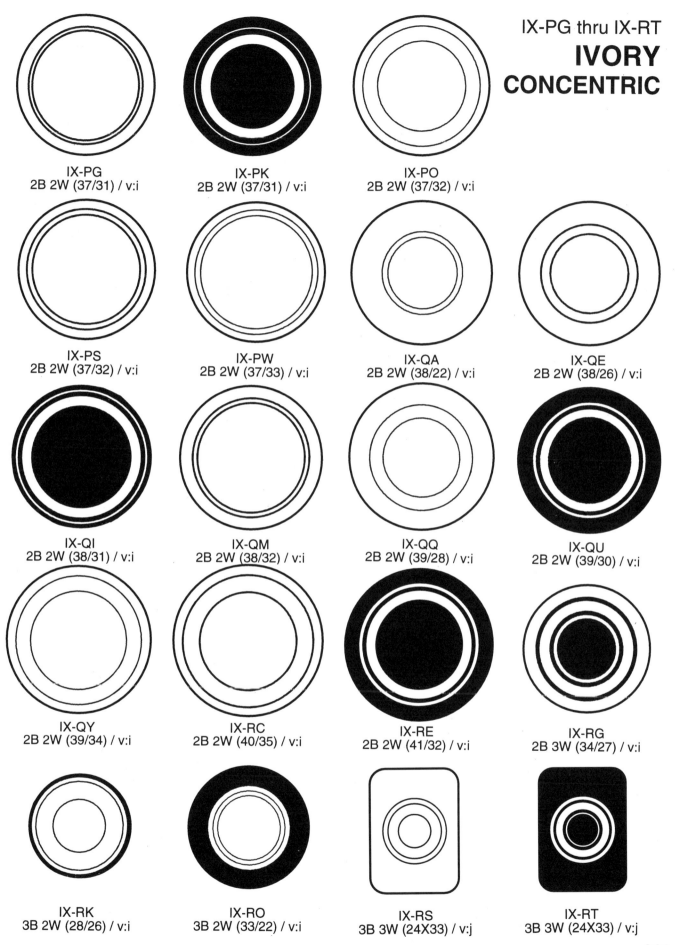

IX-PG
2B 2W (37/31) / v:i

IX-PK
2B 2W (37/31) / v:i

IX-PO
2B 2W (37/32) / v:i

IX-PS
2B 2W (37/32) / v:i

IX-PW
2B 2W (37/33) / v:i

IX-QA
2B 2W (38/22) / v:i

IX-QE
2B 2W (38/26) / v:i

IX-QI
2B 2W (38/31) / v:i

IX-QM
2B 2W (38/32) / v:i

IX-QQ
2B 2W (39/28) / v:i

IX-QU
2B 2W (39/30) / v:i

IX-QY
2B 2W (39/34) / v:i

IX-RC
2B 2W (40/35) / v:i

IX-RE
2B 2W (41/32) / v:i

IX-RG
2B 3W (34/27) / v:i

IX-RK
3B 2W (28/26) / v:i

IX-RO
3B 2W (33/22) / v:i

IX-RS
3B 3W (24X33) / v:j

IX-RT
3B 3W (24X33) / v:j

IVORY
CONCENTRIC

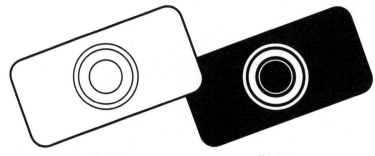

IX-RU
3B 3W (24X49) / v:j

IX-RV
3B 3W (24X49) / v:j

IX-RZ
3B 3W (25/18) / v:i

IX-SD
3B 3W (25/19) / v:i

IX-SH
3B 3W (25/19) / v:i

IX-SL
3B 3W (25/20) / v:i

IX-SP
3B 3W (26/23) / v:i

IX-ST
3B 3W (27/21) / v:i

IX-SX
3B 3W (27/21) / v:i

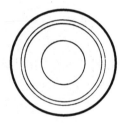

IX-TB
3B 3W (28/22) / v:i

IX-TD
3B 3W (29/22) / v:i

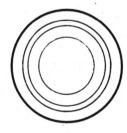

IX-TF
3B 3W (30/24) / v:i

IX-TJ
3B 3W (30/25) / v:i

IX-TL
3B 3W (31/22) / v:i

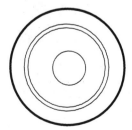

IX-TN
3B 3W (31/23) / v:i

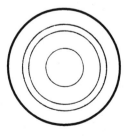

IX-TP
3B 3W (31/23) / v:i

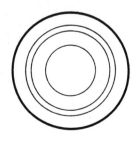

IX-TR
3B 3W (31/24) / v:i

IX-TV
3B 3W (31/27) / v:i

IVORY
CONCENTRIC

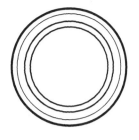

IX-TZ
3B 3W (31/28) / v:i

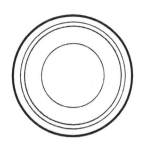

IX-UD
3B 3W (32/28) / v:i

IX-UH
3B 3W (32/29) / v:i

IX-UL
3B 3W (32/29) / v:i

IX-UP
3B 3W (33/24) / v:i

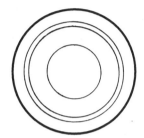

IX-UT
3B 3W (33/27) / v:i

IX-UX
3B 3W (33/27) / v:i

IX-VB
3B 3W (33/30) / v:i

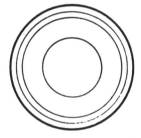

IX-VF
3B 3W (33/30) / v:i

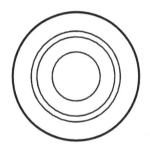

IX-VJ
3B 3W (34/27) / v:i

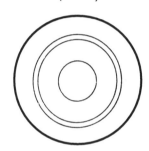

IX-VN
3B 3W (34/24) / v:i

IX-VR
3B 3W (34/26) / v:i

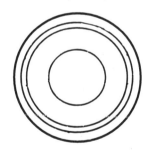

IX-VV
3B 3W (34/28) / v:i

IX-VX
3B 3W (35/28) / v:i

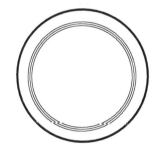

IX-VZ
3B 3W (35/30) / v:i

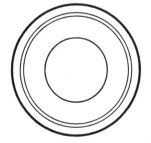

IX-WA
3B 3W (35/30) / v:i

IX-WB
3B 3W (35/31) / v:i

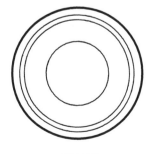

IX-WD
3B 3W (35/31) / v:i

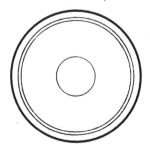

IX-WH
3B 3W (35/31) / v:i

IX-WL thru IX-ZB
IVORY
CONCENTRIC

IX-WL
3B 3W (35/31) / v:i

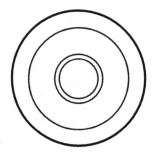

IX-WP
3B 3W (35/31) / v:i

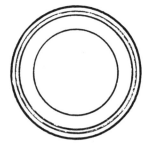

IX-WT
3B 3W (35/32) / v:i

IX-WV
3B 3W (35/32) / v:i

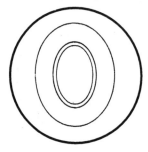

IX-WX
3B 3W (36/22X27) / v:l

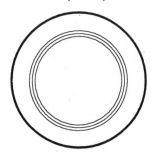

IX-XB
3B 3W (36/27) / v:i

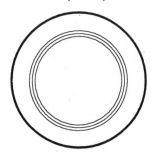

IX-XF
3B 3W (36/27) / v:i

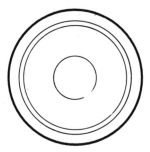

IX-XJ
3B 3W (36/30) / v:i

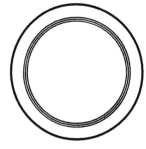

IX-XN
3B 3W (36/30) / v:i

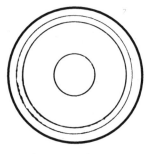

IX-XR
3B 3W (36/31) / v:i

IX-XV
3B 3W (36/31) / v:j

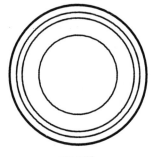

IX-XZ
3B 3W (37/34) / v:i

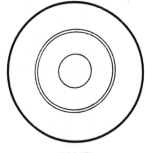

IX-YD
3B 3W (37/22) / v:i

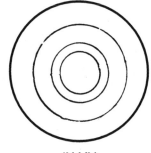

IX-YH
3B 3W (37/25) / v:i

IX-YL
3B 3W (37/26) / v:i

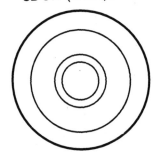

IX-YP
3B 3W 37/27) / v:i

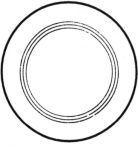

IX-YT
3B 3W (37/27) / v:i

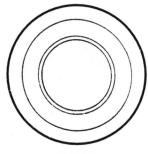

IX-YX
3B 3W (37/29) / v:i

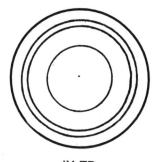

IX-ZB
3B 3W (37/31) / v:i

206

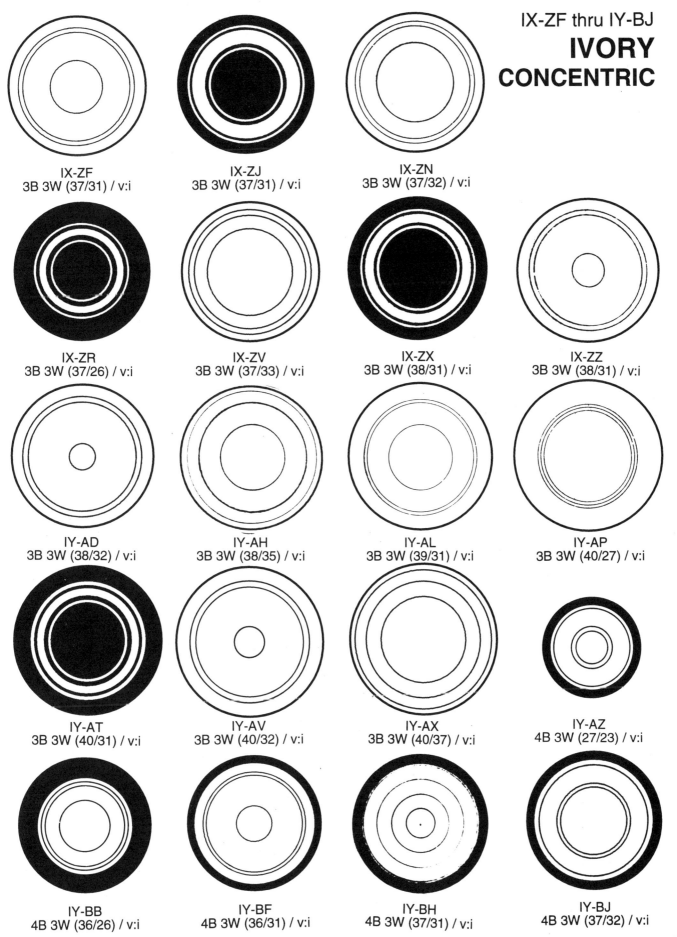

IVORY
CONCENTRIC

IX-ZF
3B 3W (37/31) / v:i

IX-ZJ
3B 3W (37/31) / v:i

IX-ZN
3B 3W (37/32) / v:i

IX-ZR
3B 3W (37/26) / v:i

IX-ZV
3B 3W (37/33) / v:i

IX-ZX
3B 3W (38/31) / v:i

IX-ZZ
3B 3W (38/31) / v:i

IY-AD
3B 3W (38/32) / v:i

IY-AH
3B 3W (38/35) / v:i

IY-AL
3B 3W (39/31) / v:i

IY-AP
3B 3W (40/27) / v:i

IY-AT
3B 3W (40/31) / v:i

IY-AV
3B 3W (40/32) / v:i

IY-AX
3B 3W (40/37) / v:i

IY-AZ
4B 3W (27/23) / v:i

IY-BB
4B 3W (36/26) / v:i

IY-BF
4B 3W (36/31) / v:i

IY-BH
4B 3W (37/31) / v:i

IY-BJ
4B 3W (37/32) / v:i

IY-BR thru IY-ED
IVORY
CONCENTRIC

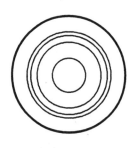

IY-BR
4B 4W (31/23) / v:i

IY-BV
4B 4W (31/27) / v:i

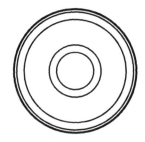

IY-BZ
4B 4W (33/32) / v:i

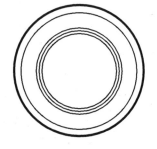

IY-CD
4B 4W (35/31) / v:i

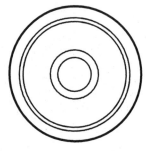

IY-CH
4B 4W (36/30) / v:i

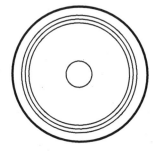

IY-CL
4B 4W (36/31) / v:i

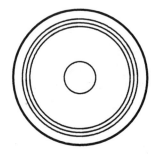

IY-CP
4B 4W (36/31) / v:i

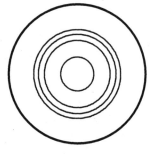

IY-CT
4B 4W (37/24) / v:i

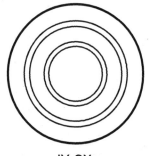

IY-CX
4B 4W (37/28) / v:i

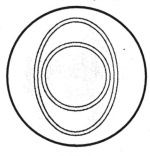

IY-DB
4B 4W (37/31x22) / v:i

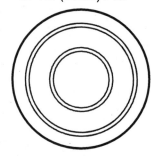

IY-DF
4B 4W (37/30) / v:i

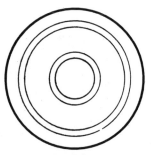

IY-DG
4B 4W (37/30) / v:i

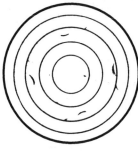

IY-DJ
4B 4W (37/31) / v:i

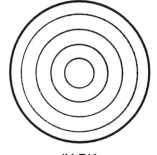

IY-DK
4B 4W (37/31) / v:i

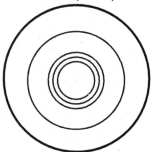

IY-DN
4B 4W (39/26) / v:i

IY-DR
4B 4W (39/32) / v:k

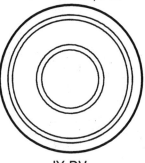

IY-DV
4B 4W (39/34) / v:i

IY-DZ
4B 4W (39/35) / v:l

IY-ED
5B 4W (37/33) / v:j

IVORY
CONCENTRIC

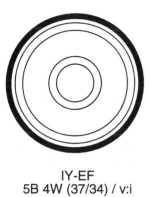

IY-EF
5B 4W (37/34) / v:i

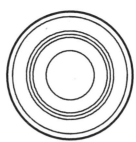

IY-EH
5B 5W (29/27) / v:i

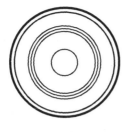

IY-EL
5B 5W (34/31) / v:i

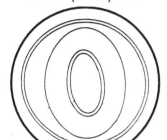

IY-EP
5B 5W (40/34) / v:l

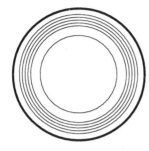

IY-ET
5B 5W (35/32) / v:i

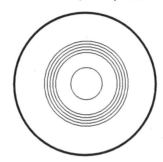

IY-EX
6B 6W (38/23) / v:i

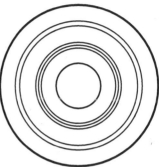

IY-FB
6B 6W (43/34) / v:l

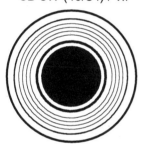

IY-FF
6B 7W (35/31) / v:j

IY-FJ
7B 7W (24/22) v:i

IY-FN
7B 7W (25/22) v:i

IY-FR
7B 7W (25/23) v:i

IY-FV
7B 7W (27/24) v:i

IY-FZ
7B 7W (27/24) v:i

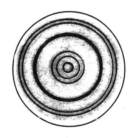

IY-GD
7B 7W (30/26) v:i

IY-GH
7B 7W (30/26) v:i

IY-GM
7B 7W (30/27) v:i

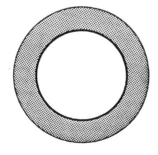

IY-JJ
3 Colors (36/24) / v:i

IY-JN
3 Colors (33/23) / v:i

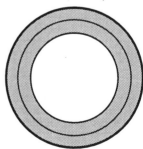

IY-JR
3 Colors (37/31) / v:i

209

IY-JV thru IY-KL
IVORY
CONCENTRIC

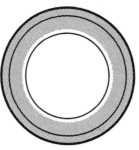

IY-JV
3 Colors (36/32) / v:i

IY-JZ
3 Colors (33/22) / v:i

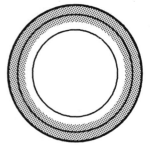

IY-KD
3 Colors (36/31) / v:i

IY-KH
3 Colors (37/31) / v:i

IY-KL
3 Colors (35/33) / v:i

IVORY
Recent Creations
& Suspected Fakes

CODES: IZ

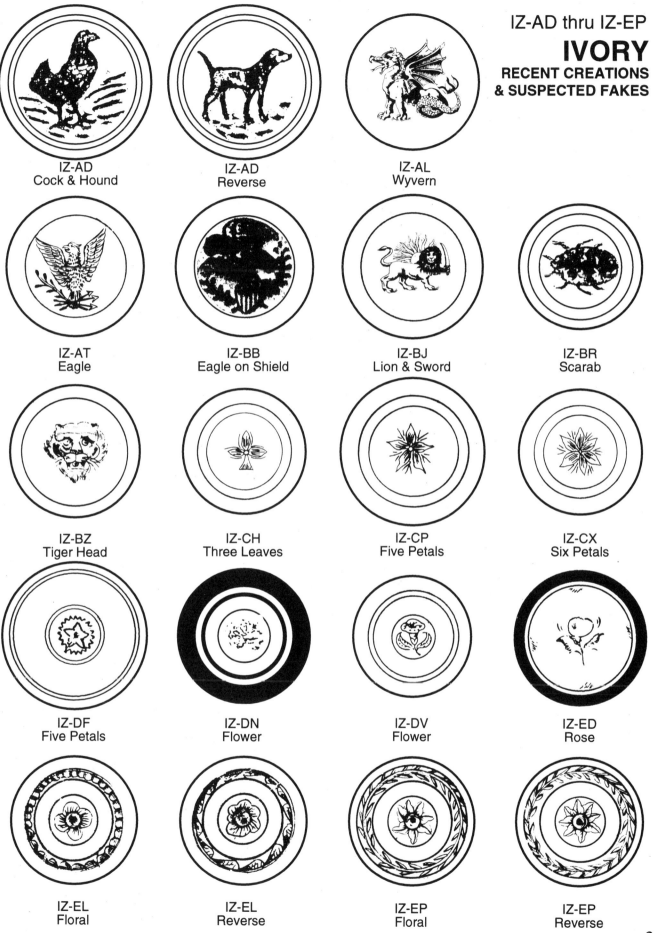

IVORY
RECENT CREATIONS & SUSPECTED FAKES

IZ-AD
Cock & Hound

IZ-AD
Reverse

IZ-AL
Wyvern

IZ-AT
Eagle

IZ-BB
Eagle on Shield

IZ-BJ
Lion & Sword

IZ-BR
Scarab

IZ-BZ
Tiger Head

IZ-CH
Three Leaves

IZ-CP
Five Petals

IZ-CX
Six Petals

IZ-DF
Five Petals

IZ-DN
Flower

IZ-DV
Flower

IZ-ED
Rose

IZ-EL
Floral

IZ-EL
Reverse

IZ-EP
Floral

IZ-EP
Reverse

213

IVORY
RECENT CREATIONS
& SUSPECTED FAKES

IZ-ET
Design

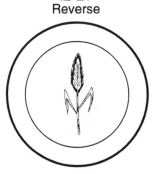

IZ-ET
Reverse

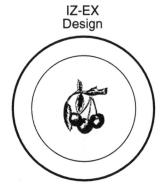

IZ-EX
Design

IZ-EX
Reverse

IZ-FF
Diamond

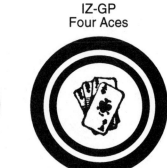

IZ-FN
Wheat

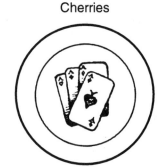

IZ-FR
Cherries

IZ-FV
Double Star

IZ-FZ
Shield

IZ-GH
Maltese Cross

IZ-GP
Four Aces

IZ-GP
Reverse

IZ-GT
Four Aces

IZ-GT
Reverse

IZ-GX
Four Aces

IZ-GX
Reverse

IZ-HB
Four Aces

IZ-HB
Reverse

IZ-HJ
Three

IZ-HL
Five

IZ-HN
Ten

IZ-HP
Twenty

IZ-HR
Fifty

IZ-HZ
Five

IZ-IB
Ten

IZ-ID
Twenty-Five

IZ-IF
Fifty

IZ-IH
One-Hundred

IZ-IP
Five

IZ-IR
Ten

IZ-IT
Twenty-Five

IZ-IV
Fifty

IZ-IX
One-Hundred

IZ-JF
Twenty-Five

IZ-JH
Fifty

IZ-JJ
One-Hundred

IZ-JN
Five

IZ-JZ
Five

215

IVORY
RECENT CREATIONS
& SUSPECTED FAKES

IZ-KH
Five

IZ-KP
Five

IZ-KX
Five

IZ-LF
Twenty-Five

IZ-LN
Twenty-Five

IZ-LV
Twenty-Five

IZ-MD
Fifty

IZ-ML
Fifty

IZ-MT
One-Hundred

IZ-NB
One-Hundred

IZ-NJ
One-Hundred

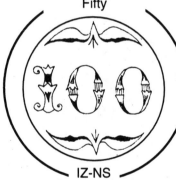

IZ-NS
One-Hundred

IZ-OA
Five

IZ-OA
Reverse

IZ-OE
Ten

IZ-OI
Ten

IZ-OI
Reverse

IZ-OK
Ten

IZ-OK
Reverse

IVORY
RECENT CREATIONS
& SUSPECTED FAKES

IZ-OM
Ten

IZ-OM
Reverse

IZ-OW
ING

IZ-OO
Ten

IZ-OO
Reverse

IZ-OQ
Ten

IZ-OQ
Reverse

IZ-OS
Twenty

IZ-OS
Reverse

IZ-PE
Anchor

IZ-PE
Reverse

IZ-PF
Indian

IZ-PF
Reverse

IZ-PH
Lady & Vase

IZ-PH
Reverse

IZ-PP
Ace Showboats

IZ-PP
Reverse

IZ-PR
Ace Entertainment

IZ-PR
Reverse

IVORY
RECENT CREATIONS
& SUSPECTED FAKES

IZ-PT
Ace Steamboats

IZ=PT
Reverse

IZ-QB
R. E. Lee

IZ-QB
Reverse

IZ-QJ
Star of Texas

IZ-QJ
Reverse

IZ-QN
Star of Texas

IZ-QN
Reverse

IZ-QV
Texas Belle

IZ-QV
Reverse

IZ-QZ
Texas Belle

IZ-QZ
Reverse

IZ-RH
Vicksburg

IZ-RH
Reverse

IZ-RP
Arcadian

IZ-RP
Reverse

IZ-RR
Arcadian

IZ-RR
Reverse

IVORY
**RECENT CREATIONS
& SUSPECTED FAKES**

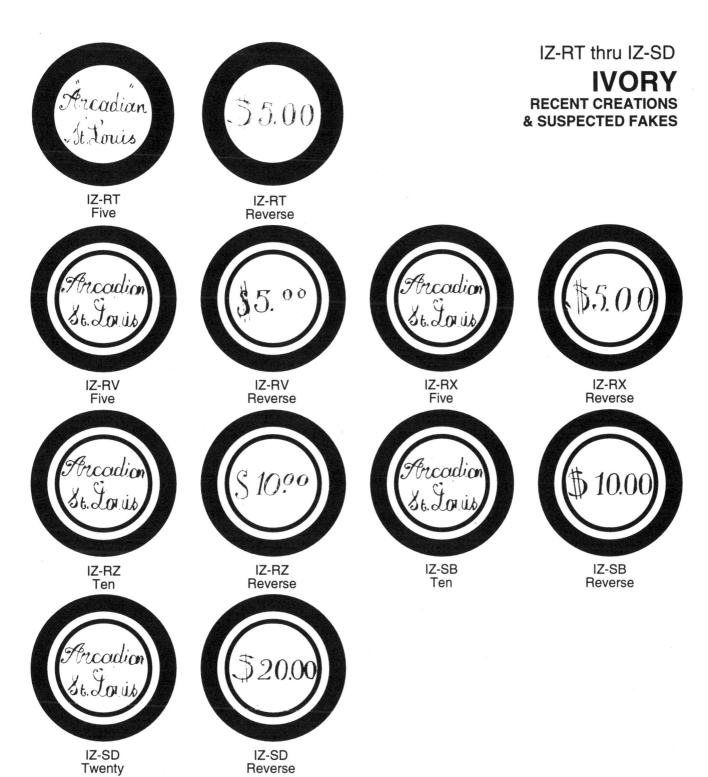

IZ-RT
Five

IZ-RT
Reverse

IZ-RV
Five

IZ-RV
Reverse

IZ-RX
Five

IZ-RX
Reverse

IZ-RZ
Ten

IZ-RZ
Reverse

IZ-SB
Ten

IZ-SB
Reverse

IZ-SD
Twenty

IZ-SD
Reverse

SELECTED EXAMPLES
IVORY ERRORS

Because ivory chips were mostly hand crafted, there were often variations and errors within a set of chips. Sometimes the front and back would be different. Sometimes the detail on one element of the chip would be omitted (probably close to quitting time.) Some samples of these kinds of errors are illustrated below:

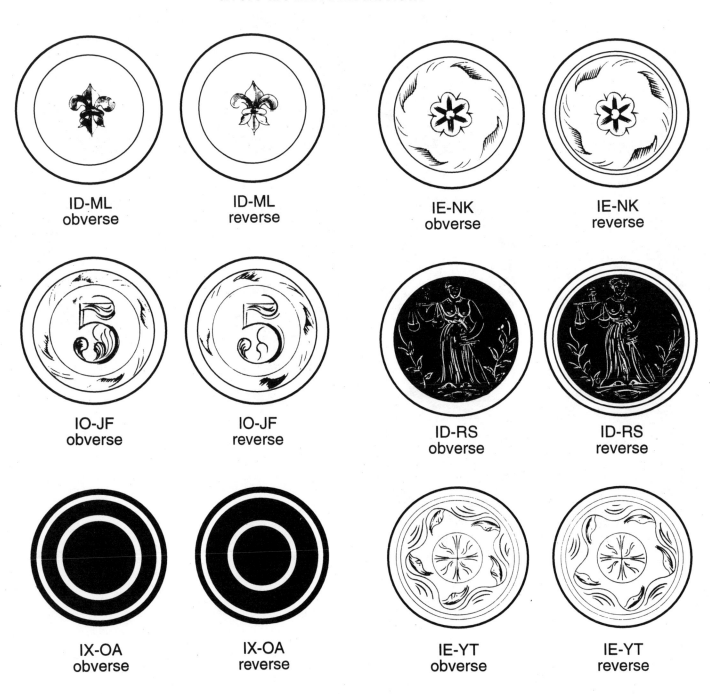

ID-ML
obverse

ID-ML
reverse

IE-NK
obverse

IE-NK
reverse

IO-JF
obverse

IO-JF
reverse

ID-RS
obverse

ID-RS
reverse

IX-OA
obverse

IX-OA
reverse

IE-YT
obverse

IE-YT
reverse

IVORY
Unusual Chips
CODES NONE

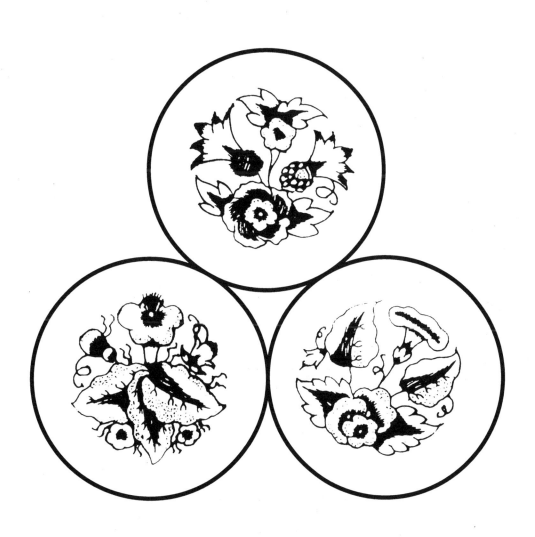

Sixteen ivory chips comprised a set used to play
Chaupat or *Viz-Gap-Tam*, a game played in India.
The 8 rounds and 8 rectangles were only engraved
on one side of the chip. Boxes designed to hold
the16 chips were usually very elaborate.

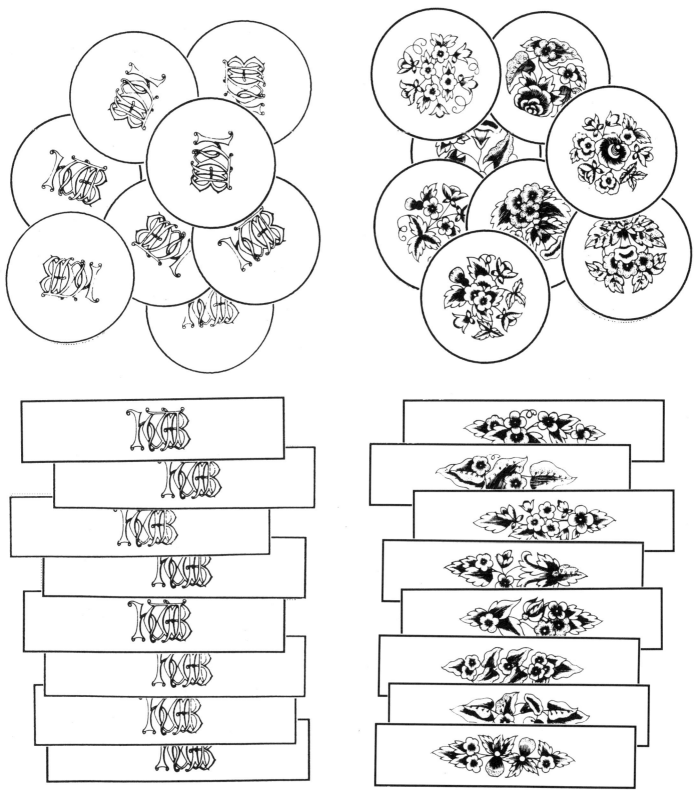

UNCODED SAMPLES
IVORY
UNUSUAL

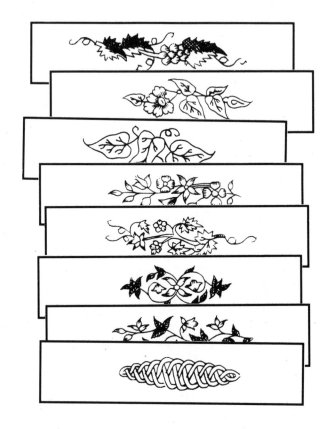

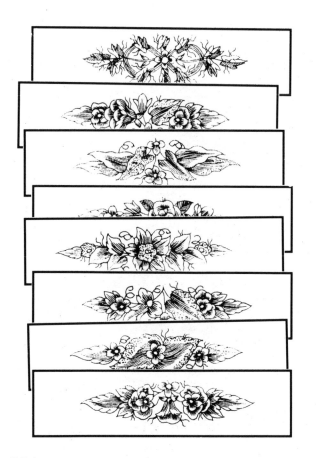

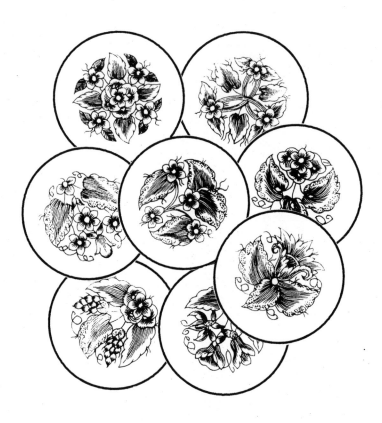

Eighteenth Century French Counters

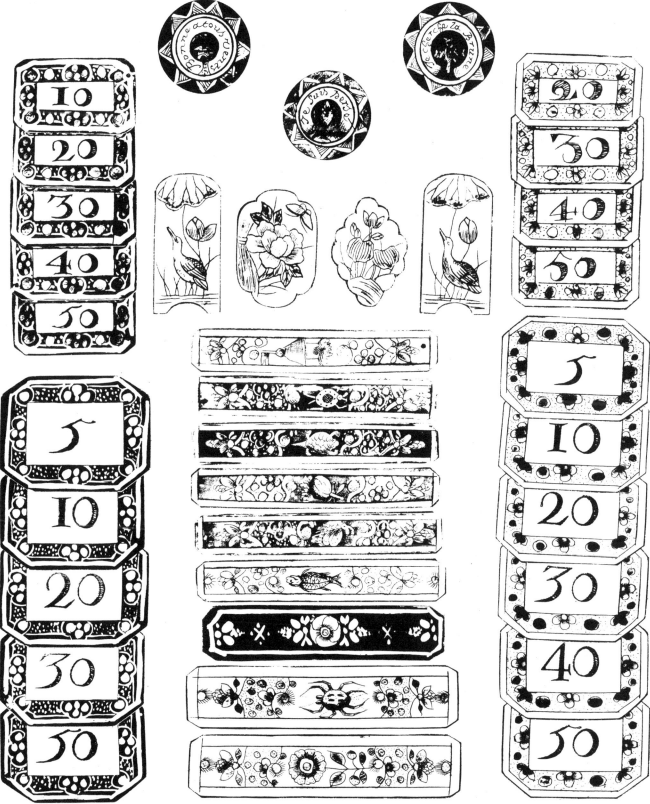

IVORY
UNUSUAL

Eighteenth Century French Counters

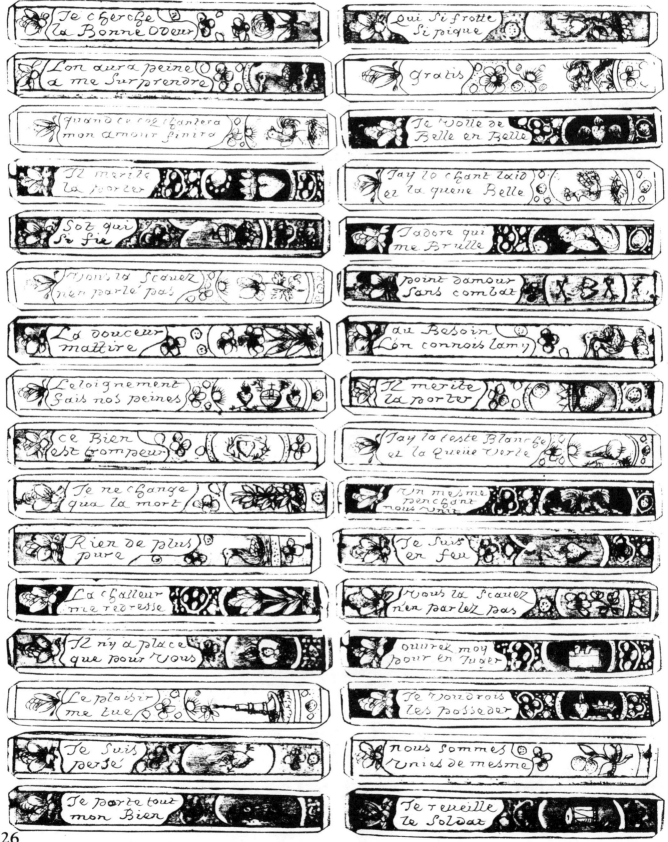

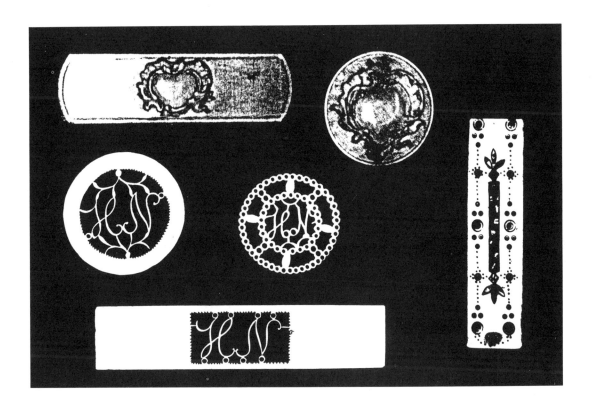

The three initialed game counters were each carved from one piece of ivory. The piece on the right contains semi-precious gems. The two French pieces at the top were carved so that initials could be added.

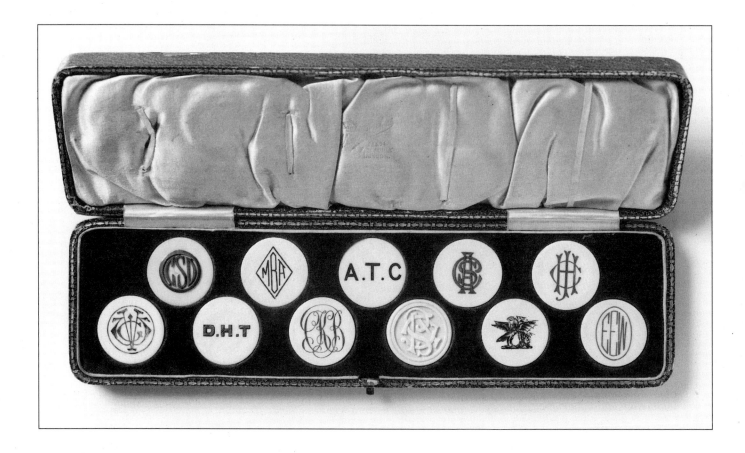

A photo of an English salesman's ivory chip sample case. The company must not have been too successful, as few of these style chips have ever been found.

POKER
Animals
& Reptiles
CODES: PA

Antique Chips
Value Rating Code*

a: 50¢   b: $1   c: $2-$3   d: $4-$5   e: $6-$7

f: $8-$9   g: $10-$14   h: $15-$19   i: $20-$29

j: $30-$39   k: $40-$49   l: $50-$69   m: $70-$89

n: $90-$109   o: $110-$149   p: $150-$199

q: $200-$299   r: $300-$399   s: $400-$499

t: $500-$699   u: $700-$999   v: $1000-$1999

w: $2000-$2999   x: $3000-$3999

y: $4000-$499   z: $5000+

*It is important to remember that quantities
of one chip or a set of chips would have
a much lower unit value per chip.

230

POKER
ANIMALS &
REPTILES

PA-AB Beaver
Inlaid Litho / v:g

PA-AF Bear
Engraved / v:f

PA-AJ Dancing Bears
Embossed / v:e

PA-AP Buffalo Head
Inlaid Litho / v:g

PA-AS Buffalo Head
Inlaid Litho / v:g

PA-AV Old Tom
Engraved / v:e

PA-AV Old Tom
Variation Example

PA-BC House Cat
Engraved / v:f

PA-BG House Cat
Engraved / v:f

PA-BK Tabby
Engraved / v:e

PA-BP Kitty
Engraved / v:e

PA-BT Kitten on Table
Engraved / v:f

PA-BZ Bull Dog
Engraved / v:c

PA-CD Dog Head
Engraved / v:e

PA-CD Dog Head
Variation Example

PA-CH Dog Head
Engraved / v:f

PA-CK Dog Head
Engraved / v:g

PA-CK Dog Head
Variation Example

PA-CN Rin Tin Tin
Inlaid Litho / v:g

POKER
ANIMALS & REPTILES

PA-CS Spaniel
Inlaid Litho / v:g

PA-CW Po Do
Embossed & Interlocking / v:b

PA-DA Dog Head
Engraved / v:g

PA-DD Retriever
Embossed / v:f

PA-DG Retriever
Engraved / v:e

PA-DG Retriever
Variation Example

PA-DP Pointer
Engraved / v:g

PA-DR Retriever w Stick
Engraved / v:e

PA-DR Retriever w Stick
Variation Example

PA-DT Scottie
Embossed / v:b

PA-DT Scottie
Embossed / v:e

PA-DZ Bull Dog
Engraved / v:h

PA-ED Bull Dog
Engraved / v:g

PA-EG Terrier
Embossed / v:d

PS-EJ Dog on a Log
In Sports Section

PA-EK Bully Boy
Engraved / v:f

PA-EP Bull Dog
Engraved / v:f

PA-ER Retriever & Rabbit
Engraved / v:f

PA-EX Fox Head
Engraved / v:g

232

POKER
ANIMALS &
REPTILES

PA-FA Elephant Head
Engraved / v:g

PA-FE Elephant Head
Engraved / v:g

PA-FJ Elephant
Engraved / v:g

PA-FL Elephant
Engraved / v:g

PA-FP Elephant
Engraved / v:e

PA-FS Elephant
Engraved / v:e

PA-FS Elephant
Variation Example

PA-FY Elephant
Engraved / v:f

PA-GE Lucky Elephant
Embossed / v:b

PA-GH Deer Head
Engraved / v:f

PA-GK Deer Head
Engraved / v:f

PA-GK Deer Head
Variation Example

PA-GR Deer
Embossed / v:g

PA-GW Elk Head
Engraved / v:f

PS-HA Elk Head
Engraved / v:f

PA-HE Elk Head
Engraved / v:d

PA-HH Elk Head
Engraved / v:c

PA-HL Elk Head
Engraved / v:c

PA-HL Elk Head
Variation Example

233

POKER
ANIMALS &
REPTILES

PA-HP Elk Head
Engraved / v:f

PA-HS Elk Head
Inlaid Litho / v:f

PA-HV Elk Head
Inlaid Litho v:f

PM-LL Eleven O'Clock
In Misc. Section

PA-HZ Elk Head
Engraved / v:b

PA-JA Elk Head
Engraved / v:f

PA-JE Moose Head
Inlaid Litho / v:f

PA-JJ Moose Head
Embossed / v:f

PA-JM Moose Head
Engraved / v:f

PA-JR Frog
Engraved / v:f

PA-JW Home Sweet Home
Engraved / v:f

PA-KA Griffin
Embossed / v:c

PA-KD Dragon
Embossed / v:c

PA-KH Dragon
Embossed / v:c

PS-KH Dragon
Variation Example

PA-KS Dragon
Engraved / v:f

PA-KW Horse Head
Engraved / v:g

PA-LA Pony Head
Engraved / v:e

PA-LA Pony Head
Variation Example

234

PA-LE Pony Head
Engraved / v:f

PA-LH Horse Head
Engraved / v:g

PA-LP Pony Head
Engraved / v:g

PA-LS Horse Head
Engraved / v:f

PA-LW Horse Head
Embossed Interlocking / v:b

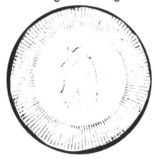

PA-MA Horse Head
Embossed Interlocking / v:b

PA-MH Horse Head
Embossed-Stamped / v:e

Words "HORSE
HEAD" on chip.
Illustration not
available

PA-ML Horse Head
Engraved / v:h

PA-MQ Horse
Inlaid Litho / v:g

PA-MY Donkey
Engraved / v:g

PA-NH Three horses
Engraved / v:e

PA-NM Three Horses
Engraved / v:e

PA-NR Major General
Engraved / v:f

PA-NX Majestic
Inlaid Litho / v:f

PA-NX Majestic
Variation Example

PA-PH Horse Head
Engraved / v:e

PA-PL Lobster
Embossed / v:c

PA-PR Crab
Engraved / v:e

PA-PT Pig Tail
Engraved / v:f

235

POKER
ANIMALS &
REPTILES

PA-PZ Pig Chef
Machined & Stamped / v:e

PA-PZ Pig Chef
Reverse

PA-RD Pony Head
Engraved / v:e

PA-RH Ram's Head
Embossed / v:e

PA-RM Ram's Head
Embossed / v:c

PA-RS Rattlesnake
Engraved / v:g

PA-RY Three Snakes
Engraved / v:e

Three Crescents
In Design Section

PA-SA Steer Head
Engraved / v:e

PA-SA Steer Head
Variation Example

PA-SH Steer Head
Engraved / v:e

PA-SH Steer Head
Variation Example

PA-SM Steer Head
Engraved / v:e

PA-SP Steer Head
Inlaid Litho / v:g

PA-ST Steer Head
Engraved / v:d

PA-TA Lion Head
Inlaid Litho / v:f

PA-TF Lion Rampant
Engraved / v:c

PA-TF Lion Rampant
Variation Example

PA-TJ Lion on Crest
Engraved / v:f

236

POKER
ANIMALS &
REPTILES

PA-TL Lion on Crest
Engraved / v:e

PA-TQ Tiger Head
Engraved / v:g

PA-TT Tiger Head
Engraved / v:f

PA-TT Tiger Head
Variation Example

PA-TZ Tiger Head
Engraved / v:f

PA-TZ Tiger Head
Variation Example

PA-UC Tiger Head
Engraved / v:f

PA-UL Tiger
Engraved / v:g

PA-UT Tiger
Inlaid Litho / v:g

237

POKER
Birds & Insects

CODES: PB

Antique Chips
Value Rating Code*

a: 50¢ b: $1 c: $2-$3 d: $4-$5 e: $6-$7

f: $8-$9 g: $10-$14 h: $15-$19 i: $20-$29

j: $30-$39 k: $40-$49 l: $50-$69 m: $70-$89

n: $90-$109   o: $110-$149   p: $150-$199

q: $200-$299   r: $300-$399   s: $400-$499

t: $500-$699 u: $700-$999 v: $1000-$1999

w: $2000-$2999   x: $3000-$3999

y: $4000-$499   z: $5000+

***It is important to remember that quantities
of one chip or a set of chips would have
a much lower unit value per chip.**

POKER
BIRDS &
INSECTS

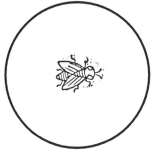

PB-AB Bee
Engraved / v:f

PB-AF Monarch Bee
Engraved & Embossed / v:f

PB-AT Bee
Engraved / v:f

PB-AN Beehive
Engraved / v:h

PB-AR Beehive
Engraved / v:e

PB-AV Beehive
Engraved / v:f

PB-AZ Beehive
Engraved / v:f

PB-AZ Beehive
Variation Example

PB-BB Beehive
Engraved / v:e

PB-BB Beehive
Variation Example

PB-BD Beehive
Embossed / v:e

PB-BF Butterfly
Engraved / v:e

PB-BF Butterfly
Variation Example

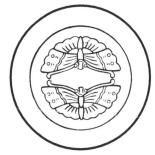

PB-BK Two Butterflies
Engraved / v:f

PB-BP Eagle
Stamped Paper / v:b

PB-BP Eagle
Reverse

PB-BT Eagle
Stamped Paper / v:b

PB-BW Eagle
Stamped Wood / v:c

PB-CA Eagle
Inlaid Litho / v:f

241

POKER
BIRDS &
INSECTS

PB-CE Eagle & Star
Stamped / v:f

PB-CH Eagle
Engraved Interlocking / v:c

PB-DA Eagle
Engraved / v:c

PB-DA Eagle
Variation Example

PB-DE Spread Eagle
Engraved / v:e

PB-DE Spread Eagle
Variation Example

PB-DG Spread Eagle
Engraved / v:e

PB-DG Spread Eagle
Variation Example

PB-DL Eagle on Sieild
Engraved / v:e

PB-DS Eagle on Shield
Embossed / v:e

PB-DW Eagle on Sieild
Engraved / v:f

PB-EG Eagle on Rock
Embossed / v:c

PB-ER Eagle on Rock
Engraved Interlocking / v:d

PB-ES Eagle w Snake
Inlaid Litho / v:f

Graphic
Unavailable

PB-EZ Soaring Eagle
Embossed / v:d

PB-FE Phoenix
Engraved / v:g

PB-OA Owl
Engraved / v:h

PB-OE Owl
Engraved / v:e

PB-OE Owl
Engraved / v:e

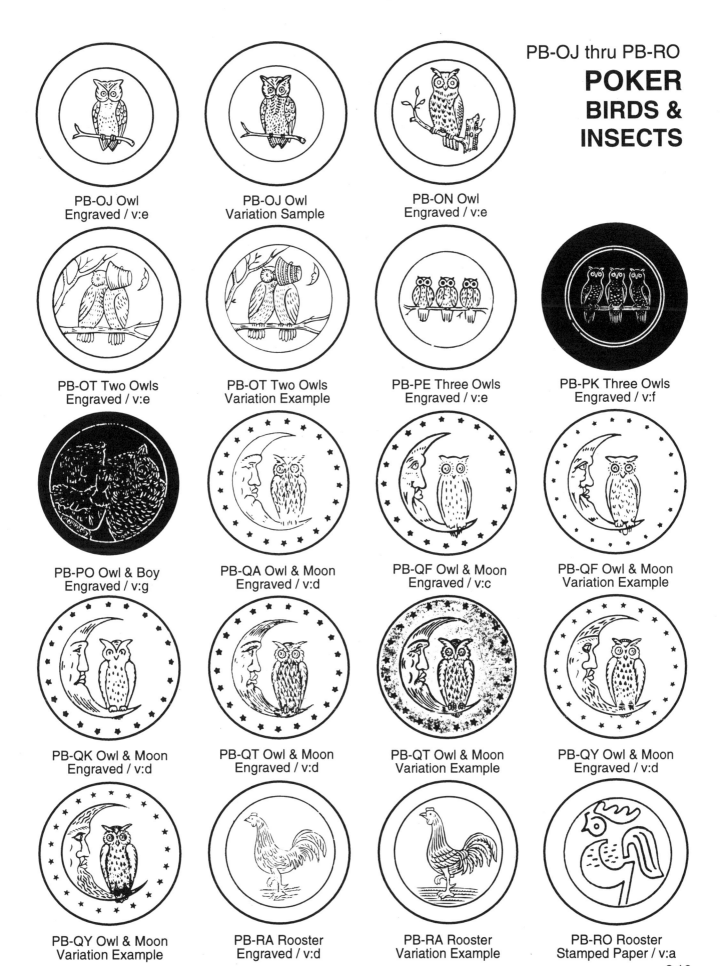

PB-OJ Owl
Engraved / v:e

PB-OJ Owl
Variation Sample

PB-ON Owl
Engraved / v:e

PB-OT Two Owls
Engraved / v:e

PB-OT Two Owls
Variation Example

PB-PE Three Owls
Engraved / v:e

PB-PK Three Owls
Engraved / v:f

PB-PO Owl & Boy
Engraved / v:g

PB-QA Owl & Moon
Engraved / v:d

PB-QF Owl & Moon
Engraved / v:c

PB-QF Owl & Moon
Variation Example

PB-QK Owl & Moon
Engraved / v:d

PB-QT Owl & Moon
Engraved / v:d

PB-QT Owl & Moon
Variation Example

PB-QY Owl & Moon
Engraved / v:d

PB-QY Owl & Moon
Variation Example

PB-RA Rooster
Engraved / v:d

PB-RA Rooster
Variation Example

PB-RO Rooster
Stamped Paper / v:a

POKER
BIRDS &
INSECTS

PB-RO Rooster
Reverse

PB-RS Rooster
Engraved /v:f

PB-SA Turkey
Engraved / v:g

PB-SQ Quail
Inlaid Litho / v:g

PB-ST Quail
Inlaid Litho / v:g

PB-TD Mallard
Inlaid Litho / v:g

PB-TG Goose
Engraved / v:h

PB-WA Swan
Engraved / v:h

PB-WH Swan
Engraved / v:d

PB-WH Swan
Variation Example

PB-WM Swan
Engraved / v:d

PB-WM Swan
Variation Example

PB-WR Swan
Engraved / v:d

PB-WS Swan
Engraved / v:e

PB-WS Swan
Variation Example

PB-XF "The Family"
Paste On / v:g

244

POKER
Playing Cards
CODES: PC

Antique Chips
Value Rating Code*

a: 50¢   b: $1   c: $2-$3   d: $4-$5   e: $6-$7

f: $8-$9   g: $10-$14   h: $15-$19   i: $20-$29

j: $30-$39 k: $40-$49 l: $50-$69 m: $70-$89

n: $90-$109   o: $110-$149   p: $150-$199

q: $200-$299   r: $300-$399   s: $400-$499

t: $500-$699 u: $700-$999 v: $1000-$1999

w: $2000-$2999   x: $3000-$3999

y: $4000-$499   z: $5000+

*It is important to remember that quantities
of one chip or a set of chips would have
a much lower unit value per chip.

POKER PLAYING CARDS

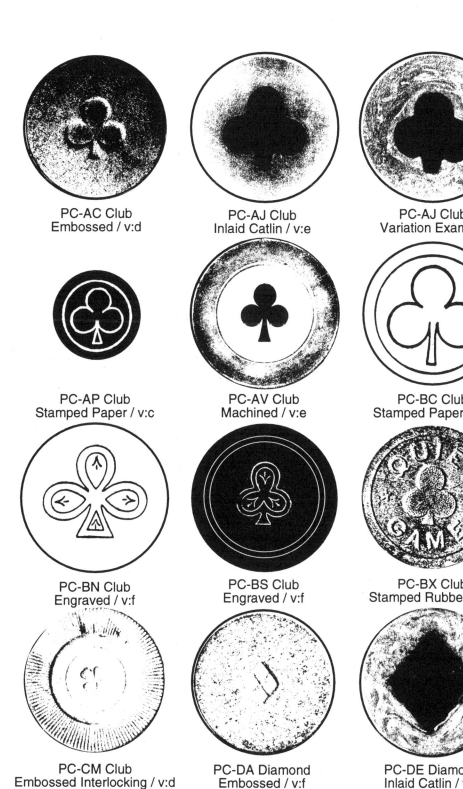

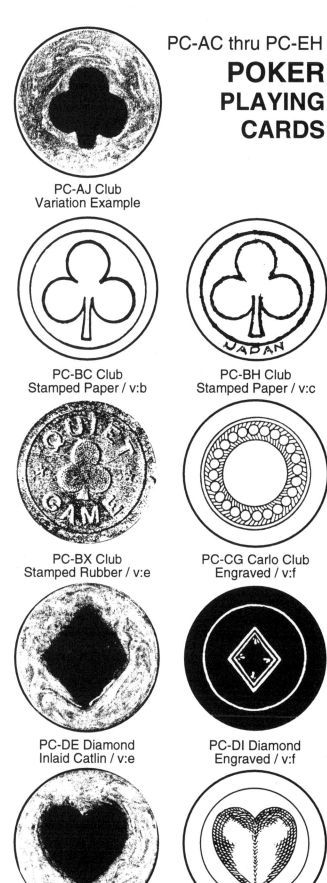

PC-AC Club
Embossed / v:d

PC-AJ Club
Inlaid Catlin / v:e

PC-AJ Club
Variation Example

PC-AP Club
Stamped Paper / v:c

PC-AV Club
Machined / v:e

PC-BC Club
Stamped Paper / v:b

PC-BH Club
Stamped Paper / v:c

PC-BN Club
Engraved / v:f

PC-BS Club
Engraved / v:f

PC-BX Club
Stamped Rubber / v:e

PC-CG Carlo Club
Engraved / v:f

PC-CM Club
Embossed Interlocking / v:d

PC-DA Diamond
Embossed / v:f

PC-DE Diamond
Inlaid Catlin / v:e

PC-DI Diamond
Engraved / v:f

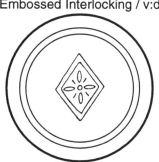

PC-DN Diamond
Engraved / v:f

PC-DR Diamond
Machined / v:e

PC-EA Heart
Inlaid Catlin / v:e

PC-EH Heart
Engraved / v:e

247

POKER
PLAYING
CARDS

PC-EN Heart
Engraved / v:f

PC-EK Heart
Engraved / v:f

PC-EW Black Heart
Machined / v:e

PC-FD Heart & Star
Engraved & Stamped / v:e

PC-FJ Spade
Inlaid Catlin / v:e

PC-FP Spade
Engraved / v:f

PC-FT Spade
Engraved / v:f

PC-GA Monarch Spade
Engraved & Embossed / v:f

PC-GF Black Spade
Machined / v:e

PC-GK Card Suits
Stamped Paper / v:b

PC-GP Card Suits
Embossed / v:g

Note:
On PC-GP, hearts
& diamonds are red
on the blue and white
chips & blue on the
red chips

PC-GP Card Suits
Embossed / v:g

PC-GT Card Suits
Stamped Paper / v:b

PC-GT Card Suits
Reverse

PC-GY Card Suits
Stamped Paper / v:b

PC-GY Card Suits
Reverse

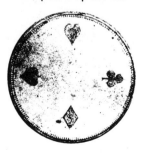

PC-HD Card Suits
Embossed / v:e

PC-HH Card Suits
Embossed & Filled / v:e

PC-HH Card Suits
Variation Example

248

POKER
PLAYING
CARDS

PC-HM Card Suits
Embossed(shallow) / v:b

PC-HP Card Suits
Embossed(deep) / v:b

PC-HT Card Suits
Inlaid Litho / v:g

PC-HX Card Suits
Inlaid Litho / v:g

PC-JA Card Suits
Embossed / v:c

PC-JF Corker
Embossed & Inlaid / v:g

PC-JJ Card Suits
Embossed Interlocking / v:b

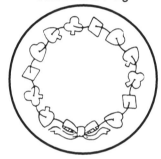

PC-KA Winner
Engraved / v:e

PC-KF Full Deck
Engraved / v:e

PC-KJ Blank Cards
Stamped Paper / v:c

PC-LA Full House
Engraved / v:e

PC-LA Full House
Variation Example

PC-LF Flush Hand
Engraved / v:d

PC-LK Flush Hand
Engraved / v:e

PC-LK Flush Hand
Variation Example

PC-LR Flush Hand
Engraved / v:h

PC-LW Flush Hand
Engraved / v:e

PC-LW Flush Hand
Variation Example

PC-MC Flush Hand
Engraved / v:e

249

POKER
PLAYING
CARDS

PC-MH Full House
Engraved / v:f

PC-PC Before/After
Embossed / v:g

PC-PC Before/After
Reverse

PC-RA Stop Monkeying
Embossed / v:d

PC-RA Stop Monkeying
Variation Example

PC-RJ Stop Monkeying
Embossed / v:e

PC-RN No Monkeying
Engraved / v:f

PC-RS Stop Monkeying
Embossed / v:g

PC-RS Stop Monkeying
Reverse

POKER
Designs
CODES: PD

Antique Chips
Value Rating Code*

a: 50¢   b: $1   c: $2-$3   d: $4-$5   e: $6-$7

f: $8-$9   g: $10-$14   h: $15-$19   i: $20-$29

j: $30-$39   k: $40-$49   l: $50-$69   m: $70-$89

n: $90-$109   o: $110-$149   p: $150-$199

q: $200-$299   r: $300-$399   s: $400-$499

t: $500-$699   u: $700-$999   v: $1000-$1999

w: $2000-$2999   x: $3000-$3999

y: $4000-$499   z: $5000+

*It is important to remember that quantities
of one chip or a set of chips would have
a much lower unit value per chip.

POKER
DESIGNS

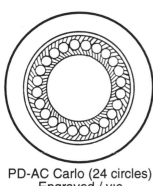

PD-AC Carlo (24 circles)
Engraved / v:c

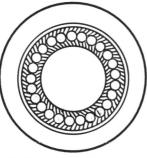

PD-AF Carlo (25 circles)
Engraved / v:d

PD-AH Carlo
Machined / v:e

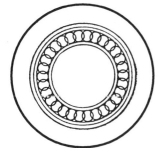

PD-AK Monaco
Engraved / v:e

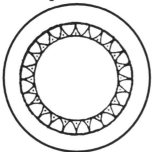

PD-AN Pointed Border
Engraved / v:f

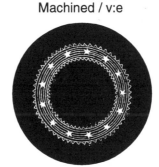

PD-AR Star Border
Engraved / v:f

PD-AU Star Border
Engraved / v:f

PD-AX Star H
Engraved / v:f

PD-BB Star 8
Engraved / v:e

PD-BE Star Cross
Engraved / v:e

PD-BG Star Cross
Engraved / v:e

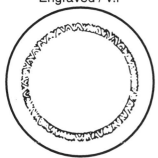

PD-BJ Wavy Border
Engraved / v:e

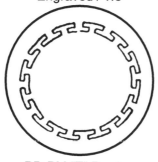

PD-BM "T" Border
Engraved / v:f

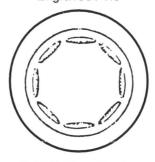

PD-BP Cigar Border
Engraved / v:f

PD-BR Rope Border
Embossed / v:e

PD-BV Newport
Embossed / v:c

PD-BZ Saratoga
Embossed / v:d

PD-CC Spirals
Embossed / v:d

PD-CC Spirals
Variation Example

253

POKER
DESIGNS

PD-CF London Club
Engraved / v:d

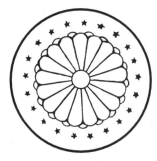

PD-CJ Petals & Stars
Engraved / v:e

PD-CM Victor
Engraved / v:e

PD-CP Petals
Engraved / v:e

PD-CS Petals
Engraved / v:f

PD-CV Petals
Engraved / v:f

PD-CY Snowflake
Engraved / v:f

PD-DC Six Loops
Engraved / v:f

PD-DF Geometric
Engraved / v:f

PD-DJ Geometric
Engraved / v:f

**Hand Done
Code Withdrawn**

PD-DR Geometric
Stamped / v:e

PD-DV Geometric
Engraved / v:f

PD-DZ Ampersand
Engraved / v:f

PD-EC Octo
Embossed / v:f

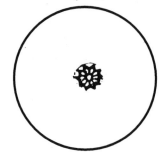

PD-EF Tiny Petals
Engraved / v:d

PD-EH Tiny Petals
Engraved / v:d

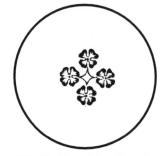

PD-EL Four Tiny Petals
Engraved / v:d

PD-EQ Quatro
Engraved / v:e

POKER
DESIGNS

PD-ET Quatro
Engraved / v:e

PD-ET Quatro
Variation Example

PD-EW Four Stems
Engraved / v:h

PD-EZ Four Stems
Engraved / v:f

PD-EZ Four Stems
Variation Example

PD-FB Four Stems
Engraved / v:f

PD-FE Crossed Spindles
Engraved / v:f

PD-FJ Four Trapezoids
Fema Style / v:f

PD-FM Maltese Cross
Engraved / v:h

PD-FP Maltese Cross
Engraved / v:f

PD-FS Maltese Cross
Engraved / v:f

PD-FY Maltese Cross
Stamped / v:d

PD-GC Maltese Cross
Inlaid Litho / v:f

PD-GC Maltese Cross
Variation Example

PD-GG Shield
Inlaid Litho / v:f

PD-GJ Fleur-de-Lis
Engraved / v:h

PD-GM Fleur-de-Lis
Engraved / v:f

PD-GQ Fleur-de-Lis
Stamped / v:d

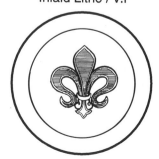

PD-GT Fleur-de-Lis
Engraved / v:e

255

PD-GW thru PD-JE

POKER
DESIGNS

PD-GW Fleur-de-Lis
Stamped Wood / v:c

PD-HA Fleur-de-Lis
Stamped Paper / v:a

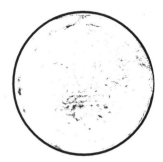

PD-HA Fleur-de-Lis
Variation Example

PD-HD Triangle
Engraved / v:f

PD-HG Triangle
Engraved / v:f

PD-HJ Triangle in Circle
Machined / v:e

PD-HN Triangle in Curves
Inlaid Litho / v:f

PD-HR Box & Arrow
Inlaid Litho / v:f

PD-HV Parallelogram & Spots
Fema Style / v:f

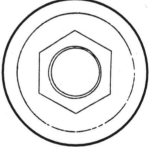

PD-HY Hex Nut
Engraved / v:f

PD-IC Hex Nut
Engraved / v:f

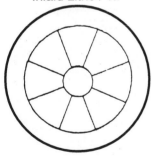

PD-IF Seven Sectors
Engraved / v:f

PD-IJ Six Sectors
Engraved / v:f

PD-IM Olympic
Engraved / v:e

PD-IQ Greek Key
Stamped / v:f

PD-IT Symmetry
Engraved / v:f

PD-IX Crescent
Engraved / v:f

PD-JB Crescent
Engraved / v:f

PD-JE Crescent
Engraved / v:f

POKER
DESIGNS

PD-JG Three Crescents
Inlaid Litho / v:g

PD-JK Star & Crescent
Inlaid Litho / v:f

PD-JN Star & Wreath
Inlaid Litho / v:f

PD-JN Star & Wreath
Variation Example

PD-JS Star & Wreath
Inlaid Litho / v:f

PD-JW Star & Wreath
Embossed / v:e

PD-JW Star & Wreath
Variation Example

PD-KD Star & Crescent
Embossed / v:e

PD-KD Star & Crescent
Variation Example

PD-KH Star
Embossed / v:e

PD-KH Star
Variation Example

PD-KL Star
Engraved / v:f

PD-KP Star
Engraved / v:d

PD-KT Star & Rings
Embossed-Engraved / v:e

PD-KW Monarch Star
Embossed-Stamped / v:e

PD-KZ Star & Rings
Embossed-Engraved / v:e

PD-LC Star & Rings
Embossed-Engraved / v:e

PD-LG Lone Star
Inlaid Litho / v:f

PD-LL New Star
Engraved / v:h

257

POKER
DESIGNS

PD-LO New Star
Engraved / v:e

PD-LO New Star
Variation Sample

PD-LT New Star
Engraved / v:f

PD-LW New Star
Engraved / v:f

PD-LW New Star
Variation Example

PD-MB New Star
Engraved / v:f

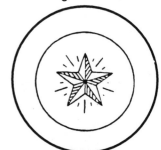

PD-MH Lone Star
Engraved / v:e

PD-MO Lone Star
Inlaid Litho / v:e

PD-MS Double Star
Engraved / v:d

PD-MW Evening Star
Engraved / v:c

PD-MW Evening Star
Variation Example

PD-NJ Double Star
Stamped / v:d

PD-NM Star of Diamonds
Engraved / v:f

PD-NQ Double Star
Engraved / v:f

PD-NT Double Star
Engraved / v:f

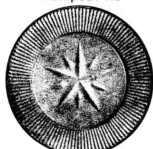

PD-NW Interlocking Star
Embossed / v:a

PD-NW Interlocking Star
Variation Example

PD-OA Four Stars
Stamped / v:e

PD-OD Circle of Stars
Engraved / v:f

PD-OF thru PD-QR
POKER
DESIGNS

PD-OF Four Corners
Engraved / v:f

PD-OH Strandwold
Engraved / v:f

PD-OJ Shaded Segment
Engraved / v:f

PD-OL Fine Grid
Embossed / v:c

PD-OP Fine Grid
Fibre Material / v:c

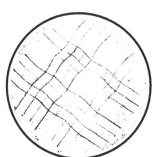

PD-OT Grid with Border
Engraved / v:c

PD-OX Wavy Grid
Engraved / v:b

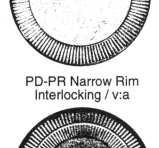

PD-PB Machined Center
Machined / v:b

PD-PF Colored Rings
Fema Stlye / v:f

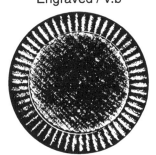

PD-PJ Ring & Rays
Engraved-Embossed / v:c

PD-PN Wood Ridge
Stamped Wood / v:b

PD-PR Narrow Rim
Interlocking / v:a

PD-PV Square Edge
Interlocking / v:a

PD-PZ Plain Center
Interlocking / v:a

PD-QC Wide Rim
Interlocking / v:c

PD-QG Cut Rim
Interlocking / v:a

PD-QK Two Rings
Interlocking / v:a

PD-QN Three Rings
Interlocking / v:a

PD-QR Three Wide Rings
Interlocking / v:a

259

POKER
DESIGNS

PD-QV Center Circles
Interlocking / v:a

PD-QZ Cut Rim
Interlocking / v:a

PD-RC Target
Interlocking / v:a

PD-RF Target
Interlocking / v:a

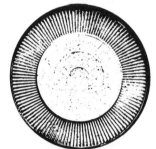

PD-RJ Target
Interlocking / v:a

PD-RM Ring of Dots
Interlocking / v:a

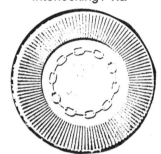

PD-RP Chain
Interlocking / v:a

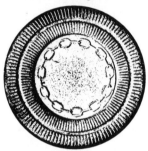

PD-RS Cut Rim Chain
Interlocking / v:a

PD-RW Open Ring
v:c

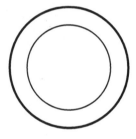

PD-SA One Circle
Engraved / v:f

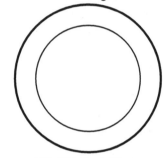

PD-SH One Circle
Engraved(39-28) / v:c-e

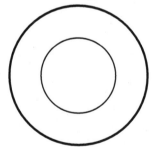

PD-SH One Circle
Variation Example(37-20)

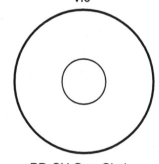

PD-SH One Circle
2nd Var. Example(38-12)

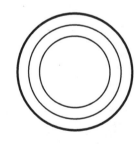

PD-ST Two Circles
Engraved / v:f

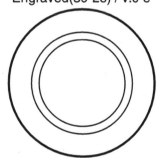

PD-TA Two Circles
Engrvd(39-27-23) / v:c-e

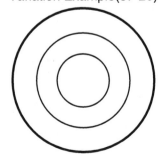

PD-TA Two Circles
Var. Example(38-25-14)

PD-TR Monarch
Embossed / v:b

PD-TR Monarch
Variation Example

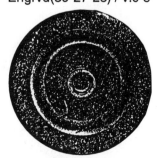

PD-TV Monarch with Circles
Embossed-Engraved / v:b

POKER
DESIGNS

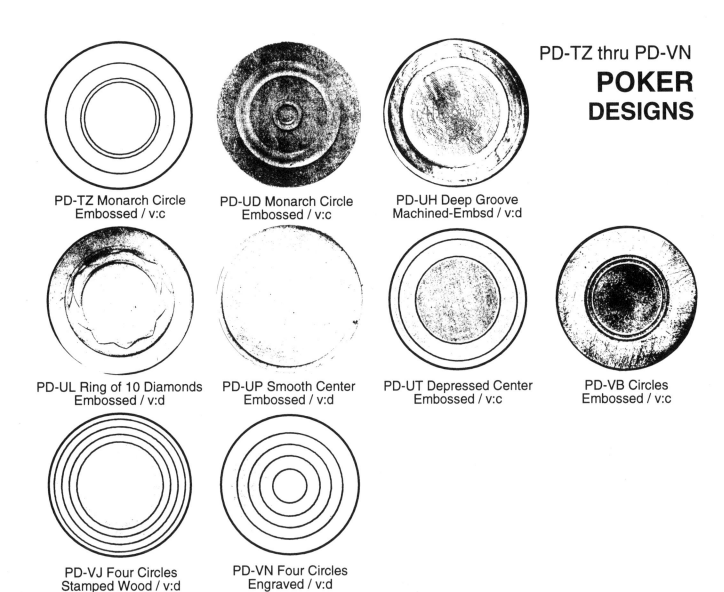

PD-TZ Monarch Circle
Embossed / v:c

PD-UD Monarch Circle
Embossed / v:c

PD-UH Deep Groove
Machined-Embsd / v:d

PD-UL Ring of 10 Diamonds
Embossed / v:d

PD-UP Smooth Center
Embossed / v:d

PD-UT Depressed Center
Embossed / v:c

PD-VB Circles
Embossed / v:c

PD-VJ Four Circles
Stamped Wood / v:d

PD-VN Four Circles
Engraved / v:d

Suggested Coding for Plain Chips

Between 1885 and 1940 there were many different plain chips manufactured which contained no designs or markings whatsoever. If every size and material of every chip ever made were coded, it might required as many as 100 different codes. Rather, it is suggested that collectors might communicate about, sort or organize their plain chips with the following coding system:

Materials:

C: clay L: celluloid
B: bone M: mother-of-pearl
I: ivory W: wood
P: paper O: other
R: rubber

PLN -☐ - ☐ ☐
(Material) *(Diameter (mm))* *(Description)*

Example:
A plain, blue round edged clay chip measuring 39mm across would be:

PLN-C-39 blue round edge

POKER
People
CODES: PE

Antique Chips
Value Rating Code*

a: 50¢   b: $1   c: $2-$3   d: $4-$5   e: $6-$7

f: $8-$9   g: $10-$14   h: $15-$19   i: $20-$29

j: $30-$39   k: $40-$49   l: $50-$69   m: $70-$89

n: $90-$109   o: $110-$149   p: $150-$199

q: $200-$299   r: $300-$399   s: $400-$499

t: $500-$699   u: $700-$999   v: $1000-$1999

w: $2000-$2999   x: $3000-$3999

y: $4000-$499   z: $5000+

*It is important to remember that quantities
of one chip or a set of chips would have
a much lower unit value per chip.

POKER
PEOPLE

PE-AC Child
Engraved / v:g

PE-AK Cupid's Kiss
Embossed / v:e

PE-AU Child w Umbrella
Inlaid Litho / v:f

PE-BG Gnome
Engraved / v:f

PE-BT Three Boys
Inlaid Litho / v:g

PE-CA My Ante
Engraved / v:f

PE-CP Punch
Engraved / v:f

PE-CR Mercury
Engraved / v:f

PE-DJ Jester
Printed Paper / v:d

PE-DK Knight's Armor
Stamped Paper / v:c

PE-DK Knight's Armor
Reverse

PE-DP Pirate
Stamped Paper / v:b

PE-DP Pirate
Reverse

PE-DS Santa Claus
Paste On Paper / v:e

PE-EM Man in the Moon
Ink Stamp / v:e

PE-ES Mascot
Embossed / v:c

PE-ES Mascot
Variation Example

PE-EX Mascot
Embossed / v:d

PE-FA Mascot
Embossed / v:c

265

POKER
PEOPLE

PE-FJ Mascot
Embossed / v:e

PE-FL Liberty
Engraved / v:h

PE-FR Liberty
Molded Rubber / v:g

PE-FR Liberty
Reverse

PE-FW Liberty
Pressed Wood / v:g

PE-FW Liberty
Reverse

PE-GL Lady & Vase
Engraved / v:f

PE-GM Mermaid
Engraved / v:h

PE-HD Ta-Ra-Ra
Engraved / v:e

PE-HF Monarch Flamenco
Embssd & Inl Litho / v:f

PE-HR Indian Maid
Stamped Wood / v:e

PE-HT Indian Maid
Embossed / v:e

PE-HW Indian Brave
Inlaid Litho / v:f

PE-JF Indian Chief
Engraved / v:e

PE-JK Indian Chief
Engraved / v:c

PE-JK Indian Chief
Variation Example

PE-JT Indian Chief
Engraved / v:h

PE-KA Arab
Inlaid Litho / v:f

PE-KE Arab
Inlaid Litho / v:f

266

POKER
PEOPLE

PE-KH Arab on Horse
Inlaid Litho / v:f

PE-RR Rough Rider
Engraved / v:d

PE-RR Rough Rider
Variation Sample

PE-SH Clasped Hands
Engraved / v:g

PE-SK Clasped Hands
Engraved / v:g

PE-SK Clasped Hands
Variation Example

PE-TA Arm & Arrow
Inlaid Litho / v:f

PE-TL Triune
Engraved / v:f

267

POKER

Plants

CODES: PL

Antique Chips
Value Rating Code*

a: 50¢   b: $1   c: $2-$3   d: $4-$5   e: $6-$7

f: $8-$9   g: $10-$14   h: $15-$19   i: $20-$29

j: $30-$39   k: $40-$49   l: $50-$69   m: $70-$89

n: $90-$109   o: $110-$149   p: $150-$199

q: $200-$299   r: $300-$399   s: $400-$499

t: $500-$699   u: $700-$999   v: $1000-$1999

w: $2000-$2999   x: $3000-$3999

y: $4000-$499   z: $5000+

*It is important to remember that quantities
of one chip or a set of chips would have
a much lower unit value per chip.

POKER
PLANTS

PL-AC Acorn
Engraved / v:e

PL-AG Acorn
Engraved / v:e

PL-AK Acorn
Engraved / v:h

PL-AO Acorn
Engraved / v:d

PL-AO Acorn
Variation Example

PL-AZ Acorn
Engraved / v:e

PL-BE Acorn
Engraved / v:e

PL-BJ Acorn
Engraved / v:e

PL-BN Monarch Acorn
Engr & Embsd / v:e

PL-BR Acorn
Engraved / v:e

PL-BV Acorn
Embossed / v:e

PL-CA Clover
Engraved / v:h

PL-CE Clover
Engraved / v:e

PL-CE Clover
Variation Example

PL-CO Clover
Engraved / v:e

PL-CO Clover
Variation Example

PL-CT Clover
Engrvd Wood / v:d

PL-CT Clover
Variation Example

PL-CY Clover
Engraved / v:e

271

POKER
PLANTS

PL-CY Clover
Variation Example

PL-DE Clover
Engraved / v:e

PL-DJ Monarch Clover
Engrvd & Embsd / v:e

PL-DO Clover
Stamped Paper / v:b

PL-DT Clover
Intrlkng Paste On / v:e

PL-DY Shamrock
Engrvd Wood / v:d

PL-ED Shamrock
Embossed / v:e

PL-EJ Clover
Engrvd Wood / v:c

PL-EO Clover
Stamped Paper / v:b

PL-ET Lily
Engraved / v:e

PL-ET Lily
Variation Example

PL-FF Lotus
Engraved / v:e

PL-FF Lotus
Variation Example

PL-FN Rose
Engraved / v:h

PL-FR Rose
Engraved / v:h

PL-FT Rose
Engraved / v:e

PL-FV Rose
Engraved / v:f

PL-FV Rose
Variation Example

PL-GB Rose
Engraved / v:f

POKER
PLANTS

PL-GB Rose
Variation Example

PL-GH Rose
Engraved / v:e

PL-GM Monarch Rose
Engrvd & Embsd / v:e

PL-HD Rose
Engraved / v:f

PL-HJ Rose
Engraved / v:f

PL-HP Rose
Engraved / v:f

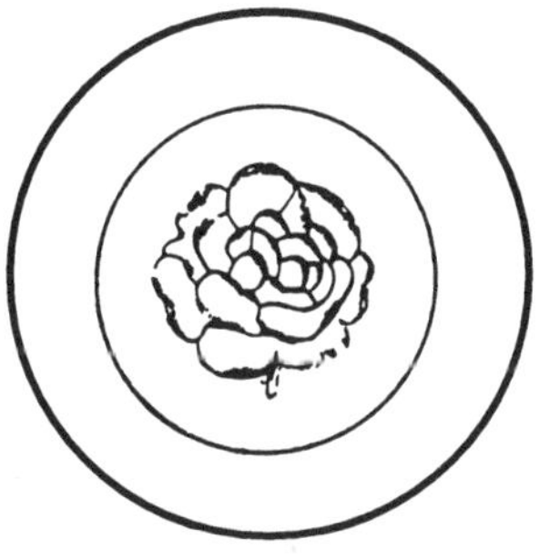

PL-HV Rose
Engraved / v:e

PL-HV Rose
Variation Example

PL-JD Rose
Engraved / v:e

PL-JD Rose
Variation Example

PL-JN Rose
Engraved / v:g

PL-JN Rose
Variation Example

PL-JT Rose
Embossed / v:e

PL-JT Rose
Variation Example

PL-KA Rose
Engraved / v:f

PL-KH Tulip
Engraved / v:h

PL-KM Tulip
Engraved / v:f

PL-KR Monarch Tulip
Engrvd & Embsd / v:e

PL-KR Monarch Tulip
Variation Example

273

POKER
PLANTS

PL-KX Rose
Engraved / v:f

PL-LF Flower
Engraved / v:h

PL-LP Pansy
Engraved / v:e

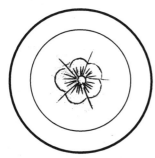

PL-LS Pansy
Engraved / v:e

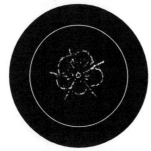

PL-LS Pansy
Variation Example

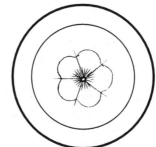

PL-LV Pansy
Engraved / v:e

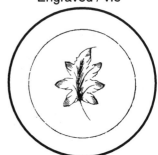

PL-ME Maple Leaf
Engraved / v:e

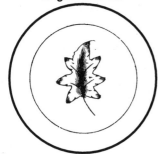

PL-ME Maple Leaf
Variation Example

PL-MO Three Leaves
Engraved / v:h

PL-MO Three Leaves
Variation Example

PL-MT Three Leaves
Engraved / v:f

PL-NA Three Leaves
Engraved / v:e

PL-NA Three Leaves
Variation Example

PL-NP Pineapple
Inlaid Litho / v:g

PL-NZ Desert
Inlaid Litho / v:g

PL-PH Palm
Machined / v:f

PL-PM Florida Palm
Inlaid Litho / v:f

PL-PT Wreath & Torch
Engraved / v:e

PL-QH Tulip Wreath
Engraved / v:e

POKER
PLANTS

PL-QW Floral Border
Engraved / v:f

PL-RH Club House
Embossed / v:d

PL-RW Oak Wreath
Engraved / v:e

PL-SW Wide Wreath
Embossed / v:e

POKER

Miscellaneous

CODES: PM

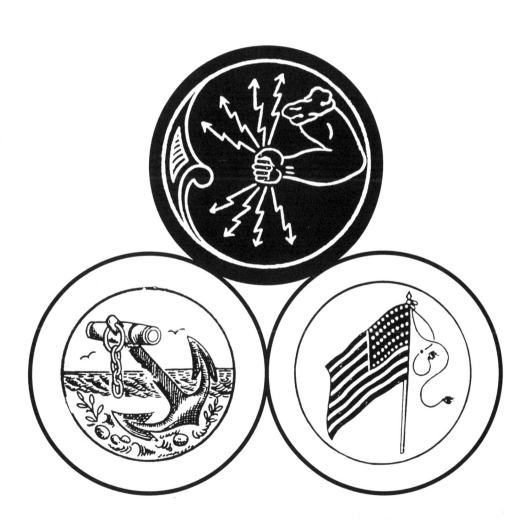

Antique Chips
Value Rating Code*

a: 50¢   b: $1   c: $2-$3   d: $4-$5   e: $6-$7

f: $8-$9   g: $10-$14   h: $15-$19   i: $20-$29

j: $30-$39   k: $40-$49   l: $50-$69   m: $70-$89

n: $90-$109   o: $110-$149   p: $150-$199

q: $200-$299   r: $300-$399   s: $400-$499

t: $500-$699   u: $700-$999   v: $1000-$1999

w: $2000-$2999   x: $3000-$3999

y: $4000-$499   z: $5000+

*It is important to remember that quantities
of one chip or a set of chips would have
a much lower unit value per chip.

POKER
MISC.

PM-AC Anchor
Engraved / v:f

PM-AH Anchor
Engraved / v:h

PM-AN Anchor
Engraved / v:f

PM-AN Anchor
Variation Example

PM-AR Anchor
Engraved / v:f

PM-AV Anchor
Engraved / v:h

PM-AZ Anchor
Engraved / v:d

PM-AZ Anchor
Variation Example

PM-BD Anchor
Embossed(deep) / v:b

PM-BF Anchor
Embossed(shallow) / v:b

PM-BK Anchor
Engraved / v:d

PM-BP Anchor
Engraved / v:e

PM-BT Anchor & Shells
Engraved / v:f

PM-CA Arrowhead
Engraved / v:f

PM-CE Arrowhead
Engraved / v:f

PM-CJ Four Arrows
Engraved / v:e

PM-CM Two Arrows
Engraved / v:e

PM-CR Boot
Engraved / v:f

PM-CT Boot
Engraved / v:f

279

POKER
MISC.

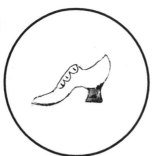

PM-CW Shoe
Engraved / v:f

PM-CW Shoe
Variation Example

PM-CZ Monarch Shoe
Engraved & Embossed / v:f

PM-DD Shoe
Engraved / v:f

PM-DG Crown
Stamped Paper / v:c

PM-DJ Crown
Engraved / v:h

PM-DN Crown
Engraved / v:e

PM-DN Crown
Variation Example

PM-DS Crown
Engraved / v:e

PM-DS Crown
Variation Example

PM-DX Crown
Engraved / v:e

PM-EC Crown
Inlaid Litho / v:f

PM-EG Crown
Engraved / v:c

PM-EL Crown
Inlaid Litho / v:f

PM-EP Crown
Embossed / v:f

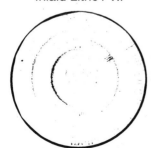

PM-EU Crown
Interlocking Embsd / v:d

PM-EY Crown
Engraved Paper / v:b

PM-FD Crown & Scepter
Engraved / v:e

PM-FJ Prince of Wales
Engraved / v:d

PM-FJ Prince of Wales
Variation Example

PM-FP Prince of Wales
Engraved / v:d

PM-FP Prince of Wales
Variation Example

PM-FT Prince of Wales
Paste On / v:g

PM-FW Prince of Wales
Inlaid Litho / v:g

PM-FW Prince of Wales
Variation Example

PM-GF Flag
Ink Stamped / v:e

PM-GJ Flag
Stamped Paper / v:c

PM-GN Flag
Engraved / v:e

PM-GT Flag
Engraved / v:e

PM-GT Flag
Variation Example

PM-GZ Flag
Engraved / v:e

PM-HD Flag
Paste On / v:g

PM-HD Flag
Variation Example

PM-HK Flag(U.S. & Gr Br.)
Paste On / v:h

PM-HK Flag(U.S. & Gr Br.)
Reverse

PM-HQ Crossed Flags
Inlaid Litho / v:g

PM-HV Four Flags
Inlaid Litho / v:h

PM-JA Lighthouse
Engraved / v:h

281

POKER
MISC.

PM-JE Lighthouse
Engraved / v:e

PM-JH Lighthouse
Engraved / v:e

PM-JJ Lighthouse
Engraved / v:e

PM-JJ Lighthouse
Variation Example

PM-JL Lighthouse
Engraved / v:f

PM-JW Windmill
Engraved / v:f

PM-KA Castle
Embossed / v:g

PM-KA Castle
Reverse

PM-KF Lighthouse
Embossed / v:g

PM-KF Lighthouse
Reverse

PM-KK Go Way Back
Engraved / v:h

PM-KW Waterfall
Inlaid Litho / v:g

PM-LA Five Forty-Eight
Engraved / v:f

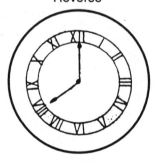

PM-LE Eight O'Clock
Engraved / v:f

PM-LL Eleven O'Clock
Engraved / v:f

PM-LS Caduceus
Stamped Paper / v:c

PM-MK Keystone
Engraved / v:e

PM-MR Power
Engraved / v:g

PM-NE Three Links
Engraved / v:g

POKER
MISC.

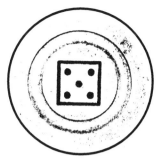

PM-NM Monarch Die
Engraved & Stamped / v:f

PM-NS Domino
Inlaid Litho / v:f

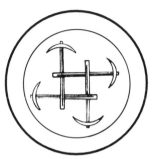

PM-PA Palette
Engraved / v:h

PM-PK Key
Inlaid Litho / v:f

PM-PP Aladdin's Lamp
Machined / v:f

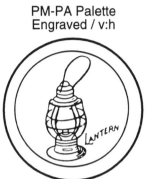

PM-PT Lantern
Engraved / v:f

PM-QP Four Picks
Engraved / v:e

PM-RH Hat & Cane
Machined / v:f

PM-WP PLA-M-WEL
Stamped Wood / v:c

283

POKER
Monograms
CODES: PO

Antique Chips
Value Rating Code*

a: 50¢   b: $1   c: $2-$3   d: $4-$5   e: $6-$7

f: $8-$9   g: $10-$14   h: $15-$19   i: $20-$29

j: $30-$39 k: $40-$49 l: $50-$69 m: $70-$89

n: $90-$109   o: $110-$149   p: $150-$199

q: $200-$299   r: $300-$399   s: $400-$499

t: $500-$699 u: $700-$999 v: $1000-$1999

w: $2000-$2999   x: $3000-$3999

y: $4000-$499   z: $5000+

*It is important to remember that quantities
of one chip or a set of chips would have
a much lower unit value per chip.

Initially made in: white, red, blue, yellow, chocolate, light blue and pink.

PO-AA PO-AB PO-AC PO-AD

PO-AE PO-AF PO-AG PO-AH PO-AI PO-AJ

PO-AK PO-AL PO-AM PO-AN PO-AO PO-AP

PO-AQ PO-AR PO-AS PO-AT PO-AU PO-AV

PO-AW PO-AX PO-AY PO-AZ

Initial Inlaid
Large Center
**Paranoid Poker Chips
Circa 1908-1938
U.S. Playing Card Co.
Values: b-d**

287

POKER
MONOGRAMS
(SINGLE)

PO-BA thru PO-BZ

Initially made in:
white, red, blue,
yellow, chocolate,
light blue and pink.

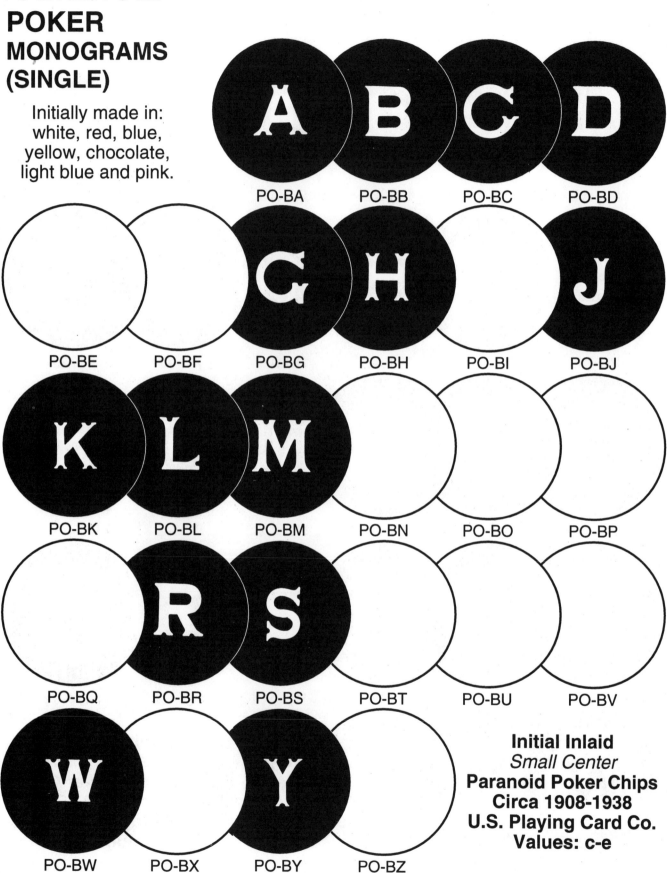

A	B	C	D
PO-BA	PO-BB	PO-BC	PO-BD

PO-BE PO-BF PO-BG (G) PO-BH (H) PO-BI PO-BJ (J)

PO-BK (K) PO-BL (L) PO-BM (M) PO-BN PO-BO PO-BP

PO-BQ PO-BR (R) PO-BS (S) PO-BT PO-BU PO-BV

PO-BW (W) PO-BX PO-BY (Y) PO-BZ

Initial Inlaid
Small Center
**Paranoid Poker Chips
Circa 1908-1938
U.S. Playing Card Co.
Values: c-e**

PO-CA thru PO-CZ

POKER MONOGRAMS (SINGLE)

Initially made in: white, red, blue, yellow, chocolate, light blue and pink.

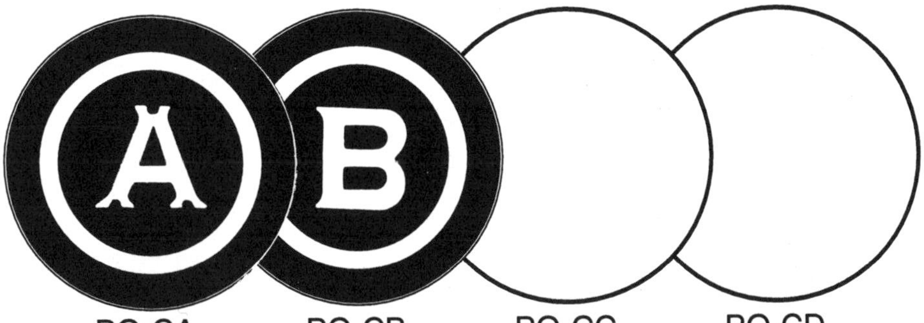

PO-CA PO-CB PO-CC PO-CD

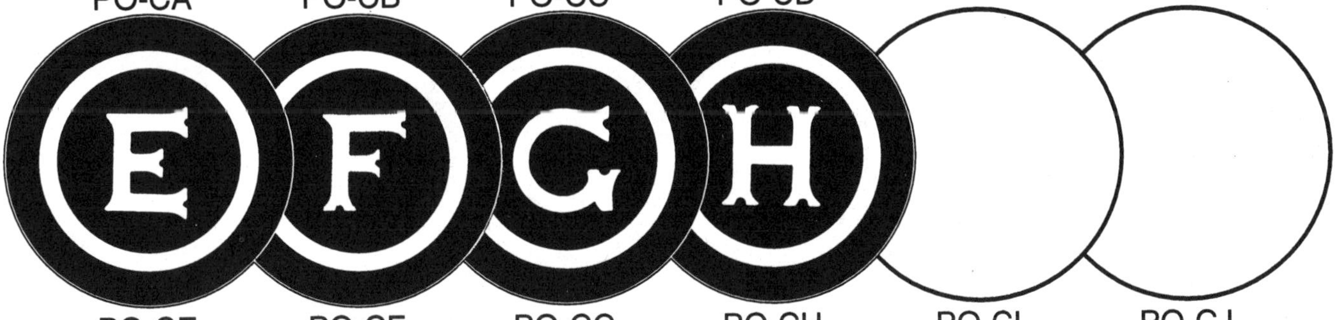

PO-CE PO-CF PO-CG PO-CH PO-CI PO-CJ

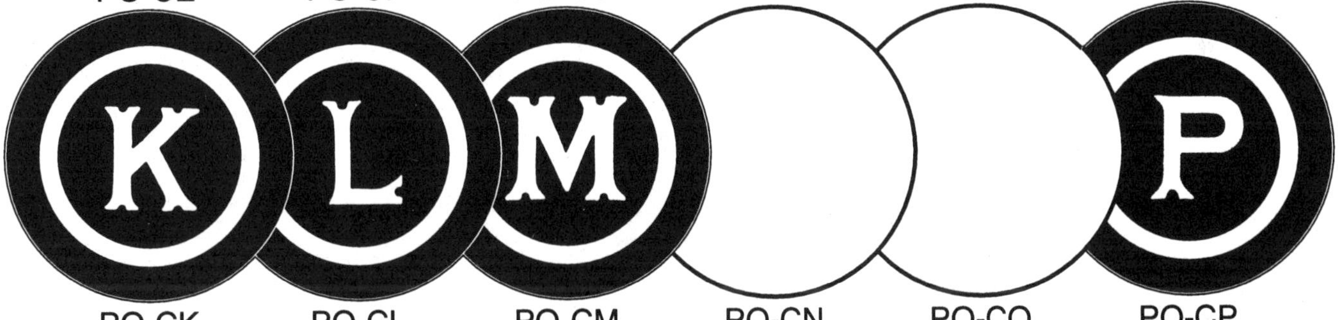

PO-CK PO-CL PO-CM PO-CN PO-CO PO-CP

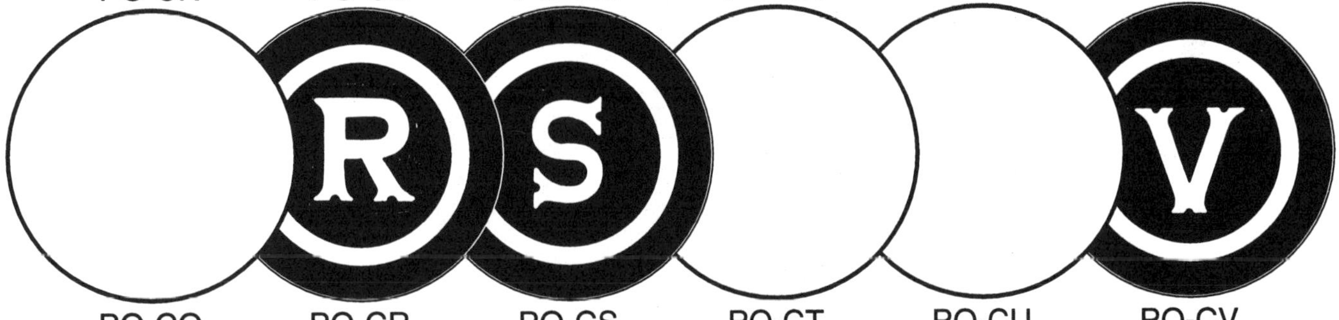

PO-CQ PO-CR PO-CS PO-CT PO-CU PO-CV

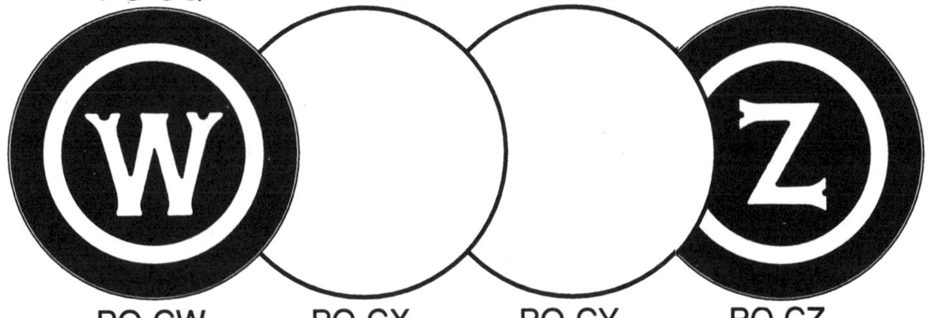

PO-CW PO-CX PO-CY PO-CZ

Initial Inlaid
Wide Ring
Paranoid Poker Chips
Circa 1908-1938
U.S. Playing Card Co.
Values: c-e

PO-DA thru PO-DZ

POKER
MONOGRAMS
(SINGLE)

Initially made in:
white, red, blue,
yellow, chocolate,
light blue and pink.

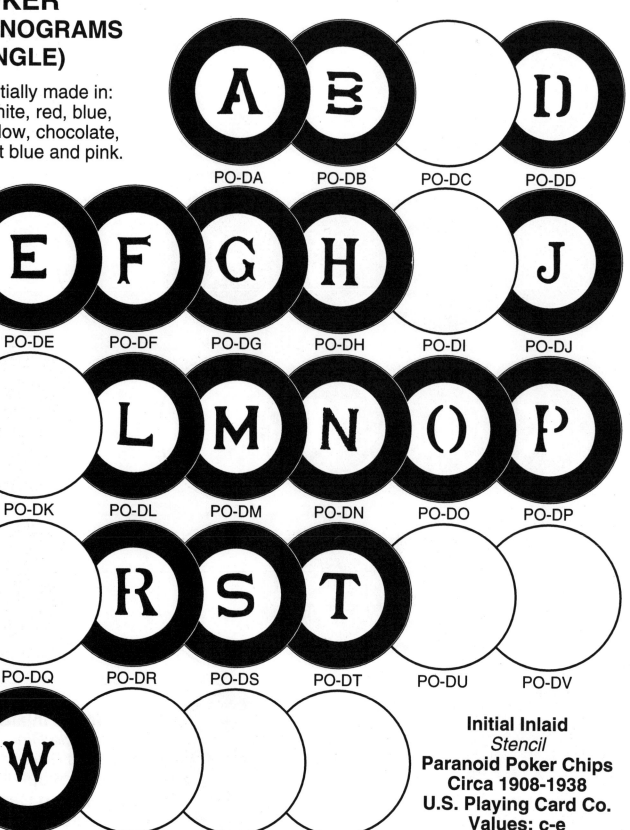

| PO-DA | PO-DB | PO-DC | PO-DD |

| PO-DE | PO-DF | PO-DG | PO-DH | PO-DI | PO-DJ |

| PO-DK | PO-DL | PO-DM | PO-DN | PO-DO | PO-DP |

| PO-DQ | PO-DR | PO-DS | PO-DT | PO-DU | PO-DV |

| PO-DW | PO-DX | PO-DY | PO-DZ |

Initial Inlaid
Stencil
**Paranoid Poker Chips
Circa 1908-1938
U.S. Playing Card Co.
Values: c-e**

290

POKER
MONOGRAMS
(SINGLE)

Initially made in:
white, red, blue,
yellow, chocolate,
light blue and pink.

PO-EA	PO-EB	PO-EC	PO-ED

PO-EE	PO-EF	PO-EG	PO-EH	PO-EI	PO-EJ

PO-EK	PO-EL	PO-EM	PO-EN	PO-EO	PO-EP

PO-EQ	PO-ER	PO-ES	PO-ET	PO-EU	PO-EV

PO-EW	PO-EX	PO-EY	PO-EZ

Initial Inlaid
Diamond
**Paranoid Poker Chips
Circa 1908-1938
U.S. Playing Card Co.
Values: e-f**

POKER
MONOGRAMS
(SINGLE)

Shown below are 4 example chips
from three different sets of monogram
chips that have been assigned codes.

PO-FA thru PO-FZ
Initial Inlaid
Wide Rim
Circa 1900
Values: b-d

PO-FH   PO-FJ   PO-FR   PO-FX

PO-GG   PO-GM   PO-GN   PO-GY

PO-GA thru PO-GZ
Initial Inlaid
Narrow Ring
Circa 1900
Values: b-d

PO-HA thru PO-HZ
Initial Engraved
Monarch Antique
Circa 1900
Values: c-e

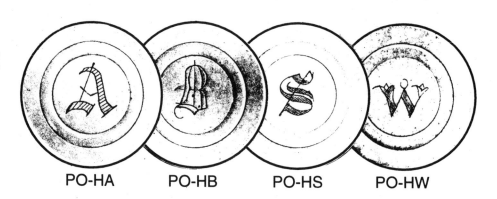

PO-HA   PO-HB   PO-HS   PO-HW

POKER
MONOGRAMS
(SINGLE)

Hundreds of additional single monogram chip designs were made during the period from 1880 - 1940.

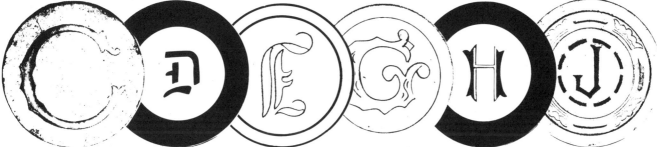

See additional monogram chips in the ivory and mother-of-pearl sections of this book.

293

POKER
MONOGRAMS

Thousands of monogram chip designs with two and three initials were made during the period from 1880 to 1940. A few examples of these chips are shown here.

POKER
Numerals
CODES: NONE

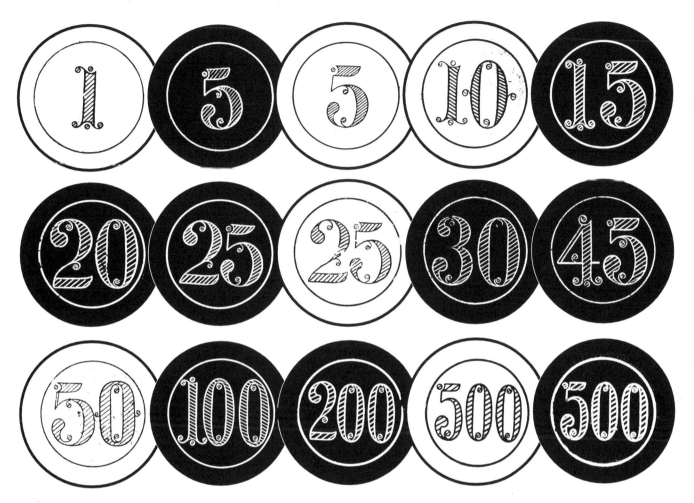

This type of engraved numeral chip was available from nearly all the major manufacturers and distributors. Several of these numeral chips were available in a variety of colors. Minor variations of these designs were also common.

These elaborately engraved numeral chips were available in different colors.

297

EMBOSSED SAMPLES
POKER
NUMERALS

Examples of the numerous embossed numeral chips available in a variety of colors and minor variations.

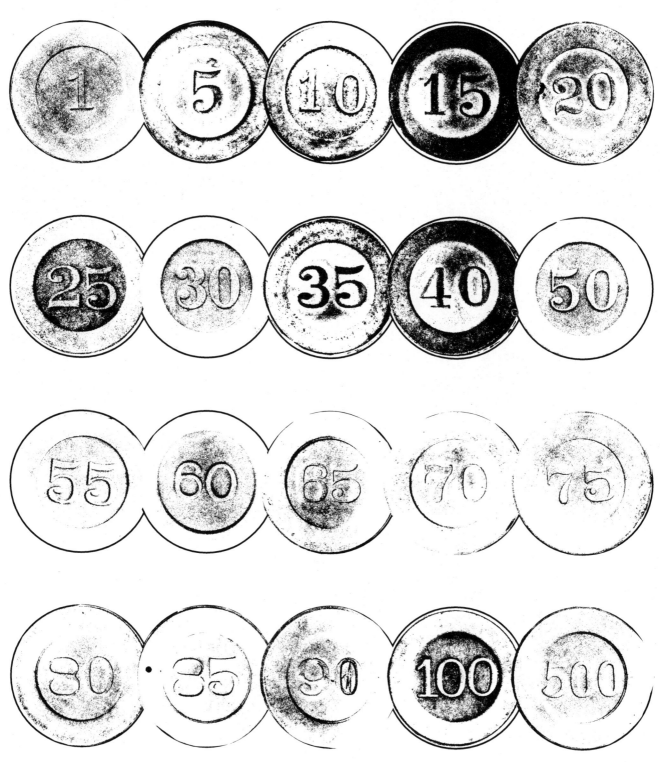

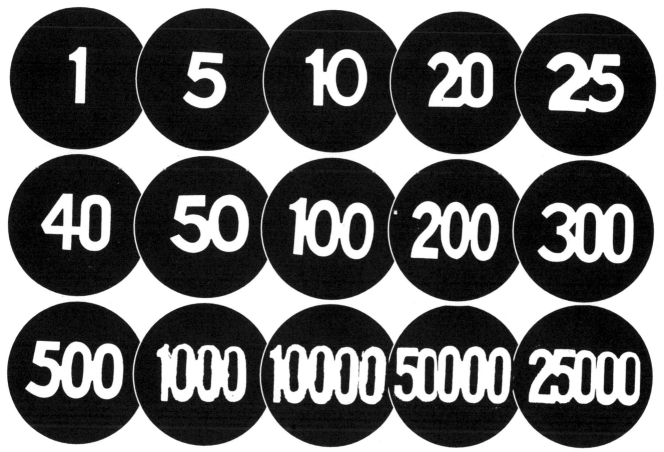

Samples of the most popular inlaid numeral chips.

This inlaid 4-stick box design was a popular numeral chip option.

POKER
NUMERALS

POKER
Sports
CODES: PS

Antique Chips
Value Rating Code*

a: 50¢   b: $1   c: $2-$3   d: $4-$5   e: $6-$7

f: $8-$9   g: $10-$14   h: $15-$19   i: $20-$29

j: $30-$39   k: $40-$49   l: $50-$69   m: $70-$89

n: $90-$109   o: $110-$149   p: $150-$199

q: $200-$299   r: $300-$399   s: $400-$499

t: $500-$699   u: $700-$999   v: $1000-$1999

w: $2000-$2999   x: $3000-$3999

y: $4000-$499   z: $5000+

*It is important to remember that quantities of one chip or a set of chips would have a much lower unit value per chip.

302

PS-AB Baseball
Engraved / v:e

PS-AH Baseball Player
Engraved / v:f

PS-AL Billiards
Inlaid Litho / v:f

PS-AR Bowling
Engraved / v:d

PS-BB Max Rosenblum
Inlaid Litho / v:g

PS-BB Max Rosenblum
Reverse

PS-BH Sportsman
Inlaid Litho / v:f

PS-BN Corbett
Engraved / v:f

PS-BQ Corbett
Engraved / v:f

PS-BT Gladiator
Embossed / v:e

PS-BT Gladiator
Variation Example

PS-CA Golf Bag & Clubs
Engraved / v:e

PS-CG Golf Bag & Clubs
Engraved / v:e

PS-CG Golf Bag & Clubs
Error Example (Reverse)

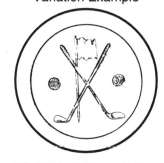

PS-CK Golf Clubs & Flag
Engraved / v:e

PS-CP Golf Clubs & Flag
Engraved / v:e

PS-CT Golfer
Inlaid Litho / v:g

PS-CW Golfers
Inlaid Litho / v:g

PS-DA Golfer
Embossed / v:b

POKER
SPORTS

PS-DD Golfer(flying turf)
Embossed / v:d

PS-DG Golfer
Engraved / v:g

PS-DJ Golfer
Inlaid Litho & Embossed / v:g

PS-DS Fishing & Hunting
Engraved / v:e

PS-DW Fishing & Hunting
Inlaid Litho / v:g

PS-ED Hunt
Stamped Wood / v:e

PS-ES "If the dog...'
Engraved / v:g

PS-EP Dog on a Log
Engraved / v:f

PS-EW Bronc Rider
Inlaid Litho / v:f

PS-EZ Bronc Rider
Inlaid Litho / v:f

PS-FE Equestrian
Engraved / v:e

PS-FE Equestrian
Variation Example

PS-FJ Famous Jockeys
Inlaid Litho / v:h

PS-FJ Famous Jockeys
Reverse

PS-FN Famous Jockeys
Inlaid Litho / v:h

PS-FN Famous Jockeys
Reverse

PS-FR Jockey
Embossed / v:a

PS-GA Shure Winner
Stamped Paper / v:c

PS-GA Shure Winner
Reverse

POKER
SPORTS

PS-GD Shure Winner
Stamped Paper / v:b

PS-GD Shure Winner
Reverse

PS-GH Monarch Cap
Engraved & Embossed / v:e

PS-GL Cap & Whip
Engraved / v:h

PS-GR Cap & Whip
Engraved / v:f

PS-GR Cap & Whip
Variation Example

PS-GX Cap, Whip & Stirrup
Engraved / v:f

PS-HC Shoe, Cap & Whip
Engraved / v:f

PS-HS Shoe, Cap & Whip
Engraved / v:d

PS-HS Shoe, Cap & Whip
Variation Example

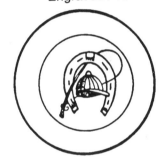

PS-JA Shoe, Cap & Whip
Engraved / v:d

PS-JA Shoe, Cap & Whip
Variation Example

PS-JS Shoe, Cap & Whip
Engraved / v:c

PS-JW Horseshoe
Engraved / v:h

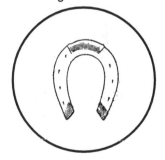

PS-SH Horseshoe
Engraved / v:f

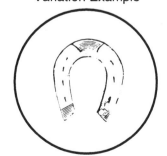

PS-SH Horseshoe
Variation Example

PS-SM Horseshoe
Engraved / v:f

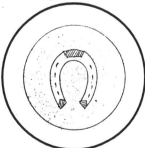

PS-SQ Horseshoe
Engraved / v:f

PS-SV Horseshoe
Engraved / v:f

POKER
SPORTS

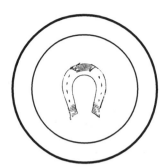

PS-TA Horseshoe
Engraved / v:f

PS-TF Horseshoe
Stamped Paper / v:a

PS-TF Horseshoe
Variation Example

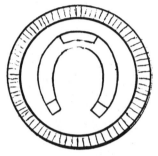

PS-TJ Horseshoe
Stamped Paper / v:b

PS-TN Horseshoe
Inlaid Litho / v:f

PS-TT Horseshoe
Inlaid Litho & Embsd / v:f

PS-UB Horseshoe
Engraved / v:e

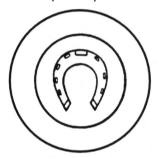

PS-UB Horseshoe
Variation Example

PS-UK Horseshoe
Engraved / v:e

PS-UR Horseshoe
Engraved / v:e

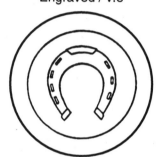

PS-UR Horseshoe
Variation Example

PS-UW Horseshoe
Engraved / v:e

PS-WA Shoe & Shamrock
Engraved / v:f

PS-WG Horseshoe & Bit
Engraved / v:f

PS-WK Shoe & Whip
Engraved / v:h

PS-WP Shoe & Whip
Engraved / v:f

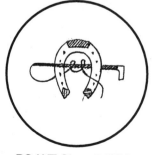

PS-WT Shoe & Whip
Engraved / v:f

PS-XA Shoe & Whip
Engraved / v:f

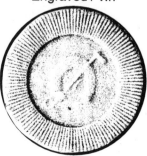

PS-XH Shoe & Whip
Interlocking & Embsd / v:b

POKER
SPORTS

PS-XL Shoe & Whip
Engraved / v:e

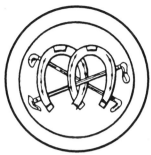

PS-XS Shoes & Whips
Engraved / v:d

PS-XS Shoes & Whips
Variation Example

PS-YH Saddle & Whip
Engraved / v:e

PS-YM Polo Player
Inlaid Litho / v:g

PS-YT Tennis Player
Engraved / v:f

307

POKER
Transportation
CODES: PT

Antique Chips
Value Rating Code*

a: 50¢   b: $1   c: $2-$3   d: $4-$5   e: $6-$7

f: $8-$9   g: $10-$14   h: $15-$19   i: $20-$29

j: $30-$39   k: $40-$49   l: $50-$69   m: $70-$89

n: $90-$109   o: $110-$149   p: $150-$199

q: $200-$299   r: $300-$399   s: $400-$499

t: $500-$699   u: $700-$999   v: $1000-$1999

w: $2000-$2999   x: $3000-$3999

y: $4000-$499   z: $5000+

*It is important to remember that quantities
of one chip or a set of chips would have
a much lower unit value per chip.

POKER TRANSPORT-ATION

PT-AD Stagecoach
Inlaid Litho / v:f

PT-AK Stagecoach
Inlaid Litho / v:g

PT-AP Automobile
Engraved / v:e

PT-AP Automobile
Variation Example

PT-AT Airplane
Embossed / v:d

PT-AY Airplane
Embossed(deep) / v:d

PT-BD Airplane
Embossed(shallow) / v:d

PT-BF Airplane
Embossed / v:f

PT-BK Airplane
Engraved / v:f

PT-BP Biplane
Inlaid Litho / v:g

PT-CH Cupid on Bike
Engraved / v:g

PT-CL Lady & Bicycle
Engraved / v:f

PT-CR Lady & Bicycle
Embossed / v:e

PT-CW Bicycle Girl
Embossed / v:d

PT-CW Bicycle Girl
Variation Example

PT-DM Motorboat
Embossed(deep) / v:c

PT-DP Motorboat
Embossed(shallow) / v:d

PT-DW Pilot's Wheel
Stamped Paper / v:a

PT-ED Sailing Ship
Engraved / v:h

PT-EH thru PT-GW
POKER TRANSPORT-ATION

PT-EH Sailing Ship
Embossed / v:c

PT-EJ Sailing Ship
Embossed / v:c

PT-EM Sailing Ship
Inlaid Litho / v:f

PT-ES Sailing Ship
Embossed / v:g

PT-ES Sailing Ship
Reverse

PT-EW Navy Ship
Engraved / v:g

PT-FN Battleship
Engraved / v:g

PT-FY Yacht
Engraved / v:e

PT-GW G. Washington Bridge
Inlaid Litho / v:f

POKER
Wheel & Faro
(Inlaid)
CODES: PW & PX

Antique Chips
Value Rating Code*

a: 50¢   b: $1   c: $2-$3   d: $4-$5   e: $6-$7

f: $8-$9   g: $10-$14   h: $15-$19   i: $20-$29

j: $30-$39   k: $40-$49   l: $50-$69   m: $70-$89

n: $90-$109   o: $110-$149   p: $150-$199

q: $200-$299   r: $300-$399   s: $400-$499

t: $500-$699   u: $700-$999   v: $1000-$1999

w: $2000-$2999   x: $3000-$3999

y: $4000-$499   z: $5000+

*It is important to remember that quantities
of one chip or a set of chips would have
a much lower unit value per chip.

POKER,
WHEEL
& FARO
(INLAID)

PW-AB Excello
Inlaid / v:e

PW-AD Excello
Inlaid / v:d

PW-AF Arrowheads
Inlaid / v:e

PW-AJ Arrowheads
Inlaid / v:e

PW-AM Arrowheads
Inlaid / v:e

PW-AQ Chevron
Inlaid / v:e

PW-AT Crown
Inlaid / v:e

PW-AW Crown & Crescent
Inlaid / v:e

PW-AW Crown & Crescent
Variation Example

PW-BC Clover Leaf
Inlaid / v:e

PW-BC Clover Leaf
Variation Example

PW-BF Clover Leaf
Inlaid / v:d

PW-BF Clover Leaf
Variation Example

PW-BN Monarch Clover
Inlaid-Embossed / v:e

PW-BQ Winner Clover
Inlaid-Engraved / v:f

PW-BP Hub Clover
Inlaid-Embossed / v:e

PW-BW Club
Inlaid / v:e

PW-BW Club
Variation Example

PW-CC Club
Inlaid / v:e

315

PW-CC thru PW-DY
POKER, WHEEL & FARO (INLAID)

PW-CC Club
Variation Example

PW-CH Club
Inlaid / v:d

PW-CH Club
Variation Example

PW-CL Club
Inlaid / v:d

PW-CL Club
Variation Example

PW-CQ Monarch Club
Inlaid-Embossed / v:e

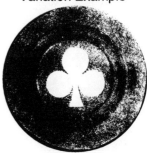

PW-CQ Monarch Club
Variation Example

PW-CT Wreath Club
Inlaid-Engraved / v:f

PW-CV Wreath Club
Inlaid-Engraved / v:f

PW-CY Carlo Club
Inlaid-Embossed / v:f

PW-DC Hub Club
Inlaid-Embossed / v:f

PW-DG Club & Crescent
Inlaid / v:d

PW-DG Club & Crescent
Variation Example

PW-DK Club & Crescent
Inlaid / v:d

PW-DK Club & Crescent
Variation Example

PW-DR Club in Heart
Inlaid / v:f

PW-DV Diamond
Inlaid / v:d

PW-DY Diamond
Inlaid / v:d

PW-DY Diamond
Variation Example

316

POKER,
WHEEL
& FARO
(INLAID)

PW-EG Monarch Diamond
Inlaid-Embossed / v:e

PW-EJ Monarch Diamond
Inlaid-Embossed / v:e

PW-EM Heart
Inlaid / v:f

PW-EP Heart
Inlaid / v:e

PW-ES Heart
Inlaid / v:e

PW-EW Small Heart
Inlaid / v:e

PW-FB Wide Heart
Inlaid / v:d

PW-FB Wide Heart
Variation Example

PW-FM Tall Heart
Inlaid / v:d

PW-FQ Monarch Heart
Inlaid-Embossed / v:e

PW-FQ Monarch Heart
Variation Example

PW-FW Wreath Heart
Inlaid-Engraved / v:f

PW-GA Winner Heart
Inlaid-Engraved / v:f

PW-GC Heart in C
Inlaid / v:f

PW-GG Spade
Inlaid / v:e

PW-GK Spade
Inlaid / v:e

PW-GP Small Spade
Inlaid / v:e

PW-GT Spade
Inlaid / v:d

PW-GZ High Spade
Inlaid / v:d

317

PW-HE thru PW-KJ
POKER,
WHEEL
& FARO
(INLAID)

PW-HE Spade
Inlaid / v:e

PW-HJ Spade
Inlaid / v:d

PW-HM Monarch Spade
Inlaid-Embossed / v:e

PW-HP Monarch Spade
Inlaid-Embossed / v:e

PW-HS Monarch Spade
Inlaid-Embossed / v:e

PW-HW Wreath Spade
Inlaid-Engraved / v:f

PW-JC Triumph
Inlaid / v:e

PW-JC Triumph
Variation Example

PW-JH Triumph
Inlaid / v:d

PW-JH Triumph
Variation Example

PW-JK Triumph
Inlaid Litho / v:f

See Playing Card
Section

PW-JN Card Suits
Inlaid / v:e

PW-JN Card Suits
Variation Example

PW-JT Club Cross
Inlaid / v:f

PW-KA Maltese Cross
Inlaid / v:e

PW-KE Maltese Cross
Inlaid / v:e

PW-KJ Monarch Cross
Inlaid-Embossed / v:d

PW-KJ Monarch Cross
Variation Example

318

PW-KM Carlo Cross
Inlaid-Engraved / v:f

PW-KQ Cross in Cloud
Inlaid / v:f

PW-KV Cross & Crescent
Inlaid / v:d

PW-KV Cross & Crescent
Variation Example

PW-LB Cross & Crescent
Inlaid / v:d

PW-LB Cross & Crescent
Variation Example

PW-LH Cross in C
Inlaid / v:f

PW-LM Chrismon Cross
Inlaid / v:e

PW-LR Chrismon Cross
Inlaid / v:d

PW-LW Monarch Chrismon
Inlaid-Embossed / v:e

PW-LZ Wreath Chrismon
Inlaid-Engraved / v:f

PW-MA Carlo Chrismon
Inlaid-Engraved / v:f

PW-MC Maltese Cross
Inlaid / v:e

PW-MC Maltese Cross
Variation Example

PW-MJ Maltese Cross
Inlaid / v:d

PW-MJ Maltese Cross
Variation Example

PW-MP Monarch Maltese
Inlaid-Embossed / v:e

PW-MP Monarch Maltese
Variation Example

PW-MT Fancy Maltese
Inlaid / v:d

319

POKER,
WHEEL
& FARO
(INLAID)

PW-MX Cross
Inlaid / v:e

PW-NB Cross & Circle
Inlaid / v:d

PW-NE Polo
Inlaid / v:d

PW-NJ Cross & Diamond
Inlaid / v:e

PW-NN Hubcap
Inlaid / v:f

PW-NR Defiance
Inlaid / v:f

PW-NV Oriental
Inlaid / v:e

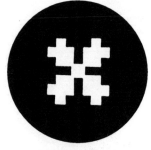

PW-NZ Cross in Circle
Inlaid / v:e

PW-PC Roman
Inlaid / v:d

PW-PC Roman
Variation Example

PW-PG Paragon
Inlaid / v:e

PW-PK Mayfair
Inlaid / v:e

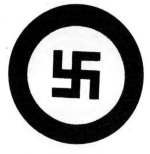

PW-PP Four Crosses
Inlaid / v:e

PW-PS Swastika
Inlaid / v:d

PW-PS Swastika
Variation Example

PW-PW Swastika
Inlaid / v:d

PW-PW Swastika
Variation Example

PW-QD Star
Inlaid / v:d

PW-QD Star
Variation Example

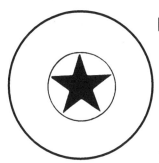

POKER, WHEEL & FARO (INLAID)

PW-QJ Star
Inlaid / v:d

PW-QJ Star
Variation Example

PW-QN Star
Inlaid-Engraved / v:e

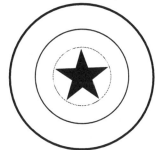

PW-QR Star
Inlaid-Engraved / v:e

PW-QV Star
Inlaid-Engraved / v:e

PW-QV Star
Variation Example

PW-QY Monarch Star
Inlaid-Embossed / v:e

PW-RB Monarch Star
Inlaid-Embossed / v:e

PW-RF Wreath Star
Inlaid-Engraved / v:f

PW-RJ Winner Star
Inlaid-Engraved / v:f

PW-RN Hub Star
Inlaid-Embossed / v:f

PW-RR Star & Crescent
Inlaid / v:e

PW-RR Star & Crescent
Variation Example

PW-RV Star & Crescent
Inlaid / v:c

PW-RV Star & Crescent
Variation Example

PW-SC Star & Crescent
Inlaid / v:c

PW-SF Arabian
Inlaid / v:d

See Design
Section

PW-SJ Star
Inlaid / v:d

321

POKER, WHEEL & FARO (INLAID)

See Design
Section

PW-SM Star
Inlaid / v:d

PW-SQ Diamond Star
Inlaid / v:e

PW-ST Monte Carlo
Inlaid / v:d

PW-ST Monte Carlo
Variation Example

PW-SX Sunburst
Inlaid / v:d

PW-SX Sunburst
Variation Example

PW-TB Sunburst
Inlaid / v:c

PW-TB Sunburst
Variation Example

PW-TF Monarch Sunburst
Inlaid-Embossed / v:e

PW-TF Monarch Sunburst
Variation Example

PW-TJ Sunburst
Inlaid / v:d

PW-TM Five Arms
Inlaid / v:f

PW-TQ Five Arms
Inlaid / v:f

PW-TU Unique
Inlaid / v:c

PW-TY Pentagram
Inlaid / v:d

PW-UC Four Petals
Inlaid / v:e

PW-UG Eight Petals
Inlaid / v:d

PW-UK Six Petals
Inlaid / v:e

POKER, WHEEL & FARO (INLAID)

PW-UN Regal
Inlaid / v:e

PW-UR Comets
Inlaid / v:c

PW-UV Comets
Inlaid / v:d

PW-UV Comets
Variation Example

PW-UX Three Crescents
Inlaid / v:f

PW-VA Six Crescents
Inlaid / v:e

PW-VA Six Crescents
Variation Example

PW-VC Three C's
Inlaid / v:e

PW-VF Champion
Inlaid / v:d

PW-VJ Champion
Inlaid / v:d

PW-VM Ideal
Inlaid / v:d

PW-VQ Oxford
Inlaid / v:d

PW-VT Perfection
Inlaid / v:d

PW-VW Geometric
Inlaid / v:c

PW-VW Geometric
Variation Example

PW-VZ Square
Inlaid / v:e

See Design
Section

PW-WC Keystone
Inlaid / v:c

PW-WG Leviathon
Inlaid / v:e

323

POKER,
WHEEL
& FARO
(INLAID)

PW-WK Reflection
Inlaid / v:e

PW-WN Dixie
Inlaid / v:e

PW-WP Dixie
Inlaid / v:e

PW-WP Dixie
Variation Example

PW-WS Greek Key
Inlaid / v:e

PW-WW Greek Key
Inlaid / v:e

PW-XB Greek Key
Inlaid-Embossed / v:e

PW-XF Olympic
Inlaid / v:d

PW-XH Olympic
Inlaid / v:d

PW-XM Ten Wedges
Inlaid / v:d

PW-XQ Dot Wedges
Inlaid / v:e

PW-XT Dotted Wheel
Inlaid / v:d

PW-XT Dotted Wheel
Variation Example

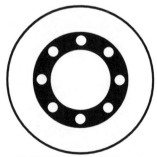

PW-XX Dotted Wheel
Inlaid / v:d

PW-YA Plain Circle
Inlaid / v:e

PW-YF Plain Circle
Inlaid / v:e

PW-YF Plain Circle
Variation Example

PW-YK Monarch Circle
Inlaid-Embossed / v:e

PW-YN Wreath Circle
Inlaid-Engraved / v:f

POKER,
WHEEL
& FARO
(INLAID)

PW-YQ One Ring
Inlaid / v:e

PW-YQ One Ring
Variation Example

PW-YV One Ring
Inlaid / v:e

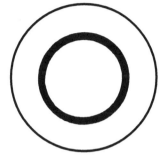

PW-YV One Ring
Variation Example

PW-YZ One Ring
Inlaid / v:e

PW-ZD One Ring
Inlaid / v:e

PW-ZJ One Ring
Inlaid / v:e

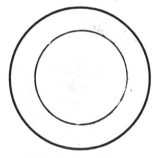

PW-ZN Two Rings
Inlaid / v:e

PW-ZS Fleur-de-Lis
Inlaid / v:d

PW-ZS Fleur-de-Lis
Variation Example

PW-ZY Fleur-de-Lis
Inlaid / v:c

PW-ZY Fleur-de-Lis
Variation Example

PX-AG Fleur-de-Lis
Inlaid-Engraved / v:e

PX-AL Monarch FdL
Inlaid-Embossed / v:e

PX-AP Fleur-de-Lis in C
Inlaid-Embossed / v:e

PX-AT Wreath FdL
Inlaid-Engraved / v:f

PX-AX Winner FdL
Inlaid--Engraved / v:f

PX-BD Horseshoe
Inlaid / v:e

PX-BH Horseshoe
Inlaid / v:d

325

PX-BL thru PX-EB
POKER,
WHEEL
& FARO
(INLAID)

PX-BL Two Horseshoes
Inlaid / v:f

PX-BQ High Hat
Inlaid / v:e

PX-BQ High Hat
Variation Example

PX-BW Aladdin's Lamp
Inlaid / v:e

PX-CC Aladdin's Lamp
Inlaid / v:e

PX-CC Aladin's Lamp
Variation Example

PX-CG Liberty Bell
Inlaid / v:d

PX-CL Lyre
Inlaid / v:d

PX-CS Scimitar
Inlaid / v:e

PX-CW Scimitar
Inlaid / v:d

PX-DA Anchor
Inlaid / v:e

PX-DA Anchor
Variation Example

PX-DG Monarch Anchor
Inlaid-Embossed / v:e

PX-DM Wreath Anchor
Inlaid-Engraved / v:f

PX-DS Pilot's Wheel
Inlaid / v:c

PX-DS Pilot's Wheel
Variation Example

PX-DX Sailing Ship
Inlaid / v:e

PX-DX Sailing Ship
Variation Example

PX-EB Viking Ship
Inlaid / v:e

326

POKER,
WHEEL
& FARO
(INLAID)

PX-EG Scottie
Inlaid / v:d

PX-EG Scottie
Variation Example

PX-EJ Scottie w Eye
Inlaid / v:e

PX-EL Lighthouse
Inlaid / v:e

PX-EV Victory
Inlaid / v:e

Errors on inlaid chips are rare because they were machine-made, but, they do exist. Some examples are shown below:

POKER
Advertising
(Products)
CODES: PY

Antique Chips
Value Rating Code*

a: 50¢   b: $1   c: $2-$3   d: $4-$5   e: $6-$7

f: $8-$9   g: $10-$14   h: $15-$19   i: $20-$29

j: $30-$39 k: $40-$49 l: $50-$69 m: $70-$89

n: $90-$109   o: $110-$149   p: $150-$199

q: $200-$299   r: $300-$399   s: $400-$499

t: $500-$699   u: $700-$999   v: $1000-$1999

w: $2000-$2999   x: $3000-$3999

y: $4000-$499   z: $5000+

*It is important to remember that quantities
of one chip or a set of chips would have
a much lower unit value per chip.

PY-AB ABC Radio
Engraved-Printed / v:f

PY-AB ABC Radio
Reverse

PY-AF ABC Cigar Co
Engraved / v:e

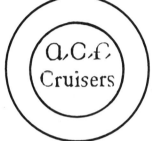

PY-AK Cruisers
Stamped Paper / v:e

PY-AP American Heat
Engraved / v:f

PY-AT Anona Cigar
Inlaid Litho / v:f

PY-AY APB Smoke Shop
Inlaid Litho / v:f

Bakelite Sample
Embossed / v:f

Bakelite Sample
Reverse

PY-BH Beam's Choice
Embossed-Stamped / v:e

PY-BH Beam's Choice
Reverse

PY-BL Boston Store
Engraved Paper / v:d

PY-BN Boston Store
Engraved Wood / v:d

PY-BR Brain Bread
Engraved / v:f

PY-BV Brooks Clothes
Engraved Wood / v:e

PY-BZ Century
Engraved / v:e

PY-BZ Century
Reverse

PY-CE Century
Stamped Paper / v:d

PY-CH Chauncey Olcott
Inlaid Litho / v:f

331

POKER, ADVERTISING (PRODUCTS)

PY-CK Chicago Press
Engraved-Embossed / v:f

PY-CN Climax
Engraved / v:E

PY-CT Climax
Printed Paper / v:f

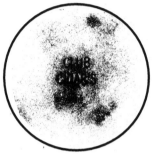

PY-CY Club Cigars
Engraved / v:e

PY-DC Coca Cola
Embossed-Stamped / v:e

PY-DC Coca Cola
Reverse

PY-DG Colt
Embossed-Stamped / v:e

PY-DG Colt
Reverse

PY-DK Cummins
Embssd-Paste On / v:c

PY-DK Cummins
Reverse

PY-DP Cunningham
Embossed / v:f

PY-DP Cunningham
Reverse

See in Animal
Section

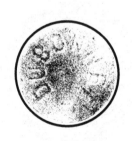

PY-DU Dubonnet
Embossed / v:e

PY-DZ Dunbars
Printed Paper / v:f

Nothing endeavored
nothing discovered.

PY-DZ Dunbars
Reverse

PY-EA Eagle Brewing
Engraved / v:f

PY-EE Engkaso
Printed Paper / v:d

PY-EJ Far West Travelers Assoc.
Inlaid Litho / v:f

POKER, ADVERTISING (PRODUCTS)

PY-EN Fortuna Home
Engraved / v:e

PY-EP Gilbey's Port
Engraved Wood / v:e

PY-ER Gilbey's Rum
Engraved Wood / v:e

PY-EW A. Girpo Ltd.
Engraved Celluloid / v:e

PY-FG Global Coal
Printed Paper / v:e

PY-FL G & W Special
Embossed / v:f

PY-FL G & W Special
Reverse

PY-FR Goodrich
Stamped Rubber / v:e

PY-FR Goodrich
Reverse

PY-FW Goodyear
Embossed-Stamped / v:e

PY-FW Goodyear
Reverse

PY-GE Gen. Greene
Printed Paper / v:f

PY-GH Harley Davidson
Embossed-Stamped / v:e

PY-GH Harley Davidson
Reverse

PY-GM Home Run Tobacco
Embossed / v:f

PY-GM Home Run Tobacco
Reverse

PY-GR H.W. Johns
Embossed / v:f

PY-GT H.W. Johns
Embossed / v:f

PY-GV H.W. Johns
Embossed / v:f

POKER, ADVERTISING (PRODUCTS)

PY-GX H.W. Johns
Embossed / v:e

PY-GZ H.W. Johns
Embossed / v:e

PY-HB H.W. Johns
Embossed / v:e

PY-HD H.W. Johns
Embossed / v:e

PY-HF H.W. Johns
Embossed / v:e

PY-HH H.W. Johns
Embossed / v:f

PY-HJ H.W, Johns
Embossed / v:f

Reverse for All
Previous 7 Chips

note:
Several of the previous 10 chips (PY-GR thru PY-HJ have a blank reverse instead of the graphic shown at the left.

PY-HN Jung Beer
Engraved Paper / v:e

PY-JK J. Klein
Embossed / v:f

PY-JT Kwikset
Embossed-Engraved / v:f

PY-LE Lennox
Embossed-Stamped / v:e

PY-LI Lithia Beer
Engraved Paper / v:e

PY-LO Lorillard's
Engraved / v:f

PY-LR Lorillard's
Embossed / v:f

PY-LX Lorillard's
Printed Paper / v:f

PY-MA Maine
Engraved / v:f

PY-MA Maine
Reverse

POKER, ADVERTISING (PRODUCTS)

PY-ME Menominee
Engraved Paper / v:e

PY-MN Minn. Brewing
Embossed / v:f

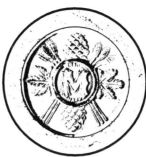

PY-MN Minn. Brewing
Reverse

PY-MS Morton's Salt
Inlaid Litho / v:f

PY-NC Nylon Cord
Molded Rubber / v:e

PY-OM Omaha Rubber
Embossed Rubber / v:f

PY-OM Omaha Rubber
Reverse

PY-OQ Oshkosh
Printed Paper / v:e

PY-OQ Oshkosh
Reverse

PY-OS Oshkosh
Engraved Paper / v:d

PY-OX Oxford Cigar
Inlaid Litho / v:g

PY-PA Pabst
Printed Paper / v:e

PY-PK Packard
Embossed-Stamped / v:f

PY-PN Penn Western
Engraved Wood / v:f

PY-PS Pepsi Cola
Embossed-Stamped / v:f

PY-PS Pepsi Cola
Reverse

PY-PW Piper Heidsieck
Engraved / v:f

PY-QA Prime Plugs
Engraved Paper / v:f

PY-QP Pullman
Inlaid / v:e

335

POKER, ADVERTISING (PRODUCTS)

PY-QR Radios
Embossed-Engraved / v:f

PY-QR Radios
Reverse

PY-QW Rawlplug
Embossed / v:d

PY-RE Renfield
Printed Celluloid / v:d

PY-RH Rhinelander
Engraved Paper / v:e

PY-RO Rose Valley
Engraved / v:f

PY-RY Royal Pepsin
Engraved / v:f

PY-SC Schneider
Engraved Paper / v:d

PY-SE Seagram's
Embossed-Printed / v:f

PY-SI Silver Age
Engraved / v:e

PY-SI Silver Age
Reverse

PY-SL Silver Age
Printed Paper / v:d

PY-SL Silver Age
Reverse

PY-SQ Silvia
Engraved Wood / v:e

PY-ST Stachelberg
Engraved / v:e

PY-SV Stromberg
Printed Paper / v:e

PY-SV Stromberg
Reverse

PY-SX Supremax
Printed Celluloid / v:e

PY-SX Supremax
Reverse

POKER, ADVERTISING (PRODUCTS)

PY-TA Taylor (red brbn)
Printed Paper / v:e

PY-TD Taylor (white brbn)
Printed Paper / v:e

PY-TH Taylor Wine
Engraved Paper / v:e

PY-TH Taylor Wine
Reverse

PY-TL Thilco
Engraved Paper / v:e

PY-UC United Cigar
Engraved-Embossed / v:f

PY-US U.S. Rubber
Stamped / v:e

PY-US U.S. Rubber
Reverse

PY-VA Valentines
Embossed / v:f

PY-VA Valentines
Reverse

PY-WA American Bourbon
Embossed / v:e

PY-WE American Rye
Embossed / v:e

PY-WK Canadian Club
Embossed / v:e

PY-WN Father Time
Embossed / v:e

PY-WP Imperial Whisky
Embossed / v:e

PY-WR Mt. Ridge
Embossed / v:e

Reverse of all
Previous 6 Chips

PY-XJ Johnnie Walker
Engraved Celluloid / v:f

PY-XJ Johnnie Walker
Reverse

337

PY-XR thru·PY-ZY
POKER,
ADVERTISING
(PRODUCTS)

PY-XR Warrens
Engraved / v:f

PY-XW Waterman's Pens
Embossed-Inlaid / v:g

PY-XW Waterman's Pens
Reverse(wood inlay)

PY-YD Willis Day
Paper Enclosed in Plastic / e

PY-YD Willis Day
Reverse

PY-YW White Horse
Engraved / v:f

PY-ZF World's Fair
Embsd-Prntd Paper / v:e

PY-ZW Wynn's
Printed Paper / v:d

PY-ZW Wynn's
Reverse

PY-ZY York-Willis
Printed Paper / v:e

338

Advertising
(Gambling Products)

CODES: PZ

Note: Normally, in this book, the cut-off date for including chips is 1940. In this section, due to collector's interest in gambling chip manufacture, the cut-off date is 1970.

Antique Chips
Value Rating Code*

a: 50¢   b: $1   c: $2-$3   d: $4-$5   e: $6-$7

f: $8-$9   g: $10-$14   h: $15-$19   i: $20-$29

j: $30-$39   k: $40-$49   l: $50-$69   m: $70-$89

n: $90-$109   o: $110-$149   p: $150-$199

q: $200-$299   r: $300-$399   s: $400-$499

t: $500-$699   u: $700-$999   v: $1000-$1999

w: $2000-$2999   x: $3000-$3999

y: $4000-$499   z: $5000+

*It is important to remember that quantities
of one chip or a set of chips would have
a much lower unit value per chip.

POKER, ADVERTISING (GAMBLING)

PZ-AE Bowman
Wave Mold / v:f

PZ-AK Calif Games
Inlaid Litho / v:d

PZ-AM Calif. Games
Inlaid Litho / v:e

PZ-AO Calif. Games
Inlaid Litho / v:e

PZ-AS Christy & Jones
Hat & Cane / v:e

PZ-AU Christy & Jones
4 Inserts / v:e

PZ-AW Christy & Jones
Hat & Cane / v:d

PZ-BC Cla-Jac Ent.
Stamped Plastic / v:e

PZ-BG Click Ent.
Stamped Celluloid / v:f

PZ-BK Codes
Heart & Dash / v:h

PZ-BP H.C. Edwards
H Mold / v:e

PZ-BS H.C. Edwards
No Inserts / v:e

PZ-BV H.C. Edwards
3 Inserts / v:e

PZ-BY H.C. Edwards
3 Double Inserts / v:e

PZ-CB H.C. Edwards
6 Inserts / v:e

PZ-CE Ewing Mfg.
3 Inserts / v:f

PZ-CH Ewing Mfg.
3 Wide Inserts / v:f

PZ-CK Ewing Mfg.
3 Inserts / v:f

PZ-CN Ewing Mfg.
3 Wide Inserts / v:f

POKER,
ADVERTISING
(GAMBLING)

PZ-GA Art Gamlin
4 Inserts / v:e

PZ-GE George & Co
Floral Mold / v:f

PZ-IS Iserco
9 Inserts / v:e

PZ-JO Bud Jones
Nevada Mold / v:d

PZ-KI T.R. King
Large Crown / v:f

PZ-KN T.R. King
Large Crown / v:e

PZ-KT T.R. King
Small Crown / v:d

PZ-LA L.A. Rubber
Embossed / v:h

PZ-LA L.A. Rubber
Reverse

PZ-LG Langworthy
Rectangles / v:g

PZ-LN Langworthy
Machined / v:f

PZ-LP Langworthy
No Inserts / v:e

PZ-LS Langworthy
3 Inserts / v:e

PZ-LV Langworthy
5 Inserts / v:d

PZ-MA Mason & Co
Hub Mold / v:f

PZ-MD Mason & Co.
2 Inserts / v:f

PZ-MF Mason & Co
2 Wide Inserts / v:f

PZ-MH Mason & Co
Co. Initials / v:g

PZ-PA Paulson
Hat & Cane / v:d

POKER,
ADVERTISING
(GAMBLING)

PZ-PD Paulson
3 Inserts / v:d

PZ-PI Pioneer Supply
3 Inserts / v:e

PZ-PK Pioneer Supply
3 Wide Inserts / v:e

PZ-PM Pioneer Supply
3 Very Wide / v:e

PZ-PO Pioneer Supply
4 Inserts / v:e

PZ-PQ Pioneer Supply
5 Inserts / v:e

PZ-PT Portland Card
Square in Circle / v:g

PZ-RI C.W. Rice
Horsehead Left / v:f

PZ-RK C.W. Rice
No Inserts / v:e

PZ-RM C.W. Rice
2 Inserts / v:e

PZ-RO C.W. Rice
2 Wide Inserts / v:e

PZ-RQ C.W. Rice
4 Inserts / v:e

PZ-RS C.W. Rice
5 Inserts / v:e

PZ-RV Rigdon & Co
Hourglass / v:g

PZ-RY Ryan's
Slanted S's / v:g

PZ-SA Salt Lake Card
Engraved / v:g

PZ-SP Spaulding
Fibre Material / v:h

PZ-SP Spaulding
Reverse

PZ-SQ Spaulding.
Fibre Material / v:h

343

POKER,
ADVERTISING
(GAMBLING)

PZ-SQ Spaulding
Reverse

PZ-SU Pat Sullivan
Horsehead Left / v:e

PZ-TA Taylor's
No Inserts / v:f

PZ-TC Taylor's
3 Inserts / v:f

PZ-TK T.K. Specialty
Horseshoe / v:f

PZ-TK T.K. Specialty
Reverse

PZ-TM T.K. Specialty
4 Inserts / v:f

PZ-TO T.K. Specialty
Horseshoe / v:f

PZ-TQ T.K. Specialty
Machined / v:g

PZ-TS Jack Todd
Engraved / v:i

PZ-TU Jack Todd
Diamond Mold / v:h

PZ-TW Jack Todd
Diamond Mold / v:h

PZ-WA Frank Walters
Machined / v:g

PZ-WE Western Supply
Rectangle / v:g

PZ-WH White's
Dot Mold / v:i

PZ-WL Wills
No Inserts / v:g

PZ-WN Wills
6 Inserts / v:g

PZ-WP Wills
No Inserts / v:g

PZ-WR Wills
4 Inserts / v:g

UNUSUAL
Mixed Examples
CODES: NONE

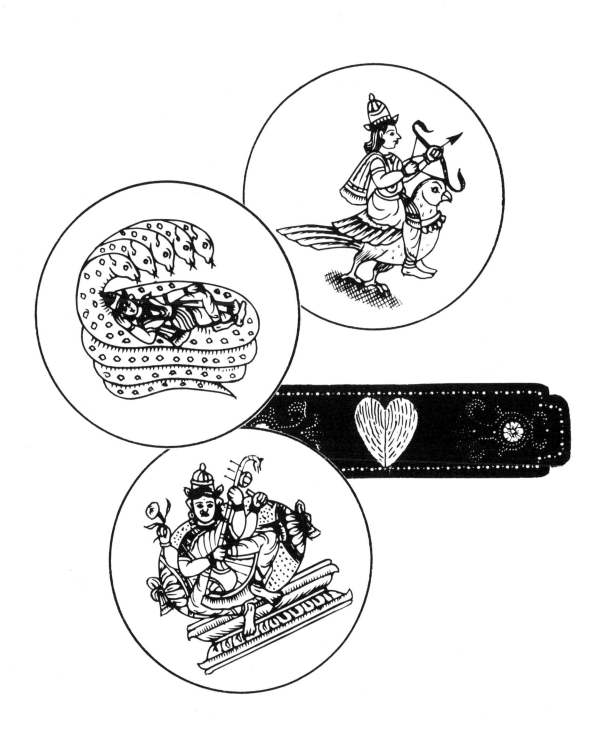

CELLULOID
Poker Chips
Trade Mark "CELLULOID," Jan. 14, 1873.
Patented July 12, 1870. Reissued June 28, 1874.
100.   **No.**

CAUTION.—The word "CELLULOID" having been patented as a Trade Mark, any parties offering goods of any description under the name of "CELLULOID," will be prosecuted to the full extent of the law.

347

SAMPLES
UNUSUAL
CELLULOID

European celluloid chips. The CDEF stands for *chemin de fer*.

UNUSUAL
PORCELAIN CHIPS

An assortment of porcelain chips from Asia.

SAMPLES
UNUSUAL
SPECIAL PURPOSE CHIPS
Each of these chips has a special purpose in various games.

UNUSUAL
TRUMP INDICATOR CHIPS

Whist markers indicated the trump suit being played. Chips on the top row are carved from bone. Rows two and three show chips that were hand-painted on china. Row four shows a set of hand-painted mother-of-pearl chips and their hand-carved mother-of-pearl case. The chips in the bottom row are brass.

SAMPLES
UNUSUAL
BRIDGE CHIPS

Aluminum bridge chips from the 1930's.

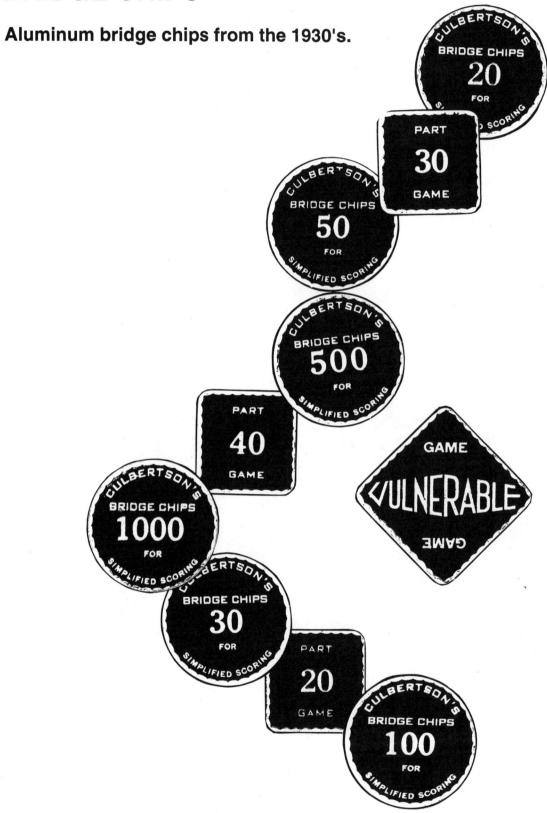

UNUSUAL
TUNBRIDGE WARE CHIPS

Tunbridge is a form of wood mosaic decoration developed by craftsmen in the area of Tonbridge (Kent) England in the 1820's. The manufacturing process is very similar to today's popular polymer clay technique of building a cane or loaf and cutting slices for the final product. Tunbridge ware is sometimes called "stickware." These chips are quite rare.

SAMPLES
UNUSUAL
PLASTIC CHIPS FROM INDIA

These unusual chips from India are made from a plastic type material similar to the French casino chips. They are decorated in red and blue colors

This set of 60 paper chips was decorated with cartoons of poker *cliches*. Advertised as "the most economical poker chips sold", the chips were made by the Dyment Company in Cleveland, Ohio in 1933. Graphics have been enlarged 42%.

UNUSUAL
CARTOONED PAPER CHIPS

UNUSUAL
CHIPS ON A WIRE

Progressive and Drive Whist Counters

..... Patent pending.

For durability and economy this Counter is the LEADER of the day. Never breaks or wears out and no limit as to the number of times used.

Winner can claim of loser one counter for each point lost. Thus a perfect score is obtained.

TRADE MARK.

Manufactured by .... G. F. WHITE & CO., 31 Bedford St., Boston.

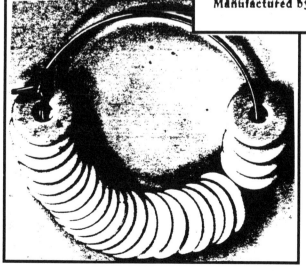

These game counters were housed on a wire ring that disengaged easily to remove chips.

UNUSUAL

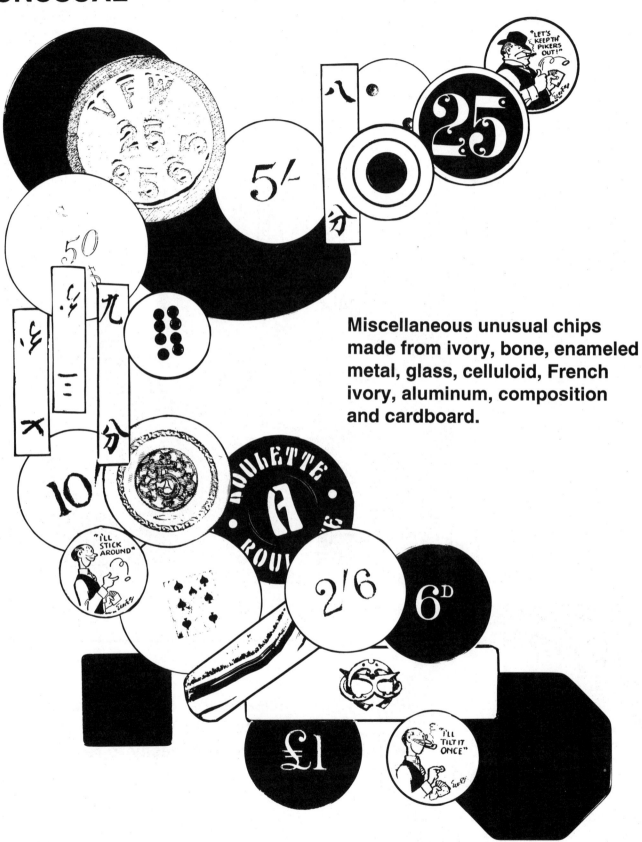

Miscellaneous unusual chips
made from ivory, bone, enameled
metal, glass, celluloid, French
ivory, aluminum, composition
and cardboard.

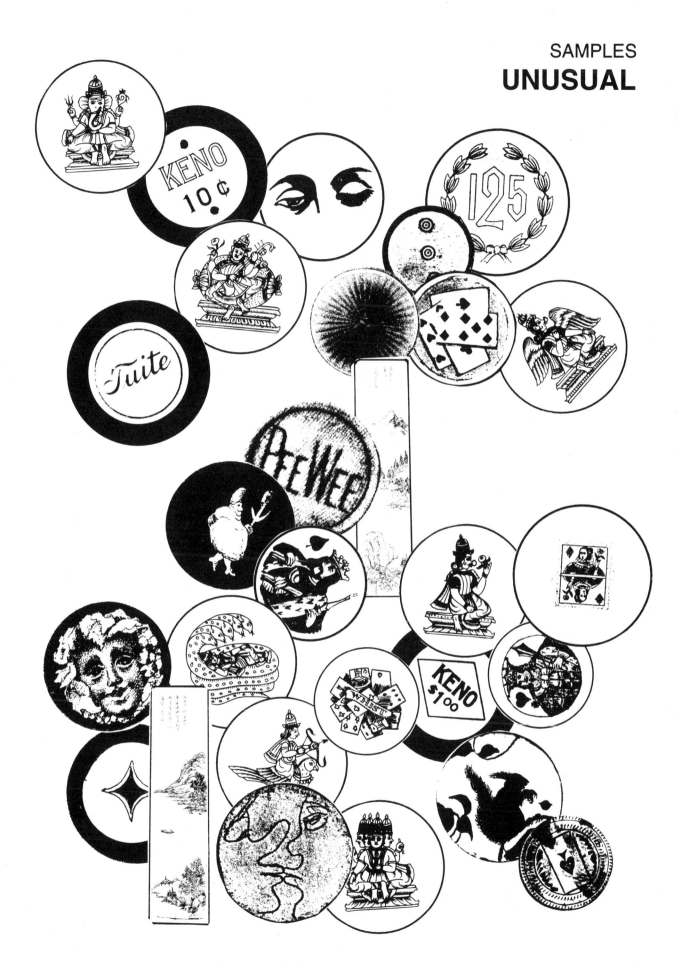

DEALER CHIPS
Selected Samples

Dealer chips were special chips that were used to indicate which player was to deal next. These chips were often very special in design. In the case of ivory dealer chips, the chips were much larger than the regular chips, and they sometimes contained silver inlays. These chips were frequently elliptical or rectangular in shape.

The advertising dealer chip (*circa* 1890) shown below came from the Piping Rock Hotel at Saratoga Springs, New York. The Piping Rock Club was known as the gambling spot of the east, if not of the U.S., at that time. These dealer chips —otherwise known as "whiskey chips" — were not only used to designate who was to deal next but also for single large-stake bets — one-deal situations only.

SAMPLES
DEALER
CHIPS

BONE CHIPS
Selected Samples

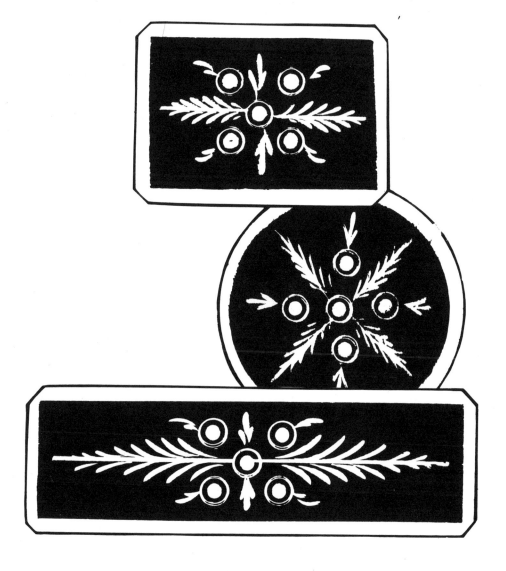

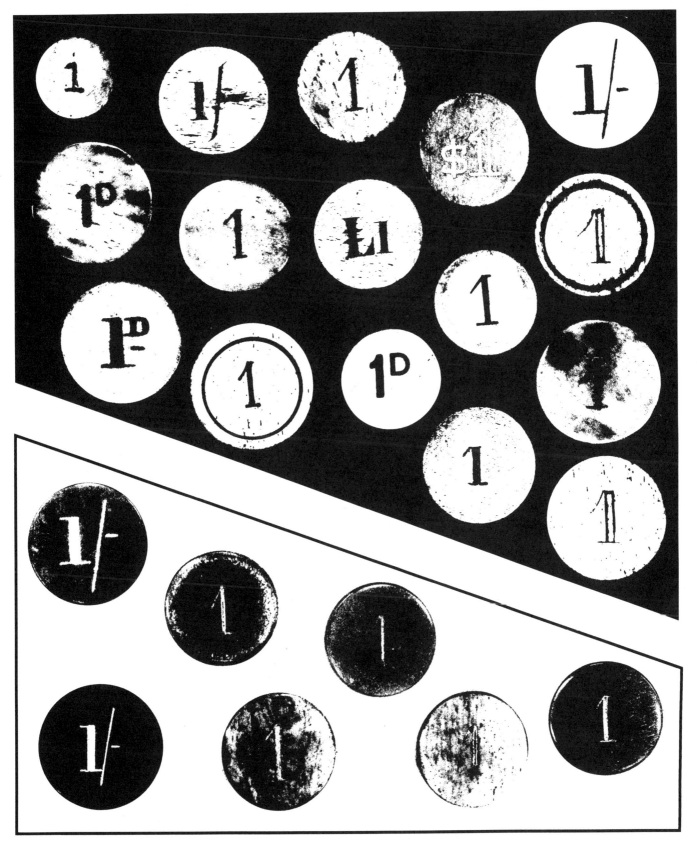

SAMPLES
BONE
CHIPS

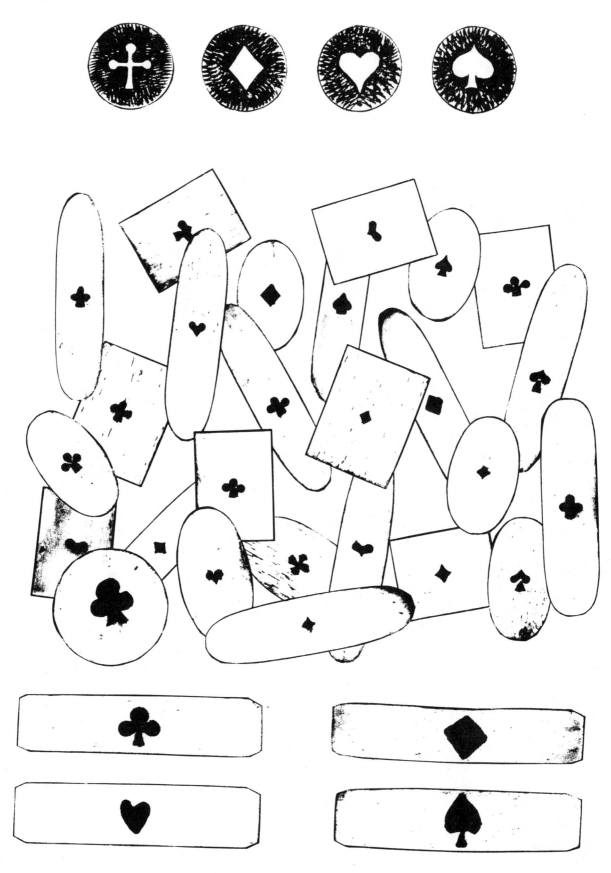

BONE
CHIPS

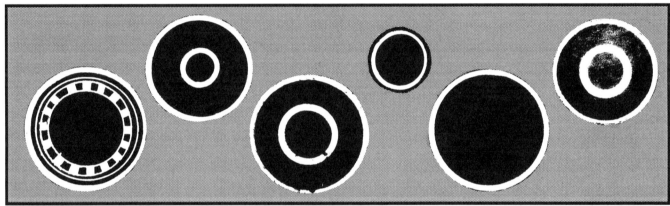

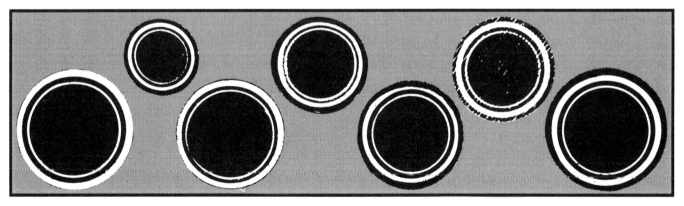

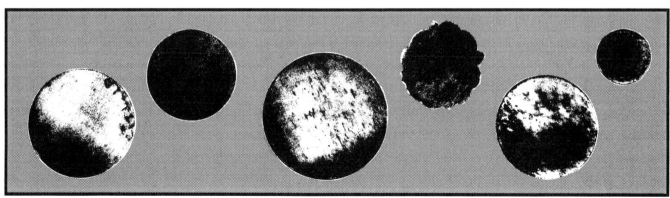

BONE
CHIPS

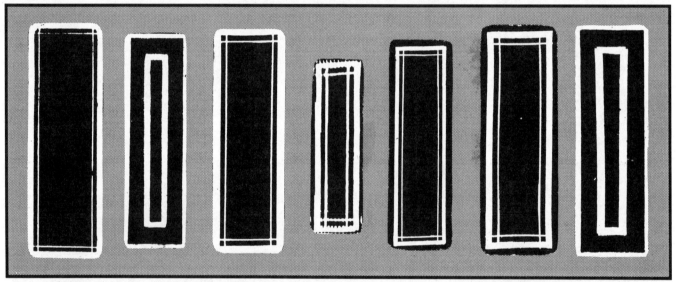

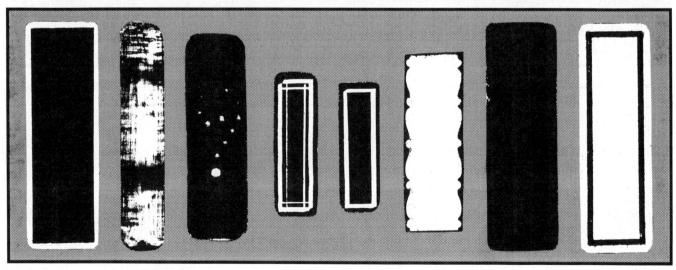

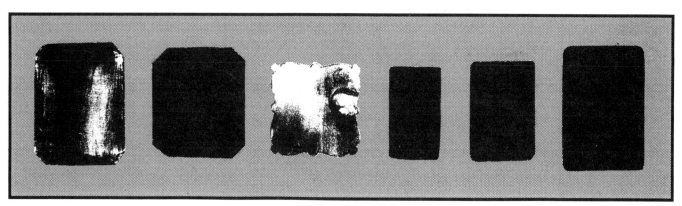

SAMPLES
BONE
CHIPS

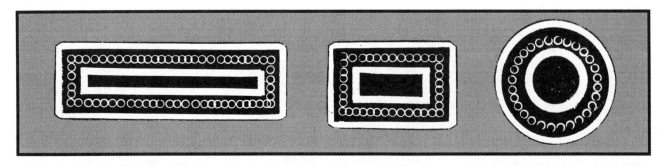

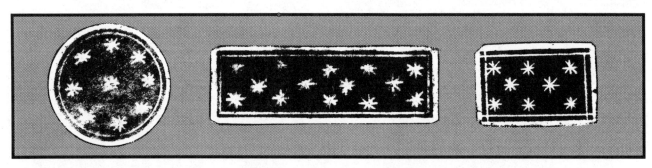

CASINO & CLUB
Selected Samples

Note: Most of the chips
shown in this section were
made after 1940.

SAMPLES

CASINO
NEVADA $100 CHIPS

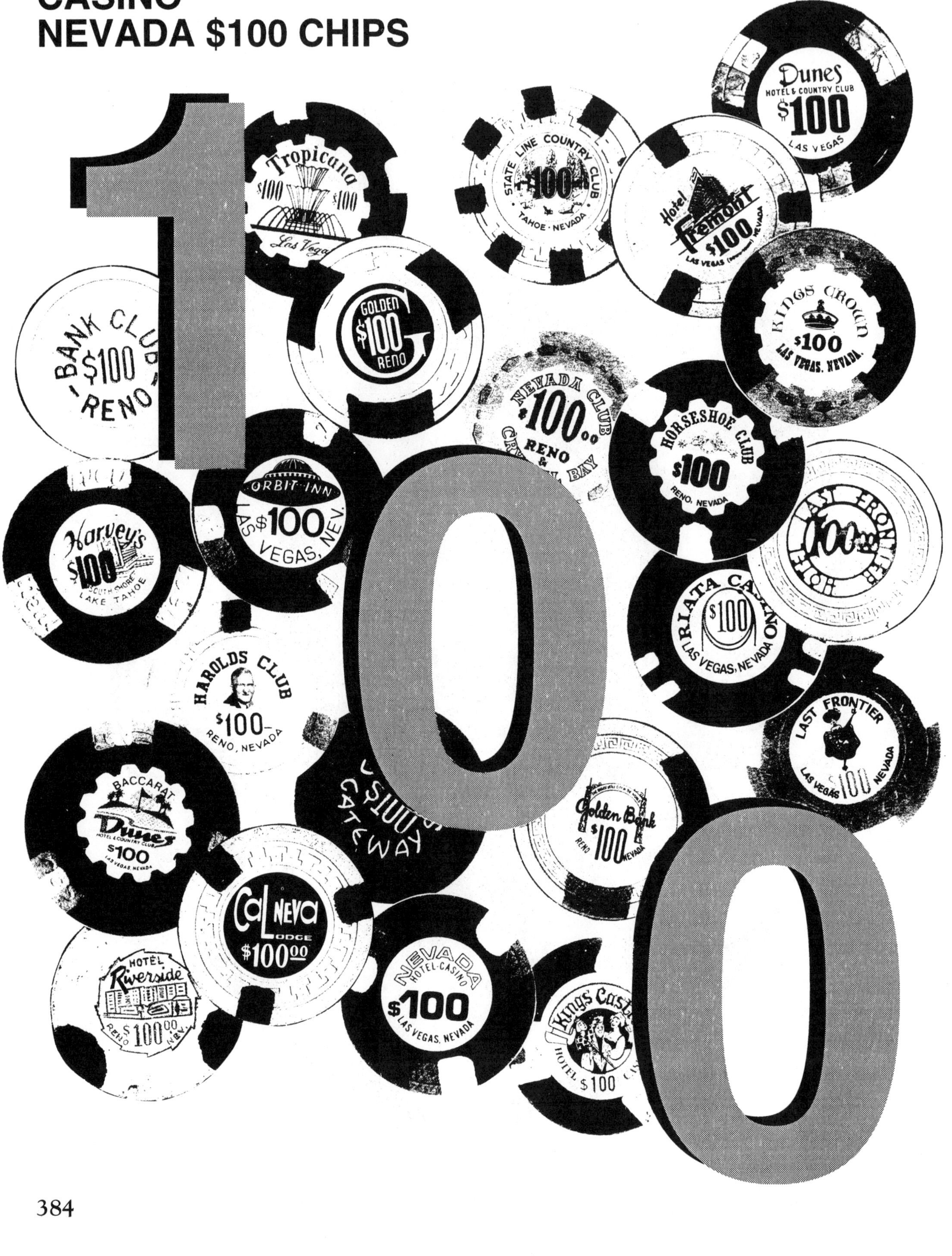

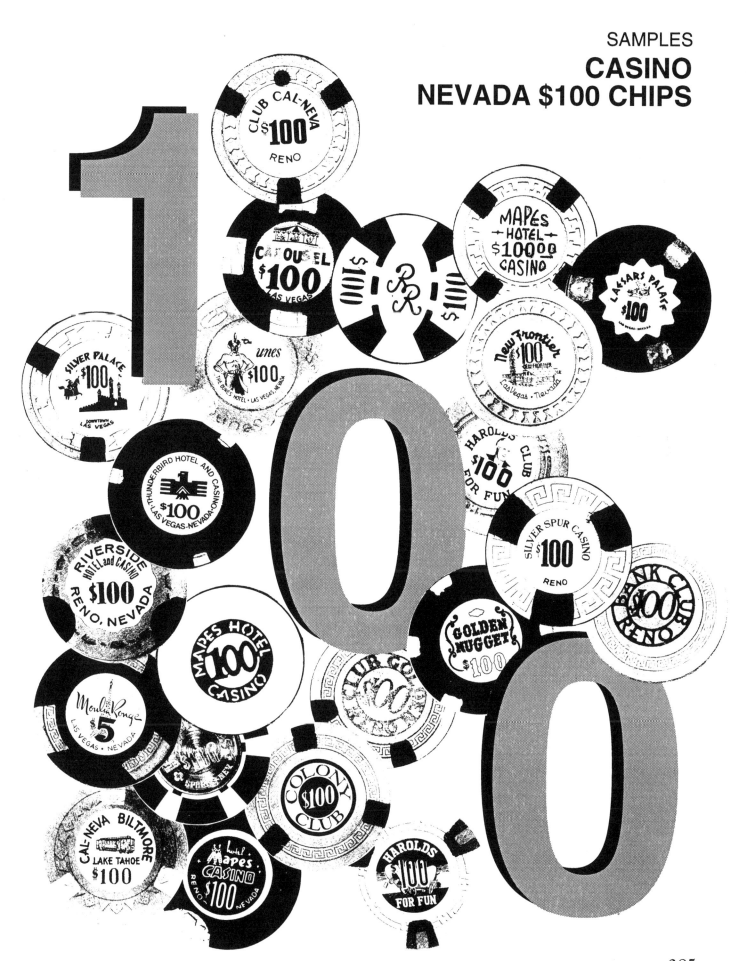

385

CASINO & CLUB
UNCODED CATEGORIES

Shown below are four types of chips that are not given codes,
even though they fit into various poker chip categories such as
transportation, design and sports.

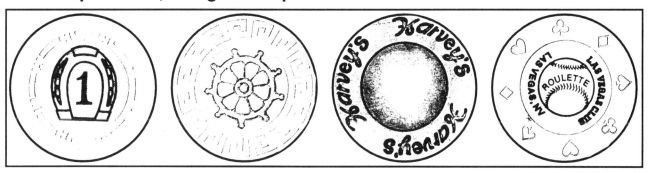

Designated roulette chips

Cruise ships & gambling ships

Yacht, tennis and athletic clubs

Molded rim chips

FOREIGN
Selected Samples

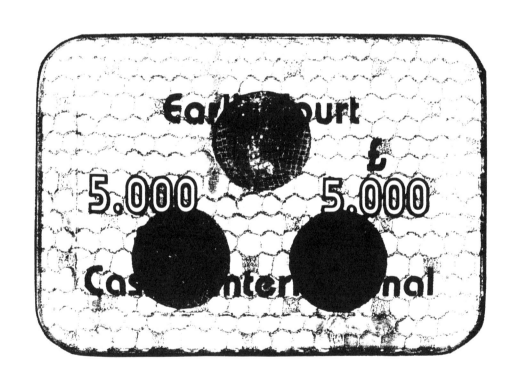

Societé des Bains de Mer
de Monaco
THE GRAND CASINO MONTE CARLO

100 FRANC

20 FRANC   20 FRANC

20 FRANC   5 FRANC

ORIGINAL 20th CENTURY
GAMING CHIPS

13806

Societé des Bains de Mer
de Monaco
GRAND CASINO MONTE CARLO

5 FRANC

10 FRANC   40 FRANC

40 FRANC   40 FRANC

ORIGINAL 20th CENTURY
GAMING CHIPS

393

OLD CATALOGS
Selected Pages

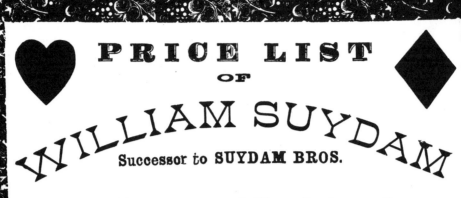

PRICE LIST
OF
WILLIAM SUYDAM
Successor to SUYDAM BROS.

Headquarters and Manufactory of
ALL KINDS OF
SPORTING GOODS,
WILLIAM SUYDAM,

22 Union Square,   **New York City.**

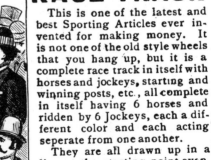

THE NEW STYLE
RACE TRACK

This is one of the latest and best Sporting Articles ever invented for making money. It is not one of the old style wheels that you hang up, but it is a complete race track in itself with horses and jockeys, starting and winning posts, etc., all complete in itself having 6 horses and ridden by 6 Jockeys, each a different color and each acting seperate from one another.

They are all drawn up in a line at the starting point even, the spring lever is pulled and away they go around and around the track and the horse stopping with his nose nearest the winning post wins the purse as there are 6 entrance fees the owner of the track takes one fee for percentage every time and pays the winning horse or the man that holds the winning ticket 5. As each horse works on a seperate wire there is no collision or no mistake and everything goes smooth and satisfactory to every one. The race track is not only adapted for Races, Fairs, etc., but is just as well intended for saloon purposes for drinks, money or anything else. Altogether it is one of the best and most attractive things ever invented for making money.

Price of Track, Cards, Box, and everything Complete, $15.00

SAVE YOUR MONEY BY SENDING ALL ORDERS TO HEADQUARTERS ONLY.

Dear Sir: In reply to yours, there is only one sure way to win at cards, etc. and that is to get Tools to work with and then to use them with discretion which is the secret of all Gambling and the way that all Gamblers make their money. Yours truly,

Wm. Suydam.

NOTICE.

In case you should send me an order, be sure and send all Money only by REGISTERED LETTER, or POSTAL MONEY ORDER to avoid all chance of loss, or delay in forwarding the Goods. N. B. Any Money sent me not in accordance with these regulations, if lost I cannot be responsible for it.

ADVANTAGE OR MARKED BACK PLAYING CARDS.

By which you can tell the color, Suit and Size as well by the backs as by the faces, they are an exact imitation of the fair Playing Cards in common use and are adapted for any Game, where it would be impossible for your opponent to win as you would know just what he had in his hand and could act accordingly. These Cards can be learned in an hour with the instructions which are sent with each pack, so that you can tell EVERY Card the instant you see it, both Size and Suit. Price with full and complete instructions $1.00 per pack, or $10 per dozen. N. B. Be sure and ask for the Key or Directions as without them the Cards would be of no use to you unless you are a first class professional Gambler.

THE COMPLETE POKER PLAYER.

The most elaborate and Satisfactory Work ever issued, in regard to any Game at Cards.

By JOHN BLACKBRIDGE, Esq., Actuary and Counselor at Law.

Price, handsomely bound in Cloth, gilt sides and back, $1.00; Paper Covers, 75 cents.

This book contains the laws of the game of Draw Poker, as laid down by the recognized authorities.
It contains full instruction as to how to play every hand that is dealt.
It contains just such information as you need to have, in order to answer, on the instant of each deal, the momentous question, "Shall I go in, or stay out?"
It contains correct calculations as to the probable and real value of any hand that can be dealt you.
It contains "Schenck's famous rules of Draw Poker," as laid down by him for the benefit of the English aristocracy, who are wild to learn this famous game.
It contains Dr. Pole's calculations on original hands, which, being based on *absolute science*, are worth alone, the price of the book.
It contains the results of 1,000 hands, actually dealt, in order to verify by *Experience* the results of Theory. It contains the "Art of Bluffing" with a proper estimate of the same, and is *par excellant*, THE BOOK OF REFERENCE wherever the game is played.
It contains results of large games, with wholesome advice as to *limits of bets*.
It contains advice as to how to play each hand for its value, thus making winning a matter of certainty in the long run.
In short, it exhausts the subject of Draw Poker, and shows the results of long study and practice, united to a sincere desire to render the game pleasant and honorable.
The oldest professional player will get some new ideas from this book.
Copies sent, postage paid, on receipt of Price.

THE POKER RING.

JUST OUT!

An ingenious little contrivance for Marking the Cards while playing, in a perfectly safe and systematic manner, so that in half an hour you can tell each card as well by the back as by the face. Although it is not as yet generally known, it is now in use by a few of the oldest and best "professional" players in the country. Anybody can use it at once.
These rings are finely chased and are all PURE SOLID SILVER, and are worth the money alone as an ornament, if they were never used as an implement of advantage playing,
For second dealing they are invaluable, and no second dealer should be without one for a day; but comment is unnecessary as anyone understanding second dealing will see in an instant its value, the moment the subject is brought to his mind. PRICE, with full instructions for using it, $1.50.
The above finely chased ROLLED GOLD $2.25.
In sending for Ring, send size of the finger you wish to wear it on so that I can give an exact fit. Send all money by registered letter only, to avoid all chance of loss or delay.

These **NUMERAL CHECKS** are 1½ inches in diameter and oval edges, and made in the following colors ; Yellow, Red, Blue, Brown, Pink, Green, Purple and Black.   Price, per 100 $2.50,   Per 1000 $20.00.   The yellow in these is used instead of the white to prevent ringing in.

Monogram Checks made to Order Only.

2 Letters, $5.50 per 100, $50.00 per 1000.

3 Letters, $7.00 per 100, $65.00 per 1000.

Reduced Prices
Of *Embossed* Faro and Poker Checks.

1¼ inch plain per 100 70 cents per 1000 $6.00

1½ inch plain per 100 75 cts. per 1000 $7.00

1½ inch lined per 100 $1.00 per 1000 $9.00

1½ inch Engraved any design on this sheet, per Hundred $1.25.   Per Thousand $12.00

WE WILL NOT DEVIATE FROM ABOVE PRICES.

N. B.—Any of the above Checks we may send you if not satisfactory in every particular send them right back and we will return your money.

These **INITIAL CHECKS** made only 1½ inch in diameter and oval edges. Colors, White, Red, Blue, Yellow, Brown, Green, Pink, Purple and Black. We can furnish all the letters in the alphabet the same as below if desired.   Price per 100, **$4.**00; per 1,000, **$35.**00.

ENGRAVED SQUARE EDGE. These styles 1½ inch in diameter only. Colors, White, Red, Blue, Pink, Yellow, Green and Brown

Price per 100, $3.00.   Per 1000, $25.00.

Price List of
MANUFACTURED
W. SUYDAM, 22 Union

Marked Back Playing Cards.

ROUND CORNERS, per pack, by mail, postpaid $1 00
" 12 packs 10 00

Marked Back Strippers.

ROUND CORNERS, per pack, by mail, postpaid $1 50
" 6 packs 7 00
" 12 packs 12 00

Fair Card Strippers.

ENAMELED ROUND CORNERS, per pack, by mail postpaid $1 00
" " 6 packs 5 00
" " 12 packs 9 00

First Quality Round Corners, Fancy Backs, Enameled Patent Squeezers, marked by hand by new shading process, $1.50 per pack, 6 packs $8.00, one dozen, $15.00.

Faro Tools.

HARTS FARO DEALING CARDS, unsq'red, per doz. $15 00
" " " squared, " 15 00
" " " " per pack 1 25
Also the same in any form, "Rounds and Straights," "End Rounds" or "Wedges," per pack 2 25
Same per dozen, by express 25 00
FARO CARDS, Linen, second quality 6 00
" " " " squared 7 50
STEAMBOATS, squared, per dozen 4 00
SQUARE DEALING BOXES, German Silver 10 00
" " heavily plated, ... $10, 15 00
" " to hold two packs 12 00
TWO CARD DEALING BOXES, top sight tell, top balance improved Lever or End Squeeze $50, 75 00
BACK UP SECOND CARD BOX FOR RED AND BLACK, Gaff and Pull Back 25 00
Dealing Boxes of every description made to order and repaired. Top balance, End Squeeze and Lever constantly on hand.
Faro Spreads, broadcloth, with or without High Card $9 00
" " on Board 14 00
" " on fold-up boards 18 00
" enameled. 3 00
" " on straight board 7 00
Folding Lay-out Boards. ⅝, 1 in. and 1⅛ in. thick.
CASE KEEPERS, Walnut Wood Markers 5 00
" " Im Ivory " 8 00
" Rosewood, Wood " 10 00
" " Ivory " 13 00
" " " " painted 18 00
CARD PRESSES, for Drawer without cover 3 00
" " " " Mahogany. 4 00
" Slide Cover & Lock, " . 5 00
" " " place for box " . 6 00
" Double, with Slide Cover & Lock " . 7 00
CHECK HOLDERS, for 600 or 800 Checks. 3 00
" " 400 or 500 " Mahogany... 3 00
" " 600 or 800 " " ... 4 00
" " 1000 or more " " ... 5 00
TRIMMING SHEARS, Double Bar, Brass Block 35 00
" " " with attachment for Brief or the Odd 40 00
CASES FOR DEALING BOXES, Morocco 1 00
" " " paper 50
" FARO CARDS, Morocco 50
SHUFFLING BOARDS, best in use, thin 1 50
CUE CARDS, per 1000 . ... 3 00
" " 5000, strongly boxed for shipping 12 00
" " 10000 " " ... 20 00
BILLIARD CLOTH, for covering Faro Tables, per yd .. 6 00
" " " " 2d quality .. 5 00
CARD PUNCHES, best $2, 3 00
GLASS PAPER, better than sand, per doz. sheets. 1 00

Best Ivory Faro Checks.

1½ in. Plain Engraving, set of 600 .... $150 00 Per 100 .. $25 00
1 9-16 " " " .... 165 00 " .. 27 50
1⅝ " " " .... 180 00 " .. 30 00
1½ Fancy " " .... 165 00 " .. 27 50
1 9-16 " " " .... 180 00 " .. 30 00
1⅝ " " " .... 195 00 " .. 32 50

Coppers, Markers and Extra Checks included.
Broken Sets of Checks filled up and re-colored on short notice.

SQUARE EDGE
Compressed Ivory Faro Checks.

1½in. Lined, per set of 600 $15 00 per 1000 .... $25 00
1½in. Double Lined, " 18 00 " 30 00
1½in. Engraved, " 22 00 " 35 00
1½in " Special Designs 27 00 " 45 00
1 9-16in Lined, per set 600 18 00 " 30 00
1 8-16in. Double lined " 22 00 " 35 00
1 9-16in. Engraved " 27 00 " 45 00
1 9-16in. " Spec'l Designs 37 00 " 55 00

Coppers, Splits, Markers and Extra Checks included.
Colors: Red, White, Blue, Yellow, Brown, or tinted if desired

Embossed Checks.

1½ in., any design on sheet, per 100 $2 00 per 1000, $20 00
1½ in., single line .... " 1 50 " 14 00
1½ in., double line .... " 1 75 " 17 00

Coppers, Markers, and Extra Checks, $2.00 per set.

Ivoroyd Checks.

1¼ in. Red—White—Blue, per 100 $ 60 per 1000, $ 5 00
1⅜ " " " " 75 " 6 00
1½ " " orange " 1 00 " 8 00
1 9-16 " " " " 1 25 " 10 00

We do not Line or engrave Ivoroyd Checks.

Dealing Games for Box and Cards.

CARD HAZARD, Cards, Box, Layout complete $25 00
" Layout 15 00
RED & BLACK Layout, best cloth, old style Jack Heads 9 00
" " " " fold-up boards ... 15 00
" " " enameled cloth 5 00
" Dealing Boxes, to lock and unlock 25 00
Faked Skeleton Boxes, German Silver, a sure thing for Dealer to win every time at Red and Black or Red, White and Blue. Price $10.00. Cards $4.00 to $10.00 per dozen packs.
SHORT FARO, or Card Chuck Luck, enameled Layout 5 00
" " " Broadcloth " 6 00
RED AND BLACK Layout, New Style, 52 cards all around, Best Broadcloth $30.00, on Board $35.00, Enameled $15.00, on Board $20.00.
RED AND BLACK Dealing Boxes, for two packs 12 00
OVER AND UNDER SEVEN, Layout only, ... 2 50
ROCKY MOUNTAIN KENO, 50, 100 or 200 cards, set, 10 00

Roulette, Rondo and Ball Games.

ROULETTE WHEELS, 32 inches diameter $150 00
" " finest in the world 500 00
" Spreads. cloth, double, 13.6x5 ft 90 00
" " " single, 7 ft 2 in. x 54 in ... 50 00
" " " " for 36 numbers 50 00
" " " double " 90 00
" " enamel cloth, double 16 00
" " " single 8 00
" Check Rack, rounded backs $3, $4, 5 00
" Ivory Balls, each .... 50c., 60c., and 75
RONDO BALLS, 1⅛ in, 8 in set 5 00
" 1¼ " 7 00
HAP HAZARD 00
HIGH BALL POKER, leather bottle, 25 Ivory Balls .. 9 00
" " " " 50 " 18 00
" " BALLS, Ivory, flat face, each .. 35

MERCHANDISE BY MAIL.

When sufficient money is remitted to cover postage, we can send packages of merchandise, not exceeding 4 lbs. in weight, by mail, *not sealed*, at the rate of 1 cent per oz., and 10 cents additional for registering package. ☞ *Otherwise we will ship by express.* Parties ordering small quantities of goods, or cards, from a distance, or from towns having no express office, will find this a cheap and comparatively safe way to get them. When, however, a quantity of goods is desired, by express will usually be the proper way to ship.

PRICE LIST. 5

FARO CHECKS.

MADE OF BEST QUALITY IVORY.

1½ in., plain engraving, set of 600					$160 00
1½ in., " " "		700			180 00
1½ in., fancy " "		600			165 00
1½ in., " "		700			192 50

Coppers, splits, markers, and extra checks in each set. Larger sets furnished to order of any pattern desired, and broken sets filled and re-colored. Single checks, best ivory from 30 cents to 40 cents each. Coloring checks, 6 cents each. Coloring and sizing up to stack even with the whites, 12 cents each. Coloring, sizing up, and re-engraving, so they will be equal to new, 15 cents each.

WILL & FINCK'S EXTRA QUALITY

COMPRESSED IVORY CHECKS.

1½ in., plain	per 600	$15 00
1½ in., lined	" "	20 00
1½ in., double lined	" "	25 00
1½ in., engraved, our own designs, (patent applied for)		35 00

These engraved checks are entirely new designs—no danger of ringers, cannot be furnished by any other house in the United States. Coppers, markers, splitters, and extra checks to each set. Larger sets at the same proportionate rate. Sets also engraved to order.

SECOND QUALITY COMPRESSED IVORY CHECKS,

Such as the country is flooded with.

1½ in., plain	per 600	$12 00
1½ in., lined	" "	15 00
1½ in., double lined	" "	20 00
1½ in., engraved, either anchor, rose, shamrock, or horseshoe		25 00

---

6   WILL & FINCK'S

WILL & FINCK'S EXTRA QUALITY

COMPRESSED IVORY CHECKS.

1¼ in., plain	per 100	$ 1 75
1⅜ in., "	" "	2 00
1½ in., "	" "	2 50
1½ in., lined	" "	3 50
1½ in., double lined	" "	4 00

SECOND QUALITY COMPRESSED IVORY CHECKS.

1¼ in., plain	per 100	$ 1 25
1⅜ in., "	" "	1 50
1½ in., "	" "	1 75
1½ in., lined	" "	2 25
1½ in., double lined	" "	3 25
1½ in., engraved, either horseshoe, shamrock, rose, or anchor	per 100	3 75

WILL & FINCK

San Francisco, Cal.

1896

FARO CHECKS

IVORY.

1½-inch, engraved, set of 600			$150 00
1½ " " " 700			175 00
1½ " fancy, engraved, set of 600			170 00
1½ " " " " 700			197 00

Coppers, splits, markers, and extra checks in each set. Larger sets furnished to order of any pattern desired, and broken sets filled and recolored. Single checks, best ivory, 30 cts. each. Coloring checks, 4 cts. each. Coloring and sizing up to stack even with the whites, 9 cts. each. Coloring, sizing-up, and re-engraving, so that they will be equal to new, 12 cts. each.

WILL & FINCK CO.'S EXTRA QUALITY COMPRESSED IVORY CHECKS

1½-inch, inlaid patterns, per set of 1000. $40 00

This is one of the finest checks on the market. Samples sent on application.

COMPRESSED IVORY CHECKS

1⁹⁄₁₆-inch, embossed, per 1000		$20 00

Designs, eagle, ship, cat, or harvest.

1½-inch, embossed, per 1000		12 50

Designs, swan, fullhand, sunflower, horseshoe, horsehead, doghead, elephant, lighthouse, acorn, beehive.

Markers, coppers, or splitters, per doz.	0 25
Coppers, per 100	2 00
1½-inch plain, with any initial in center, per 100	3 50
1¼-inch, plain, per 100	25
1½ " " "	50
1½ " lined " per 100	1 00
1½ " double lined, per 100	1 25
1½ " engraved "	1 50
1⁹⁄₁₆ " " "	2 00

NEW DESIGNS IN POKER CHIPS.

Any of the following designs can be had in either red, white, blue, green or yellow, and in any quantity of each, all at the same price. Are packed 100 in a box. When they are to be sent by mall, a box of 100 weighs 35 ozs., and will cost 35 cents additional in postage. Are all 1½ inches in diameter.

Plain Chips, 1½ inch, per 100	................$	25
" " " " per 1000	....	2 50
Engraved Chips, 1½ inch, per 100	....	1 00
" " " " per 1000	....	10 00

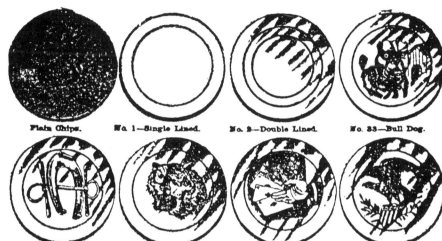

Plain Chips. No. 1—Single Lined. No. 2—Double Lined. No. 33—Bull Dog.

No. 44—Horse Shoe. No. 55—Tiger. No. 66—Full Hand. No. 77—Spread Eagle.

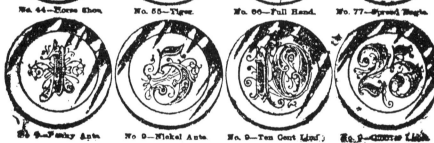

No. 4—Fancy Ante. No. 5—Nickel Ante. No. 6—Ten Cent Limit. No. 7—Quarter Limit.

No. 111—Bee Hive. No. 122—Crown. No. 133—Elephant. No. 144—Swan.

No. 177—Anchor. No. 188—Horse Head. No. 199—Dog's Head. No. 200—Light House.

B. A. STEVENS, Toledo, O.

NEW DESIGNS IN POKER CHIPS.

These chips are the handsomest pattern that have ever been made in composition. They can be had in red, white, blue, green or yellow, and in any quantity of each. Are all 1½ inches in diameter.

Per 100, $1.00.   Per 1000, $10.00.

No. 211—Owl.   No. 222—Rose.   No. 333—Acorn.   No. 344—Shamrock.

No. 255—Cap and Whip   No. 275—Ram's Head.   No. 300—Home, Sweet Home.

The following three designs we are making a specialty of, at an extremely low price. The composition is good, and the colors red, white and blue. For a design chip that is better than a plain one, they are the thing. 1½ inches in diameter.

75c per 100. $7.50 per 1,000.

No. 30.   No. 40.   No. 50.

Per 100, 75 Cts.   Per 1000, $7.50

Stevens' Noiseless Poker Chips.

These poker chips are made from soft rubber, of the same thickness; will stack perfectly; have rounded edges; and are 1½ inches in diameter. Made only in red, white and blue. These three colors are each the same price, and will be sold in any quantity of each wanted.

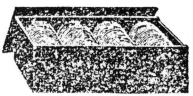

1½ Inches in Diameter.   Each 100 packed as above, 25 Red, 25 Blue and 50 White.   Perfectly Noiseless Clean and Indestructible.

Per 100, $1.25.   Per 1000, $12.50.

B. A. STEVENS, Toledo, O.

ROYAL POKER SET.

Handsome Solid Mahogany or English Oak Cabinet, containing 200 metal poker checks, three denominations or values—three colors: gold, silver and copper, and two packs of high-grade enameled playing cards.

Price, $5.00

The checks are made of an aluminum alloy metal representing gold, silver and copper, and have on the one side their respective values, while on the other is a beautiful design suggestive of the game. This set has been pronounced by competent critics the Ideal Family Combination. Each cabinet fitted with substantial nickel plated lock and key. In appearance, novelty and utility it cannot be equaled by anything in the market.

The same outfit with only one pack of cards, in a stained wooden box with clasp **$3.50**

Metallic Poker Chips, three colors and denominations of 200 in a cartoon . **2.50**

Chips are the size of a silver half dollar. Cabinets 10 inches long.

Samuel Nafew Co., 392 Broadway, New York, and 167 Dearborn Street, Chicago.

We carry the largest assortment of Poker Chips in Engraved, Fibret Inlaid, Embossed, Square and Round Edged, of any House in America. Chips are made in the colors of red, white, blue, green and yellow. They are all packed 100 chips to a box of any color, or assorted to suit purchaser. Cuts show one-half size only. Note prices.

New Styles of Composition Poker Chips.—THE DESIGN IS THE SAME ON BOTH SIDES OF THE CHIPS. All of these 16 hand-some designs are put up in neat boxes containing 100 chips each, either Red, White, Blue, Green, Yellow or in assorted colors to suit the purchaser. Any two of the designs or any different colors of the same design will stack together perfectly as every one of the entire 16 are gauged to the same thickness. They are all 1½ inches in diameter and sold at the following uniform price:

Per 100, $1.00.   Per 500, $4.50.   Per 1000, $8.00.

A single box of 100 packed weighs 35 oz. and can be sent by mail for 35c. additional. Superior quality, polished edges, warranted to stack.

Engraved Diamond Poker Chips, 1½-inch Diameter.   Five Colors.   All poker chip cuts ½ size.

No. 93—Whip and Horseshoe.

No. 95—Texas Steer.

No. 91—Lily.

No. 84—Light-house.

No. 94—Golf.

No. 92—Prince of Wales.

No. 83—Crown.

No. 88—Home, Sweet Home.

No. 82—Anchor.

No. 87—Three Links.

No. 81—Swan.

No. 86—Elephant.

No. 80.—Acorn.

No. 85—Dog's Head.

No. 89.—Clover Leaf.

No. 90—Old Glory

EMBOSSED DIAMOND POKER CHIPS

All Poker Chips One Half Size.

75c. PER HUNDRED, $6.00 PER THOUSAND.

Round Edged, 1½-inch Diameter, Four Colors, Polished Edges.

No. 38—Gladiator.

No. 37—Bicycle Girl.

No. 36—Griffin.

No. 35—Mascot.

No. 34—Stop Mon-keying.

Indestructible Poker Chips
Four colors. 1½-inch diameter, guaranteed noiseless and to stack perfectly. Price, 75c. per 100; $6.00 per 1000.

PATENT IVORY CARD CASE.
An exact imitation of Ivory. Will hold one deck of cards, and is indestructible. The very thing to carry in the vest pocket. Made in imitation of Ivory.
Price each........................85c

PLAIN CHIPS.

Diamond Brand.

Polished Edges, Warranted to Stack.

Sizes.		Per 1000.
1¼-inch, assorted		$2.00
1⅜-inch, "	"	2.25
1½-inch, "	"	2.50

Nafew Brand Paranoid Unbreakable Solid Inlaid Colored Square Edged Poker Chips.

ANY COLORS. CUTS ONE-HALF SIZE. SIZE, 1 9-16 INCHES.

No. **66.**
Fleur-de-Lis.

No. **67**—Club and Crescent.

No. **68**—Star.

No. **69**—Club.

The Nafew Brand and designs are made only for our house. The designs are **solid colors** that extend through the entire chip. Stacks absolutely, square edged, and guaranteed **non-breakable**. Furnished in any colors desired. Highest quality and an ivory polish. Our Paranoid chips are appreciated by those who wish to keep a rack or set of chips intact and last a life time. All colors.
When ordering mention colors wanted and proportion. Samples postpaid free.

PRICE, $30.00 PER THOUSAND.

Can also furnish the Nafew Paranoid Brand in a plain chip, size 1½-inch. Price, **$10.00** per thousand.

JACK POTS.	**BUCKS.**	**IVORY JACKS.**

Made from composition. Center part stands out in relief and different color from balance.	Made from composition. Center part is in relief and different color from balance, very neat.	Made from imitation ivory and will not break; head is in relief, very handsome and cannot be told from genuine ivory
Price per doz 40c	Price per doz $1 28	Price per doz.........$2 25

COPPERS, SPLITS AND MARKERS.

COPPERS.

Case Keepers' Markers.

SPLITS.
Are 1¼ inches in diameter, made in red, white or blue. Material is composition.
Price per 100....... 25c.

MARKERS
Made of durable composition, in red, white or blue. Cut shows full size.
Price per 100..........50c.

Made of durable composition, in red, white or blue. Cut shows full size.
Price per 100...50c.

Suitable for case keeper, also good for billiard markers; made of durable composition, in red, white or blue. Cut shows full size.
Price per 100.....50c.

DUPLICATE WHIST.

KALAMAZOO METHOD. This method is purely a game of skill, and is the most perfect system yet introduced. The maxims of the standard game are not interfered with in any way, and under its workings no plea of poor hands as a cause of defeat can be made, and the score is a proof of superior skill of the victors.

DUPLICATE WHIST TRAYS.

Set No. **8.** Containing 8 Trays, best cloth covered board, gold embossed, 6 celluloid poker chips and 25 score cards, ...	**$3.00**
Set No. **8 A.** Same as Set No. 8, with 8 packs of enameled cards,	**4.00**
Set No. **12.** 12 Trays, 26 celluloid chips and 25 score cards, .	**4.00**
Set No. **12 A.** Same as Set No. 12, with 12 packs of enameled cards,	**5.50**
Set No. **16.** 16 trays, 26 celluloid poker chips and 25 poker chips,	**5.00**
Set No. **16 A.** Same as Set No. 16, with 16 packs of enameled cards,	**7.00**
Set No. **20.** 20 Trays, 26 celluloid poker chips and 50 score cards,	**6.00**
Set No. **20 A.** Same as Set No. 20, with 24 packs of enameled cards,	**8.50**
Set No. **24.** 24 Trays, 26 celluloid poker chips and 50 score cards,	**7.00**
Set No. **24 A.** Same as Set No. 24, with 24 packs of enameled cards,	**10.00**
Book of Rules and Instruction sent with each set.	
Score cards, bristol board, ... Per 100,	**1.50**
Score books and rules, ... Per dozen,	**.75**

A. G. Spalding & Bros., New York, Chicago, Philadelphia.

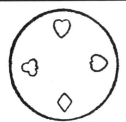

Poker Chips.

53561 Embossed Poker Chips, depressed colored spots, 4 "ace" embossed on red, white and blue chips, 1½ inches in diameter, one hundred in a box, assorted as follows: 50 white, 25 red, 25 blue, weight packed 30 ounces.

Per box of one hundred........................$1.10
Per one thousand............................. 9.00

53563 Composition Ivory, 1½ inches in diameter, superior quality and finish, one hundred in box, assorted as follows: 25 red, 25 blue, 50 white, weight, packed, 27 ounces.
Per box of one hundred..$ 1.20
Per one thousand..........10.00

**1897
SEARS ROEBUCK
CATALOGUE**

53565 Composition Poker Chips, ivory finish, warranted not to chip or warp, 1¼ inches in diameter, one hundred in a box, assorted as follows: 50 white, 25 red, 25 blue; weight, packed, 25 ounces.
Per box of one hundred......................$0.30
Per one thousand............................. 2.75

53567 Plain Poker Chips, composition, ivory finish, warranted not to chip or warp, one hundred in box, assorted as follows: 50 white, 25 red, 25 blue; weight, packed, 30 ounces.
Per one hundred...........$0.65
Per one thousand.......... 5.20

1905 SEARS, ROEBUCK

Inlaid Unbreakable Poker Chips for Professional Use.

No. 29B1928 Fleur de Lis design. Inlaid celluloid on highest grade of composition ivory; 1 9/16 inches in diameter and put up 100 to the box; assorted, 50 white, 25 red and 25 blue; or can be ordered in the solid colors, 100 to box; red, white, blue, yellow, pink or brown. Absolutely perfect in every respect, warranted to stack perfectly, and used a great deal by professionals.

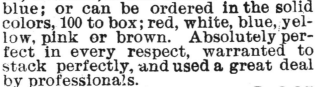

Price, per box of 100..........$ 2.25
Per 1,000........................ 21.90
Shipping weight, 34 ounces.

OGDEN & CO. CHICAGO, ILL.

UNIVERSAL ENGRAVED POKER CHECKS.

IN RED, WHITE, BLUE AND YELLOW.

100 of one color in a box.　　　Size 1½ inch.　　　Price $6.00 per Thousand.

EXTRA QUALITY.

TIGER

DEER'S HEAD

BUTTERFLY

ELEPHANT

ARROWS

PRINCE OF WALES

SWAN

THE SQUEEZER AUTOMATIC CARD AND CHIP RACK.

THE
SQUEEZER AUTOMATIC
CARD AND CHIP
RACK
PATENTED 1899.

A handsomely finished hardwood revolving rack, containing three hundred chips and four packs of cards.
A complete portable outfit for all card games,　　$7.50
The same with handsome leather case,　　9.00

NOISELESS POKER CHECKS.

These checks are the best quality of soft rubber. Cannot be broken. Will size perfectly, and are first class in every respect. They are just what you need for a quiet game, making not the slightest noise. They are made in three colors, red, white and blue, 100 in a box, assorted or one color, as you want them, but not less than 25 of one color. Regular size, 1 ½ inch.

Price per 100, $ 1.60
Price per 1,000, 15.00

PAPER POKER CHECKS.

RED, WHITE AND BLUE

Size, 1 ½ in.   100 assorted or one color in a box.
Price per 100, $ .75.
Price per 1,000,   6.50.

...INDESTRUCTIBLE HARRIS CHECKS...

ROUND EDGE

These Engraved chips are made of the finest quality composition, guaranteed to stack perfect. Full size, 1 9-16 inches in diameter.
Colors—Red, white, blue, yellow and chocolate.

$1.40 per 100   **$14.00 per 1000**

Evening Star

Victor

Carlo

$14.00 per 1000   **$12.00 per 1000**

MONARCH.

These checks have a raised sunken line although the surface is smooth. The centers are made so they do not touch one another. The contact being on the outer rim, will avoid sticking together. This is what is called a live check. Stacking qualities perfect. Most durable check made. 1 9-16 inch.
Colors—Red, white, blue, yellow, pink and light blue.

PLAIN.

Our plain checks are made of the same composition as all Harris Patented Indestructible Poker Checks. Guaranteed to stack and are perfect in every way. 1 9-16 inch.
Monarch
Colors—Red, white, blue, yellow, chocolate or pink. Other colors to order.
Plain

RUBBER CHECKS   PAPER CHECKS

FOR A QUIET GAME

RUBBER CHECKS—Absolutely noiseless, as well as being indestructible. Round edge, 1½ inch in diameter.
Colors—Red, white, blue and yellow.
Price, $1.60 per 100. $15.00 per 1000
PAPER CHECKS—This check is made from a process of compressed paper and so hardened that it is absolutely unbreakable, is finished with an enameled surface, smooth as glass, and stacks perfectly. Square edge.
Colors—Red, white, blue and yellow.
Price, 55c. per 100. $5.00 per 1000.

GENUINE HARRIS CHECKS.

Square Edge Patented Inlaid Checks, 1 9-16 inch in Diameter.

$3.30 per 100 $33.00 per 1000

Monarch Four Leaf Clover
Square Edge

Monarch Fleur de Lis
Square Edge

Monarch Large Club
Square Edge

Maltese Cross
Square Edge

Winner Star
Square Edge

Ideal
Square Edge

All Harris Poker Checks represented by the designs here are fully guaranteed to be the genuine chips by the manufacturers, and you are therefore fully protected in the knowledge that when you buy from us you get the real article.
Colors: Red, white, blue, yellow, tan and chocolate.

HARRIS INITIAL POKER CHECKS

$3.30 per 100   **CASH WITH ORDER.** $33.00 per 1000

The C and Inlaid S represents a new check. The letter C standing for club and by inlaying the initial inside of the C gives each club desiring it a distinctive poker check, which cannot be duplicated by any other manufacturer, and will prevent ringers. We can furnish you initials in club checks or the plain initials inlaid in the following letters:
B C D F G H J M S T W Y

Square Edge

Initials other than mentioned will cost extra on account special die.
We can also furnish these letters inlaid in the Monarch or Winner designs.

Square Edge

OUR SUPERIOR NON-BREAKABLE CHECKS

$1.00 per 100   **$9.00 per 1000**

Star

Carlo

Crown

No Monkeying

Eagle

FULL DECK

Old Tom

Three Horses

Navy

These checks are first class in every respect and stack perfect. **Guaranteed not to break**, being as strong and durable as any check on the market.
Colors:—Red, white, blue, yellow and chocolate.
We do not sell less than 100 of a color.

ENGRAVED HARRIS POKER CHECKS.

NEW DESIGNS.

60c. per 100   Round Edge.   1½ inches in diameter.   **$6.00 per 1000**

These checks are perfectly matched, have a high finish and guaranteed to stack at all times.

Prince of Wales

Rough Rider

Texas Steer

Lily

Good Luck

Dog Head

Golf

Owl and Crescent

Flush Hand

Colors: Red, white, blue and yellow. Packed 100 solid colors to a box; no less than 100 of a color sold, as we do not break boxes.

1901

INCORPORATED 1896   ESTABLISHED 1885

CATALOGUE

—OF—

SUPPLIES FOR SALOON, BILLIARD HALL AND CLUB ROOM USE.

—ADDRESS—

Kernan Manufacturing Co.

192-194 E. VAN BUREN ST,

CHICAGO, - - ILLINOIS.

~~~TERMS~~~

WE DESIRE TO MAKE OUR TERMS ON SHIPMENTS AS LIBERAL AS POSSIBLE. WE POSITIVELY REQUIRE CASH IN ADVANCE FOR GOODS AND POSTAGE WHEN GOODS ARE TO BE SENT BY MAIL.

MAIL SHIPMENTS. Postage on goods by mail is one cent per ounce or fraction thereof, being 16 cents per pound. No one package must exceed 4 pounds. Packages can be sent by registered mail for 8 cents per package extra. We are not responsible for goods sent by open mail. If you enclose 8 cents extra, above cost of goods and postage fee, your goods will be registered, and in case they fail to reach you, order will be refilled.

GOODS SENT BACK FOR EXCHANGE must have the sender's name and address written plainly on the outside of package; also send a letter explaining why goods are returned.

EXPRESS SHIPMENTS. All heavy goods, such as Club Room Furniture, Spindles, Canes, etc., will be sent by express or freight. See Special Terms on each individual line.

C. O. D. (Collect on Delivery.) When sent in this manner must have a sufficient amount paid in advance or deposited with Express Agent, and his written guarantee of same, to cover express charges both ways. Examination allowed on all goods, except one or two special lines. On these our written guarantee to the effect that they are as represented, or money refunded, will be given.

FREIGHT SHIPMENTS. Parties wishing goods by freight, must either send full amount with the order, or one-half the amount, and we will ship in our own name, with sight draft on you. To ascertain the freight rates, you must consult your local freight agent.

OUR REFERENCES. We have been doing business in Cleveland, Ohio, and Chicago, Illinois, for a number of years, and the chances are that in your own town you can find out in regard to our reliability and promptness in filling orders. Our aim is to please the trade, and we have succeeded in doing so in the past and shall do so in the future. We expect to fill all orders within twenty-four hours after their arrival, and in event of not doing so (which rarely happens), we will notify you by mail. In case you want goods in a hurry you can make out your order and give it to your express agent, with the money, and he will send it to the Chicago office and buy the goods for you. This will avoid any delay in looking up our reliability. As we are located near to all the express companies, we can handle Express Orders with dispatch. Remember, we claim to be the CHEAPEST house in our line, and a trial order will prove to you that our claim is a good one.

IF YOU DESIRE INFORMATION regarding any line of our goods, we will give it most cheerfully; or if desirous of anything not found in our Catalogue, write us, and we will quote you the lowest market price on any line of goods.

GENUINE HARRIS CHECKS

The genuine Harris Celluloid inlaid center checks. Guaranteed to stack and color in matching up old racks.

Semi square edges. Colors red, white, blue, brown, yellow and lavender. Other colors to order only.

1 9-16 INCHES IN DIAMETER.

| No. 2004 | No. 2005 | No. 2006 |
| ANCHOR | HORSESHOE | 4-POINT STAR |

| No. 1955 | No. 1956 | No. 1957 |
| ROMAN | CRESCENT STAR | SMALL CLUB |

| No. 1959 | No. 2001 | No. 1960 |
| STAR | MONTE CARLO | CROSS AND CRESCENT |

Any of the above designs, price per 100, $4.00; per 1000, $40.00.
GENUINE HARRIS INLAID INITIAL CHECKS, AT $50.00 PER 1000.

NEW DESIGNS
IN THE
HENRY FARO AND POKER CHECKS

Elegant New Designs in Best Quality Composition. Inlaid Celluloid Centers. Made expressly for us, in any color desired. We always carry in stock:—RED, WHITE, BLUE, YELLOW, DRAB and BROWN. **Guaranteed to Stack Perfectly.** FULL 1 9-16 INCHES IN DIAMETER.

+ YOUR CHOICE OF DESIGNS +

$3.50 PER 100. —AT— **$30.00 PER 1000.**

| CLUB—No. 2052. | SPADE—No. 2053. | DIAMOND—No. 2058. |

| HEART—No. 2957. | FLEUR de LIS, Small, No. 2054. | STAR—No. 2058. |

| FLEUR de LIS, Large, No. 2055. | CLUB and CRESCENT, Small—No. 2051. | CLUB and CRESCENT, Large—No. 2050. |

N. B. Remember 3 PER CENT. DISCOUNT FOR CASH IN ADVANCE, FROM CATALOGUE PRICES.

ENGRAVED CHECKS

Fine engraved, superior finish, 1 9-16 inch checks. Guaranteed to stack. New designs.
COLORS RED, WHITE, BLUE, YELLOW AND BROWN

| No. 2007 | No. 2008 | No. 2009 |
| SADDLE | FISHING TACKLE | SINGLE LINE |

| No. 2010 | No. 2011 | No. 2012 |
| DEER HEAD | NEW STAR | CARLO |

| No. 1997 | No. 2140 | No. 1998 |
| STAR | MAJOR GENERAL | EAGLE |

Price of any of the above designs, $2.00 per 100; $15.00 per 1000

Check Rack
SPECIAL.

Holds over 2000 checks, made of solid Mahogany, Walnut or Oak; lined throughout with billiard cloth. Finest hand polished rack made.

PRICE $8.00.

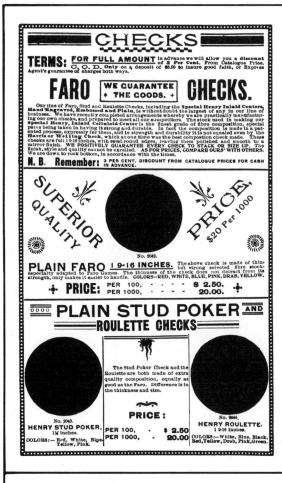

CHECKS

TERMS: FOR FULL AMOUNT in advance we will allow you a discount of 3 Per Cent. From Catalogue Price. C.O.D. Only on a deposit of $5.00 to insure good faith, or Express Agent's guarantee of charges both ways.

FARO — WE GUARANTEE THE GOODS. — CHECKS.

Our line of Faro, Stud and Roulette Checks, including the Special Henry Inlaid Centers, Hand Engraved, Embossed and Plain, is without doubt the largest of any in our line of business. We have recently completed arrangements whereby we are practically manufacturing our own checks, and prepared to meet all our competitors. The stock used in making our Special Henry, Inlaid Celluloid Center is the finest grade of fibre composition, special pains being taken in having it strong and durable. In fact the composition is made in a patented process, expressly for them, and in strength and durability it is not equaled even by the Harris or Welling Check, which at one time was the best composition check made. These checks are full 1 9-16 inches, with semi round edges, leaving them polished and smooth to a mirror finish. WE POSITIVELY GUARANTEE EVERY CHECK TO STACK OR SIZE UP. The finish, style and quality cannot be excelled. AS FOR PRICES, COMPARE OURS' WITH OTHERS. We are down to rock bottom, in accordance with the times.

N. B. Remember: 3 PER CENT. DISCOUNT FROM CATALOGUE PRICES FOR CASH IN ADVANCE.

SUPERIOR QUALITY — PRICE, $20 Per 1000

No. 2042.

PLAIN FARO 1 9-16 INCHES. The above check is made of thin but strong selected fibre stock, especially adapted to Faro Games. The thinness of the check does not detract from its strength, only makes it easier to handle. COLORS—RED, WHITE, BLUE, PINK, DRAB, YELLOW.

PRICE: PER 100, - - - $2.50 / PER 1000, - - - 20.00

PLAIN STUD POKER AND ROULETTE CHECKS

The Stud Poker Check and the Roulette are both made of extra quality composition, equally as good as the Faro. Difference is in the thickness and size.

No. 2043. HENRY STUD POKER, 1¼ inches. COLORS:— Red, White, Blue, Yellow, Pink.

No. 2044. HENRY ROULETTE, 1 9-16 inches. COLORS:— White, Blue, Black, Red, Yellow, Drab, Pink, Green.

PRICE: PER 100, - $2.50 / PER 1000, - 20.00

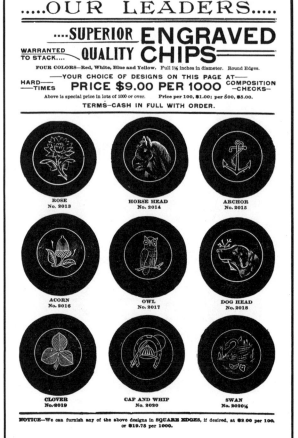

.....OUR LEADERS.....

...SUPERIOR ENGRAVED QUALITY CHIPS

WARRANTED TO STACK....

FOUR COLORS—Red, White, Blue and Yellow. Full 1½ inches in diameter. Round Edges.

—YOUR CHOICE OF DESIGNS ON THIS PAGE AT—

HARD-TIMES **PRICE $9.00 PER 1000** COMPOSITION—CHECKS—

Above is special price in lots of 1000 or over. Price per 100, $1.00; per 500, $5.00.

TERMS—CASH IN FULL WITH ORDER.

ROSE No. 2013 — HORSE HEAD No. 2014 — ARCHOR No. 2015

ACORN No. 2016 — OWL No. 2017 — DOG HEAD No. 2018

CLOVER No. 2019 — CAP AND WHIP No. 2020 — SWAN No. 2020½

NOTICE—We can furnish any of the above designs in SQUARE EDGES, if desired, at $2.00 per 100, or $19.75 per 1000.

KERNAN COMPANION POKER SET

100 Checks. THE One Pack Cards. COMPANION POKER SET KERNAN MFG. CO. CHICAGO. ILL.

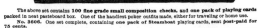

The above set contains 100 fine grade small composition checks, and one pack of playing cards packed in neat pasteboard box. One of the handiest poker outfits made, either for traveling or home use.
No. 3606. One set complete, containing one pack of Steamboat playing cards, sent post-paid for 75 cents.
No. 3607. One set complete containing one pack of 808 Bicycle playing cards, sent post-paid for 80 cents.

WHO IS SHY? Price 12 Cents.

Attractive Pocket Pieces ...For... Poker Players

YOUR NEXT DEAL Price 15 Cents.

CHECK RACK WITH LOCK and COVER.

Solid Mahogany

PRICE $10.00

No. 2103.

No. 2106.
Box Complete, - - $4.25
Box is 8x6½x3½ inches, neatly made; mahogano or oak finish, strong clasp, contains 250 engraved checks, four packs cards, and one sole leather dice box and five dice.
No. 2106, Mahogany, Oak or Walnut finish......$4.25
No. 2107. Same style as No. 2106, size 12x7x8½ inches; contains 400 engraved checks, 4 packs of cards, one sole leather dice box and 5 dice. Price, all complete......$5.25

A SOLID MAHOGANY CHECK BOX
Will hold 1000 to 1500 checks. Solid Mahogany box, size 20x9x3¾, has drop front lined with best grade billiard cloth, and a substantial lock and key. Elegantly made and finished with a fine French polish, same as pianos and all high grade furniture. Convenient to carry checks in. Can always be kept from dust and dirt when not in use. No first class club room complete without one.
No. 2103. Solid Mahogany; price without checks $12.00
No. 2104. Solid Walnut; price without checks $10.00
No. 2105. Mahogany Satin Veneer, Rosewood inlaid corners, very elegant; price $20.00
Prices quoted is for box without checks (See check pages for all grades of checks.)

ROULETTE CHECK RACK.

No. 2027.
Lined with Billiard Cloth. Price, $5.00

CHECK RACK

WALNUT OAK OR Mahogany.

No. 2025. Lined with Billiard Cloth. Holds from 500 to 800
PRICE, $4.00
No. 2026. Walnut, Oak or Mahogany. Holds from 1000 to 1500. **PRICE, $5.00**

IVORY DICE TOP

No. 214. PRICE, - $2.00

No. 214½ BONE DICE TOP. PRICE - $1.50

OLD CATALOGS

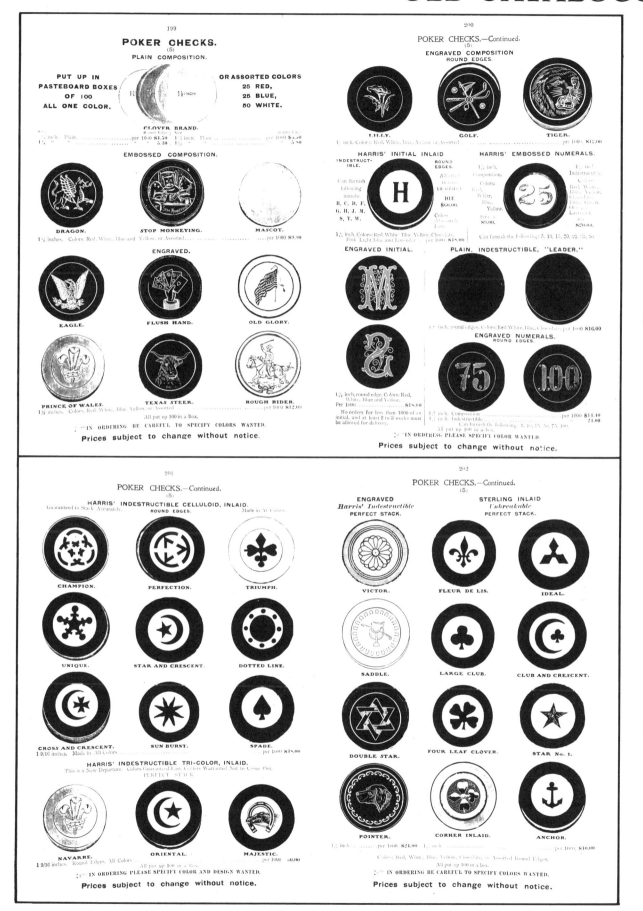

199

POKER CHECKS.
(5)

PLAIN COMPOSITION.

PUT UP IN
PASTEBOARD BOXES
OF 100
ALL ONE COLOR.

OR ASSORTED COLORS
25 RED,
25 BLUE,
50 WHITE.

CLOVER BRAND.

EMBOSSED COMPOSITION.

DRAGON.   STOP MONKEYING.   MASCOT.

1½ inches. Colors: Red, White, Blue and Yellow, or Assorted........ per 1000 $9.00

ENGRAVED.

EAGLE.   FLUSH HAND.   OLD GLORY.

PRINCE OF WALES.   TEXAS STEER.   ROUGH RIDER.

1½ inches. Colors: Red, White, Blue, Yellow, or Assorted ...... per 1000 $12.00

All put up 100 in a Box.

IN ORDERING BE CAREFUL TO SPECIFY COLORS WANTED.

Prices subject to change without notice.

200

POKER CHECKS.—Continued.
(5)

ENGRAVED COMPOSITION.
ROUND EDGES.

LILLY.   GOLF.   TIGER.

1½ inch. Colors: Red, White, Blue, Yellow or Assorted ...... per 1000, $12.00

HARRIS' INITIAL INLAID
INDESTRUCTIBLE.   ROUND EDGES.

Can furnish following initials:
B, C, D, F, G, H, J, M, S, T, W.

DIE
$60.00.

Colors Absolutely Fast.

1½ inch. Colors: Red, White, Blue, Yellow, Pink, Light Blue and Lavender ...... per 1000 $18.00

HARRIS' EMBOSSED NUMERALS.

Can furnish the following: 5, 10, 15, 20, 25, 35, 50.

ENGRAVED INITIAL.

1 7/16 inch, round edge. Colors: Red, White, Blue and Yellow.
Per 1000 .... $18.00

No orders for less than 1000 of an initial, and at least 2 to 3 weeks must be allowed for delivery.

PLAIN, INDESTRUCTIBLE, "LEADER."

1½ inch, round edges, Colors: Red, White, Blue, Chocolate, per 1000 $16.00

ENGRAVED NUMERALS.
ROUND EDGES.

1½ inch. Composition ...... per 1000 $14.40
1½ inch. Indestructible 21.00

Can furnish the following: 5, 10, 25, 50, 75, 100.

All put up 100 in a box.

IN ORDERING PLEASE SPECIFY COLOR WANTED

Prices subject to change without notice.

201

POKER CHECKS.—Continued.
(5)

HARRIS' INDESTRUCTIBLE CELLULOID, INLAID.
Guaranteed to Stack Accurately.   ROUND EDGES.   Made in All Colors.

CHAMPION.   PERFECTION.   TRIUMPH.

UNIQUE.   STAR AND CRESCENT.   DOTTED LINE.

CROSS AND CRESCENT.   SUN BURST.   SPADE.

1 9/16 inches. Made in All Colors.   per 1000 $18.00

HARRIS' INDESTRUCTIBLE TRI-COLOR, INLAID.
This is a New Departure. Colors Guaranteed Fast. Centers Warranted Not to Come Out.
PERFECT STACK.

NAVARRE.   ORIENTAL.   MAJESTIC.
per 1000   50.00

1 9/16 inches. Round Edges. All Colors.   All put up 100 in a box.

IN ORDERING PLEASE SPECIFY COLOR AND DESIGN WANTED.

Prices subject to change without notice.

202

POKER CHECKS.—Continued.
(5)

ENGRAVED
Harris' Indestructible
PERFECT STACK.

STERLING INLAID
Unbreakable
PERFECT STACK.

VICTOR.   FLEUR DE LIS.   IDEAL.

SADDLE.   LARGE CLUB.   CLUB AND CRESCENT.

DOUBLE STAR.   FOUR LEAF CLOVER.   STAR No. 1.

POINTER.   CORKER INLAID.   ANCHOR.

1½ inch ...... per 1000 $24.00   1½ inch ...... per 1000 $40.00

Colors: Red, White, Blue, Yellow, Chocolate, or Assorted. Round Edges.
All put up 100 in a box.

IN ORDERING BE CAREFUL TO SPECIFY COLORS WANTED.

Prices subject to change without notice.

Wholesale Catalogue Price List.
JANUARY 1, 1906.

The United States Playing Card Company,
Cincinnati, U. S. A.

No. 56.   July 1, 1908.

Wholesale
Catalogue Price List

The United States
Playing Card Company,
Cincinnati, U. S. A.

Playing Cards,
nal Playing Cards,
ational Games,
icate Whist Trays,
d Dominoes,
S. Poker Chips.

No. 18 E.

WHOLESALE
NET EXPORT LIST
U. S. and NATIONAL Playing Cards.

October 1, 1915.

The United States
Playing Card Co.

Factories and General Offices:
CINCINNATI, U. S. A.
Cable Address: "Bicyclcard, Cincinnati."
Branch Factory:
College Street and Manning Avenue,
Toronto, Canada.
Branch Office: Branch Office:
432 Fourth Ave.,   68-69 Shoe Lane,
New York.   London, E. C.
Cable Address:
"Bicyclcard, New York."   Cable Address:
                              "Mautarot, London."

Largest Manufacturers of Playing Cards in the World.
Again classed "Above Competition."
Two Grand Prizes, St. Louis, 1904. Highest Award, Buffalo, 1901.
Grand Prix, Paris, 1900   Highest Award, Chicago, 1893.

CABLE CODES:
A B C Telegraphic Code—Fourth Edition.
A B C Telegraphic Code—Fifth Edition.
Western Union Telegraphic Code—Universal Edition.
Universal Wireless and Cable Code (Marconi's).
Manufacturer's Export Code (Seeger's).
Atlantic Cable Directory Code.
Gurnee's Cipher Code.   Lieber's Code.
All previous lists hereby canceled. Subject to change without notice.

No. 57.

esale Catalogue Price List.
JULY 2, 1906

WI
Catalog

The United States
Playing Card Company,
Cincinnati, U. S. A.

U. S. Playing Cards,
National Playing Cards,
Educational Games,
Duplicate Whist Trays,
Card Dominoes,
U. S. Poker Chips.

THE U.S.   ARD CO.
BICYCLE
TRADE   MARK
RIDER BACK
PLAYING CARDS
Revised box adopted 1905

THE UNITED STATES PLAYING CARD CO.
CINCINNATI, U. S. A.

U. S. Composition Poker Chips

For illustrations see following pages.

Plain 1½ inch	- - - -	$5 00
" 1⅜ "	- - - -	4 83
" 1¼ "	- - - -	4 66
" ⅞ "	- - -	4·17
Embossed 1½ inch	- - -	6 67
Engraved 1½ "	- - -	8 33
Plain Paranoid	- - -	10 00
Engraved Paranoid	- - -	15 00
Large Center Paranoid	- -	25 00
Small " "	- - -	25 00

All chips are packed 50 white, 25 red, 25 blue to each box of 100, unless otherwise ordered.

The U. S. Playing Card Co.

Cincinnati, U. S. A.

U. S. Unbreakable Poker Chips

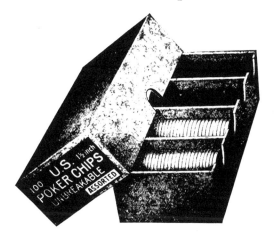

Light, noiseless, easy to handle.

Uniform in thickness.   Beautifully finished edges.

100 in a box, assorted, 50 white, 25 red and 25 blue, unless otherwise ordered.   A fourth color, yellow, if desired.

$5.00 per 1000, list.

Thin Unbreakable Chips

About two-thirds the thickness of the above.   100 in a box, assorted, 50 white, 25 red and 25 blue, unless otherwise ordered. A fourth color, yellow, if desired. Have all the superior qualities of the thicker chips.

$5.00 per 1000, list.

U. S. Poker Chips

For Prices see Page 28

1½ INCH   1⅜ INCH   1¼ INCH   ⅞ INCH

Plain—Made in white, red and blue.

DRAGON   STOP MONKEYING   MASCOT   BICYCLE

Embossed—1⅜ inch—Made in white, red, blue and yellow.

BULL DOG   AUTOMOBILE   KITTY   LION RAMPANT

INDIAN   ELK   YACHT   BOWLING

LANTERN   GOLF   PRINCE OF WALES   CROWN

Engraved—1⅜ inch—Made in white, red, blue and yellow.

These cuts are reduced size for illustration purposes. All chips are packed 50 white, 25 red, 25 blue to each box of 100, unless otherwise ordered.

29

U.S. Poker Chips—Engraved—Continued

For Prices see Page 28

OWL AND CRESCENT   BEE HIVE   STEER HEAD

FLAG   SPREAD EAGLE   ROOSTER

CAP AND WHIP   FLUSH HAND   HORSE SHOE

Engraved—1⅜ inch—Made in white, red, blue and yellow.

PARANOID PLAIN   OAK LEAF   LONDON CLUB   CUPID

LAUREL   SPREAD EAGLE   DOUBLE STAR   CARLO

Paranoid, engraved—1 9-16 inch—Made in white, red, blue, yellow, chocolate, light blue and pink.

Above cuts are reduced size for illustration purposes. All chips are packed 50 white, 25 red, 25 blue to each box of 100, unless otherwise ordered.

30

U. S. Poker Chips

For Prices see Page 28

CLOVER LEAF   MALTESE CROSS   FLEUR DE LIS   SUN-BURST

STAR   STAR AND CRESCENT   CROSS AND CRESCENT   CLUB AND CRESCENT

HEART   DIAMOND   CLUB   SPADE

Paranoid Inlaid — Small Center

1 9-16 inch.

Made in white, red, blue, yellow, chocolate, light blue and pink.

Above cuts are reduced size for illustration purposes. All chips are packed 50 white, 25 red, 25 blue to each box of 100, unless otherwise ordered.

31

U. S. Poker Chips

For Prices see Page 28

CLOVER LEAF   MALTESE CROSS   FLEUR DE LIS   SUN-BURST

STAR   STAR AND CRESCENT   CROSS AND CRESCENT   CLUB AND CRESCENT

HEART   DIAMOND   CLUB   SPADE

DOTTED CIRCLE   PLAIN CIRCLE

Paranoid Inlaid — Large Center

1 9-16 inch

Made in white, red, blue, yellow, chocolate, light blue and pink.

These cuts are reduced size for illustration purposes. All chips are packed 50 white, 25 red, 25 blue to each box of 100 unless otherwise ordered.

32

No. 7.　　　　　　　　　　　　　　　　　　　　　July 1, 1908.

Wholesale Price List
of
U. S. Poker Chips.

Plain—neatly put up and of a quality to thoroughly satisfy customers on these cheaper grades.

	1½-inch	1⅜-inch	1¼-inch	⅞-inch
Less than 5,000—list per 1,000	$5.00	$4.84	$4.67	$4.17
5,000 lots or over— " "	4.75	4.59	4.42	3.92
10,000 " " — " "	4.59	4.42	4.25	3.75
20,000 " " — " "	4.17	4.00	3.84	3.34

Made in white, red and blue.

List per 1000.

Embossed —a new line of designs.　Long use does not deface the design—1½-inch, $ 6.67

Engraved —21 designs.　Well made—convenient, and neat put-up—1½-inch, 8.34

Engraved Numeral - - - - - - - - 1½-inch, 10.00

Made in white, red, blue and yellow.

Raised Numeral—with figures 1, 5, and all multiples of 5, up to 100—1½-inch, $8.34
Made in white, red, blue, yellow, chocolate, light blue, pink, lavender, orange, purple, green and black.　Additional special colors can be supplied in Numeral Chips if necessary.

Pinochle Chips—put up ten sets to a carton, each set in a tubular box, list per carton, $2.67
A set consists of the following 1½-inch Raised Numeral Chips:

4 chips—figure 5—white,	8 chips—figure 20—blue,
2 chips—figure 10—red,	18 chips—figure 100—brown.

32 chips to a set.

We take especial pride in our fine Paranoid Chips, as follows :

Plain Paranoid, - - - - - - - - 1⁹⁄₁₆-inch, $15.00
Engraved Paranoid, - - - - - - - - 1⁹⁄₁₆-inch, 20.00
Inlaid Paranoid—large center—22 designs - - - 1⁹⁄₁₆-inch, 30.00
Inlaid Paranoid-small center stock design surrounded by 1¼-in. ring- 1⁹⁄₁₆-inch, 33.34
Initial, Inlaid Paranoid—all letters of the alphabet - - - 1⁹⁄₁₆-inch, 33.34
Initial, Inlaid Paranoid-with different letter on each side - 1⁹⁄₁₆-inch, 36.67
Initial, Inlaid Paranoid small center letter surrounded by 1¼-in. ring-1⁹⁄₁₆-inch, 36.67
Monogram Inlaid and Special Design Chips to order.

Paranoid Chips are made from the best and toughest stock procurable, for clubs and exacting players desiring perfect chips.　They stack accurately—colors are permanent and shades uniform.　Made in seven colors : white, red, blue, yellow, chocolate, light blue and pink.

Special Raised Numeral, Paranoid - - - - 1¼-inch, $11.67
Made in white, red, blue, yellow, chocolate, light blue, pink, lavender, orange, purple, green, and black.　Additional special colors if necessary.

The U. S. Playing Card Co.,
Cincinnati, U. S. A.

U. S. Poker Chips.

If you have none of our new chips let us send you samples and quote discounts from our list. Chips can come with your shipments of Bicycle and Congress, and other grades of our playing cards.

PACKING.

All chips are packed 50 white, 25 red, 25 blue in each box of 100, unless otherwise ordered.

TUBULAR PACKING.

If desired, all sizes of plain chips—⅞, 1¼, 1⅜ and 1½ inches—can be put up, without extra charge, in tubular boxes holding 25 chips each. There are 10 boxes to a carton, 4 cartons containing 1000 chips.

U. S. PINOCHLE CHIPS.

32 chips to a set, each set consisting of the following 1½ inch Raised Numeral Chips:

4 chips, figure 5, white,
2 " " **10, red,**
8 " " **20, blue,**
18 " " **100, brown.**

Put up 10 sets to a carton, each set in a tubular box.
For price, see page 31.

32

U. S. Poker Chips.

For prices see page 31

Embossed—1½ inch—Made in white, red, blue and yellow.

RAM'S HEAD — DRAGON — LOBSTER
STOP MONKEYING — MASCOT — BICYCLE

Engraved—1½ inch—Made in white, red, blue and yellow.

BULL DOG — AUTOMOBILE — KITTY
INDIAN — ELK — YACHT
LANTERN — GOLF — PRINCE OF WALES.

These cuts are reduced size for illustration purposes. All chips are packed 50 white, 25 red, 25 blue to each box of 100, unless otherwise ordered.

33

U. S. Poker Chips.

Engraved—Continued—1 1-2 inch.

Made in white, red, blue and yellow.

LION RAMPANT — OWL AND CRESCENT — BEE HIVE — STEER HEAD
BOWLING — FLAG — EAGLE — ROOSTER
CROWN — CAP AND WHIP — FLUSH HAND — HORSE SHOE

For prices see page 31.

RAISED NUMERAL—with figures 1, 5, and all multiples of 5, up to 100—1 1-2 inch.

Made in white, red, blue, yellow, chocolate, light blue, pink, lavender, orange, purple, green and black. Additional special colors if necessary.

5 — **25** — **100**

Raised Numeral Chips can be had in either regular Composition or Paranoid quality.

For prices, see page 31.

These cuts are reduced size for illustration purposes. All chips are packed 50 white, 25 red, 25 blue to each box of 100 unless otherwise ordered.

34

U. S. Poker Chips.

For prices see page 31.

Paranoid Engraved—1 9-16 inch.

Made in white, red, blue, yellow, chocolate, light blue and pink.

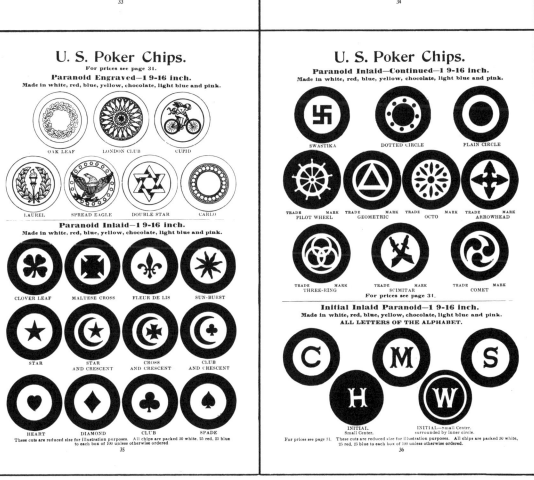

OAK LEAF — LONDON CLUB — CUPID
LAUREL — SPREAD EAGLE — DOUBLE STAR — CARLO

Paranoid Inlaid—1 9-16 inch.

Made in white, red, blue, yellow, chocolate, light blue and pink.

CLOVER LEAF — MALTESE CROSS — FLEUR DE LIS — SUN-BURST
STAR — STAR AND CRESCENT — CROSS AND CRESCENT — CLUB AND CRESCENT
HEART — DIAMOND — CLUB — SPADE

These cuts are reduced size for illustration purposes. All chips are packed 50 white. 25 red, 25 blue to each box of 100 unless otherwise ordered.

35

U. S. Poker Chips.

Paranoid Inlaid—Continued—1 9-16 inch.

Made in white, red, blue, yellow, chocolate, light blue and pink.

SWASTIKA — DOTTED CIRCLE — PLAIN CIRCLE
TRADE MARK PILOT WHEEL — TRADE MARK GEOMETRIC — TRADE MARK OCTO — TRADE MARK ARROWHEAD
TRADE MARK THREE-RING — TRADE MARK SCIMITAR — TRADE MARK COMET

For prices see page 31.

Initial Inlaid Paranoid—1 9-16 inch.

Made in white, red, blue, yellow, chocolate, light blue and pink.
ALL LETTERS OF THE ALPHABET.

C — M — S
H — W

INITIAL. Small Center. — INITIAL—Small Center, surrounded by inner circle.

For prices see page 31. These cuts are reduced size for illustration purposes. All chips are packed 50 white, 25 red, 25 blue to each box of 100 unless otherwise ordered.

36

U. S. POKER CHIPS.

Net per 1000

Plain	{ neatly put up and of a quality to thoroughly satisfy customers on these cheaper grades. Made in white, red and blue.	1½-inch,	$2.50
		1⅜-inch,	2.40
		1¼-inch,	2.30
		⅞-inch,	2.00

Made in white, red, blue and yellow.

Unbreakable Paper—Plain		1½-inch,	3.90
Etched, same designs as 1½ inch engraved		1½-inch,	3.00
Embossed		1½-inch,	4.00

A new line of designs. Long use does not deface the design.

Engraved	1½-inch,	4.50

22 designs. Well made—convenient, and neat put-up.

Engraved Numeral	1½-inch,	5.00

Figures 1, 5, 10, 15, 20, 25, 50 and 100.

Raised Numeral	1½-inch,	5.00

With figures 1, 5, and all multiples of 5 up to 100. Made in white, red, blue, yellow, chocolate, light blue, pink, lavender, orange, purple, green and black. Additional special colors can be supplied in Numera' chips if necessary.

Special Raised Numeral, Paranoid	1½-inch,	6.00

Made in white, red, blue, yellow, chocolate, light blue, pink, lavender, orange, purple, green and black. Additional special colors if necessary.

Pinochle Chips, put up 10 sets to a carton	per carton,	1.60

Each set is in a tubular box. A set consists of the following 1 4-inch Raised Numeral Chips: 4 chips—figure 5—white, 2 chips—figure 10—red, 8 chips—figure 20—blue, 18 chips—figure 100—brown; 32 chips to a set.

We take especial pride in our fine Paranoid Chips, as follows:

Plain Paranoid		1⁹⁄₁₆-inch,	7.50
"	" square edge	"	9.00
"	" thick—square edge	"	11.50
"	" thick—knurled edge	"	12.50
Engraved Paranoid		"	9.00
"	" square edge	"	10.50
Inlaid Paranoid, large center—22 designs		"	15.00
"	" square edge	"	17.50
Inlaid Paranoid		"	17.00

Small center stock design surrounded by 1¼ inch ring.

Inlaid Paranoid, square edge	"	19.50
Initial, Inlaid Paranoid, all letters of alphabet	"	18.00
" " " " sq. edge	"	20.50
Initial, Inlaid Paranoid, different letter on each side	"	20.00
" " " " sq. edge	"	22.50
Initial, Inlaid Paranoid	"	20.00

Small center letter surrounded by 1¼-inch ring.

Initial, Inlaid Paranoid, square edge	"	22.50

Small center letter surrounded by 1¼-inch ring.

Thick Paranoid, Inlaid or Initial Inlaid, sq. edge	27.50
" " " " " knurled "	30.00

Monogram Inlaid and Special Design Chips to order.

Paranoid Chips are made from the best and toughest stock procurable, for clubs and exacting players desiring perfect chips. They stack accurately—colors are permanent and shades uniform. Made in seven colors: white, red, blue, yellow, chocolate, light blue and pink.

All above Paranoid Chips furnished with round edges unless otherwise ordered.

The U. S. Playing Card Co., Cincinnati, U. S. A.

37

U. S. POKER CHIPS.

If you have none of our new chips let us send you samples and quote discounts from our list. Chips can come with your shipments of Bicycle and Congress, and other grades of our playing cards.

PACKING.

All chips are packed 50 white, 25 red, 25 blue to each box of 100, unless otherwise ordered.

TUBULAR PACKING.

If desired, all sizes of plain chips—⅞, 1¼, 1⅜ and 1½ inches—can be put up, without extra charge, in tubular boxes holding 25 chips each. There are 10 boxes to a carton, 4 cartons containing 1000 chips.

U. S. PINOCHLE CHIPS.

32 chips to a set, each set consisting of the following 1½ inch Raised Numeral Chips:

4 chips, figure 5, white.
2 " " 10, red.
8 " " 20, blue.
18 " " 100, brown.

Put up 10 sets to a carton, each set in a tubular box.

38

U. S. Poker Chips.

EMBOSSED—1½ inch.
Made in white, red, blue and yellow.

RAM'S HEAD.　　LOBSTER.　　STOP MONKEYING.

DRAGON.　　MASCOT.　　BICYCLE.

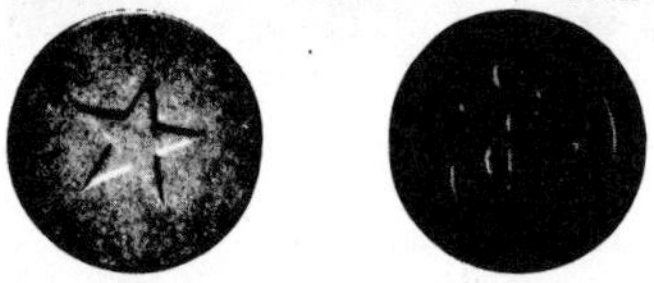

STAR.　　ANCHOR.

ENGRAVED OR ETCHED—1½ inch.
Made in white, red, blue and yellow.

BASEBALL.　　BULL DOG.　　AUTOMOBILE.

These cuts are reduced size for illustration purposes All chips are packed 50 white, 25 red, 25 blue to each box of 100, unless otherwise ordered.

39

ENGRAVED OR ETCHED—1½ INCH—Continued.

KITTY.　　INDIAN.　　ELK.

YACHT.　　LANTERN.　　GOLF.

PRINCE OF WALES.　　LION RAMPANT.　　OWL AND CRESCENT.

BEE HIVE.　　STEER HEAD.　　BOWLING.

FLAG.　　EAGLE.　　CROWN.

These cuts are reduced size for illustration purposes.

40

CATALOGUE

OUR MOTTO:
*A Satisfied Customer is Our
Best Advertisement.*

H. C. EVANS
& CO.

125 Clark Street

CHICAGO, ILL.

**1909
1910**

**Inventors and Manufacturers
OF ELECTRICAL DEVICES,
SPORTING GOODS and CLUB
ROOM FURNITURE**

H. C. EVANS & CO.
INCORPORATED   ESTABLISHED 1892

SALESROOM *and* FACTORY

· · ·

MANUFACTURERS — ORIGINATORS

Casino Supplies   Trade Stimulators
Pocket Novelties

Amusement Park Supplies
Fair Ground Games   Shooting Galleries

FORTY YEARS OF QUALITY SERVICE

The
SECRET BLUE BOOK

H.C. EVANS & COMPANY
1528 W. ADAMS STREET
CHICAGO

---

26   H. EVANS & CO., CHICAGO.

GENUINE HARRIS PATENTED INLAID POKER CHECKS
SEMI ROUND EDGE

ATTENTION IS INVITED to this line of Genuine HARRIS Checks which are SUPERIOR to all other makes. They are absolutely INDESTRUCTIBLE, guaranteed to be a perfect stack and uniform in color at all times. The centers can never fall out. They are made of the finest composition material with a high mirror finish and are absolutely reliable. We recommend them as absolutely the highest quality of chips on the market. They are all uniform size, 1 9-16 inches in diameter.

Price per 100 $2.20   Price per 1000 $22.00

We carry these checks in White, Red, Blue, Yellow and Chocolate at all times. Special Colors can be had with a slight delay. We carry 2 million Checks in stock the year round.
Never before has the HARRIS Check been offered for sale at our Prices. Compare them and see for yourself. We lead in everything even LOW PRICES.

Perfection No. 6690

Fleur de Lis, large center No. 4111   Unique No. 6499

Dotted Line No. 4268

Triumph No. 1015   Ideal No. 1065   Star Inlaid No. 2060

4 Leaf Clover, No. 1001   Maltese Cross, No. 1000   Crescent and Cross, No. 1963

ALL CHECKS ON THIS PAGE ARE SEMI ROUND EDGES.

H. C. EVANS & CO., CHICAGO.   27

GENUINE HARRIS INLAID SQUARE EDGE CHECKS INDESTRUCTIBLE

$35 per M   FARO CHECKS   **$35 per M**

The chips hereon represented are to genuine original square edge HARRIS Check and are absolutely guaranteed as being exactly as herewith represented. There are no other checks made to equal these square edge chips. They are always uniform in stack color, perfection of finish and are made of the very finest materials. Red, White, Blue, Yellow and Chocolate colors always in stock.

Perfection No. 79   Unique No. 82

Horse Shoe No. 709 Square Edge   Star and Crescent No. 788 Sq. Edge   Roman No. 707 Square Edge

Inlaid Monarch Fleur de Lis No. 34 Square Edge   Triumph No. 77 Square Edge   Initial No. 11 Square Edge

We can furnish you **Initial Checks** in the following letters: B C D F G H J S W Y T M Square Edge at $3.50 per 100; $35 per M; Round Edge $25 per M.

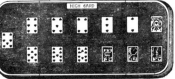

FARO SPREADS

Broadcloth with high card - $10
"   on straight board - 12
"   on fold-up boards - 15
Enameled cloth
"   on straight board 7
Faro layouts are made of Black Walnut. Rims, highly polished. Piano finish. Are ⅜ and ½ thick, all layouts being made of Best Simmons cloth.

Tabs or Cue Cards $3.00 per 1000

H. C. EVANS & CO., CHICAGO.   29

HARRIS

Plain and Engraved Checks guaranteed to be unbreakable and to stack perfect.

These goods are particularly adapted to Poker Games, Roulette Wheels, etc. Red, White, Blue, Yellow and Chocolate Colors always in stock

Roulette Check, Plain, No. 4042
Price per 100 $1.00; per M $10.00
In any color you wish them

Lone Star Engraved No. 100 Square Edge
Price per M $16.00

Engraved Carlo No. 1999
Price per 1000 $12.00   Engraved Evening Star No. 1997
Price per 1000 $12.00   Victor No. 608
Price per 1000 $10.00

The Roulette Watch.

An exact Duplicate to the regulation Roulette Wheel. Comes in a handsome Silver Plated Watch Case, with this we also give you one fold-up layout, size 12x22 inches.

This game can be used for amusement or otherwise.

PRICE, COMPLETE,   - $2.00

"The Watch" HORSE RACE Game.

Every Heat a Race. No Jockeys to pull the Horses. This handsome miniature Race Horse Game, comes in a Handsome Silver Plated Case. There are 9 Horses in each Race numbered from 1 to 9.

Can be operated for amusement or for wagers. We guarantee it to please you.

PRICE,   -   -   - $2.00

---

30   H. C. EVANS & CO., CHICAGO.

HARRIS CHECKS   Continued

ENGRAVED HARRIS CHECKS

Guaranteed to stack Perfect, and to be unbreakable. Particularly adapted for Poker, Craps, &c. White, Red, Blue, Yellow and Chocolate Colors always on Hand.

Eagle No. 66
Per 1,000 $12.   Saddle No. 64
Per 1,000 $12.

THIS FARO CHECK is one of the latest Designs, has Square Edge and is guaranteed to Stack Perfect. Remember we can fill your order for Special Checks with your initial in Inlaid Work. It requires 10 days' time to produce these goods. Made in any colors you wish them.

No. 200. Regal Square Edge Inlaid (Just out) Per 1,000 $35.   For Round Edges we charge $22 per 1,000. Square Edges $35 per 1,000.

The Evans "UP-TO-DATE Check

There is no tool used in a "CLUB ROOM" that is as hard to get perfect as a Check. Some break easily, some do not stack perfect, and last but by no means least all of them more or less are continually sticking together. In the Evans Up-To-Date Check we have overcome all these obstacles. The Up-To-Date Check is what we call a live check, the centers all being MADE SO THEY DO NOT TOUCH ONE ANOTHER the contact being on the outer rim only, they can be stacked higher and more rapidly handled than any check made. WE GUARANTEE these checks to be the most perfect most durable and best check ever made or money refunded.

PLAIN
Price $15.00 per thousand
Size 1 9/10 inch

ENGRAVED COMPOSITION POKER CHIPS

These chips are of much better quality than those listed below and are engraved in the designs shown. Size 1½ inches in diameter, packed 100 to the box assorted 50 white, 25 red and 25 blue. State design when ordering, also second choice.

No. 30F233. Engraved poker chips........................Per 100 **$2.00** Per 1000 **$18.00**

POKER CHIPS

 We carry a line of inexpensive but practical Poker Chips that will prove entirely satisfactory for everyday use. These chips are all 1½ inches in diameter and come packed 100 to the box, colors assorted 50 white, 25 red and 25 blue.

Composition Poker Chips are well liked and always satisfactory, made with round edges, nicely finished. Compressed Paper Chips are also popular and practically silent during play. Made with an enamel finish and square edges. Another popular Chip is the Noiseless Rubber Chip, made of pure rubber and uniform in size and thickness, these chips are well finished and will stack evenly.

No. 30F230. Composition Poker Chips..............Per 100 $0.70   Per 1000 $ 6.25
No. 30F231. Compressed Paper Chips ....Per 100 .60   Per 1000   5.50
No. 30F232. Rubber Poker Chips...................Per 100 1.25   Per 1000 11.50

MINIATURE POKER CHIPS

These chips are made of very good quality composition and are particularly adapted for use with our Miniature Casino Games or wherever small chips are desired. Size 1¼ inches in diameter.

No. 30F187. Miniature Poker Chips..................Per 100 $0.65   Per 1000 $6.00

NOTICE: We also carry in stock a complete line of EMBOSSED and INLAID POKER CHIPS in both round and square edge. If interested in Poker Chips of this quality write for our Club and Casino Equipment catalog FREE.

EMBOSSED CASINO CHIPS

 EMBOSSED Casino Chips are the latest development in Protection Chips and particularly suited for use in connection with a Crap Game. These Chips offer the greatest protection possible as each design whether special or of standard lettering is individual, no design ever being duplicated except for the person originally ordering. Any special design supplied on orders for 1,000 or more to show personal monogram, trade-mark, etc., without extra charge. These chips are standard 1⁹⁄₁₆ inch diameter, thick square edge and made with a non-slip satin finish.

No. 30F188. Embossed Casino Chips ....Per 100 $ 6.75
                                                              Per 1000 65.00

Casino Supplies

ALADDIN
Specialty Company

3439 Indiana Avenue
CHICAGO, ILL.

NON-DUPLICATE CHECKS

Style No. 1   Style No. 2

We can now offer you PROTECTION and also a beautiful check. The two checks shown h e r e are controlled exclusively by us and cannot be obtained elsewhere. They afford absolute protection against "ringers", as we will not sell or ship the same checks in the same community.

Aladdin Lamp   Aladdin Lamp—With Ring

These are standard size checks 1 9/16" in diameter, made in either round or thick, square edge and are guaranteed to size and stack perfectly. The designs are inlaid in white celluloid and these checks will meet the demands of the most discriminating.

Thick, square edge checks particularly adapted for Craps, Roulette, Faro and other games where dealer handles the checks. Round edge for Stud or Draw Poker and other games.

A complete stock of these checks carried at all times and we can make immediate shipment of any quantity. Furnished in the ten following colors: Red, White, Dark Blue, Yellow, Chocolate, Pink, Light Green, Light Blue, Purple and Black.

PRICES

Thick, Square Edge		Round Edge	
100	$ 7.75	100	$ 5.00
500	37.50	500	23.50
1000	72.50	1000	45.00
5000	350.00	5000	200.00

We can also supply these checks in Milled or Knurled edges, for $10.00 per thousand additional.

CREST OR SEAL CHECKS
Non-Duplicate

This is the most beautiful non-duplicate check obtainable. This check can be furnished with any design, monogram, number or picture desired.

These are Paranoid checks made from the best and toughest stock obtainable. Made for Clubs and individuals desiring absolutely the best.

These are 1 9/16" checks furnished only in Thick, Square Edge and are guaranteed to size and stack perfectly. Can be had in following twelve colors:—Red, White, Blue, Yellow, Chocolate, Pink, Light Blue, Light Green, Dark Green, Lavender, Purple and Black.

As these checks are made to order, only, it will take from three to six weeks to fill orders. Deposit of, at least one-half amount must accompany order.

PRICES

Thick, Square Edge			
1000	$125.00	3000	$300.00
2000	225.00	4000	370.00
	5000	$435.00	

We can also supply these checks with milled or knurled edges for $10.00 per 1000 additional.

SPECIAL MINIATURE POKER CHECKS

These checks are made of a very good quality plain composition and are particularly adapted for use with our miniature Roulette wheel or wherever small checks are desired. Size 1¼". Can be had in eight different colors. Packed 100 of a color to a box.

Per 100 ....$1.50   Per 1000 ....$13.00

GAME CHECKS (Continued)
SPECIAL INITIAL POKER CHECKS

We are prepared, at all times, to furnish special initial checks, in either of the above styles. These checks can be furnished with the same initial on each side, or with different initial on each side. Made in eight different colors, either round or thick square edge. These checks guaranteed to size and stack perfectly.

As these checks are made to order, we require ten days to make shipment.

Large Center   Small Center

PRICES

Large Center or Small Center			
Same Initial on Both Sides		**Different Initial on Each Side**	
100 Round Edge	$ 7.00	100 Round Edge	$ 8.00
100 Thick, Square Edge	8.00	100 Thick, Square Edge	9.00
1000 Round Edge	65.00	1000 Round Edge	72.50
1000 Thick Square Edge	75.00	1000 Thick Square	85.00

Paranoid Inlaid Poker Checks

Paranoid checks are of the finest quality. They can be furnished in ten different designs, of which we show three, above. These checks can be had in either round or thick square edge. They are 1 9/16" in diameter and guaranteed to size and stack perfectly. We require ten days time to fill orders for these checks.

PRICES

Round Edge		Thick Square Edge	
Per 100	$ 5.00	Per 100	$ 6.50
Per 1000	45.00	Per 1000	60.00

Made in eight different colors: Red, White, Blue, Yellow, Chocolate, Pink, Green and Light Blue. Colors are uniform and guaranteed permanent.

Harris Monarch and Single Line Engraved Checks

These are high grade exclusive checks, made of the same material as our other checks. These famous checks are made only by the Harris Check Co. They are "live" checks, dished in the center, that is it is made so the centers do not touch, the contact being on the outer rim only. These checks can be stacked higher and handled more rapidly than any other checks made.

They are high class checks at a moderate cost. Can be furnished in nine different colors: Red, White, Blue, Chocolate, Green, Pink, Yellow and Burnt Orange. Packed 100 of a color to a box. Standard size 1 9/16;. Thick square edge only. Sample on request.

PRICES

100	$ 4.50	1000	$ 40.00
500	21.00	5000	190.00

Roulette Markers and Marker Rack

The accompanying illustration shows our special unbreakable composition Roulette Markers, together with the Rack for containing them. The Markers are 1¼ inches in diameter, made in eight denominations, each denomination a different color with figures inlaid in white celluloid. Denominations are 5, 10, 20, 25, 50, 100, 500 and 1000. When ordering be sure and state denomination and number desired.

The Marker Rack is made of solid mahogany, beautifully polished, designed specially to contain the above markers.

Roulette Markers, each $0.15
Roulette Marker Rack, 6 hole, each 3.00
Roulette Marker Rack, 8 hole, each 4.00

BIBLIOGRAPHY

BIBLIOGRAPHY

_____. 1995. *U. S. Casino Directory.* U. S. Casino Directories, P.O. Box 22006, Bullhead City, AZ 86439.

Alfoldi, Elizabeth. "Romans Chose Muses to Grace Game Counters," *Coin World*, June 23, 1976, pp. 65–66.

Apling, Henry. "The Casting Counter (Jeton, Abbey Piece, Nuremberg Token)," *Seaby's Coin and Medal Bulletin*, 1962, pp. 188–194.

Birl, Jerry. 1995. *Catalog and Checklist of Atlantic City Roulette Chips.* Roulette International Chip Hunters, P.O. Box 126, Millsboro, DE 19966.

Black, Archie. 1996. *Black's Catalog of Atlantic City Casino Chips and Gaming Tokens.* P.O. Box 63, Brick, NJ 08723.

Draper, Margo (Seymour). "Collecting Old Poker Chips," *Antique Trader*, January 12, 1983, pp. 52–55.

Emmons, Andrea L. "The Awful Truth About French Ivory," *American Collector*, April 1982, p. 31.

Fauver, Benjamin. 1983. *American Counters, Part I, Double Eagle & Eagle Gold.* Oak Grove Publications, P.O. Box 521, Menlo Park, CA 94025.

Fauver, Benjamin. 1982. *Exonumia Symbolism & Classification.* Oak Grove Publications, P.O. Box 521, Menlo Park, CA 94025.

Fuld, Melvin. "English Card Counters, Gaming House Inns, Lottery Pieces, Racing Tokens, Spiel Marken, German Whist, Whist and Other Gaming Pieces," *Token and Medal Society Journal*, August 1974.

Fuller, Harvey J. 1992. *Index of Nevada Gambling Establishments.* The Coin Company, P.O. Box 1000, Minden, NV 89423.

Hamilton, Peter F. "The Subject Is Jetons," *The Numismatist*, 1969, pp. 1659–1667.

Herz, Howard W. and L. Kregg. 1995. *A Collector's Guide to Nevada Gaming Checks and Chips.* Gaming Archaeology, The Coin Company, P.O. Box 1000, Minden, NV 89423.

Lighterman, Mark; Myrna Ginsburg; and Robert Ginsburg. 1996. *A Guide to Florida's Gaming Chips, Checks and Tokens.* (305) 271-8387.

Massaro, Clyde. 1996. *Colorado Casinos Chip & Token Guide.* P.O. Box 471, Lafayette, CO 80026.

Myers, Allen; Ernie Wheelden; and Michael Knapp. 1997. *The Chip Rack: A Price Guide to the Casino Chips and Checks of Nevada, 4th ed.* KMW Publishing, P.O. Box 17002, Louisville, KY 40217.

Myers, Allen; Ernie Wheelden; and Michael Knapp. 1997. *The Gaming Table (Chip, Check and Token, 2nd Edition Collectors Guide).* KMW Publishing, P.O. Box 17002, Louisville, KY 40217.

O'Connor, Eugene. 1979. *The Casino*. Historical Society of Saratoga Springs, Saratoga Springs, NY.

Pfaender, Armin, and Mel Jung. 1996. *California Chips*. P.O. Box 2032, No. Hills, CA 91393.

Rulau, Russell and George Fuld. 1972. *American Game Counters (Spiel Marken)*. The Token and Medal Society.

Schneir, Leonard. 1993. *Gambling Collectibles—A Sure Winner*. Schiffer Publishing Ltd., 77 Lower Valley Road, Atglen, PA 19310.

Seymour, Dale; Ken Craig; and Allan Myers. 1996. *19th Century Ivory Gambling Chips*. Past Pleasures, P.O. Box 50863, Palo Alto, CA 94303. (Spiral-bound collector's edition with old codes and space for notes and inventory recording.)

Seymour, Dale; Robet Eisenstadt; and Alan Myers. 1997. *Old Poker Chips*. Past Pleasures, P.O. Box 50863, Palo Alto, CA 94303. (Spiral-bound collector's edition with old codes, space for notes and inventory master sheets.)

Spencer, Donald D. 1994. *Casino Chip Collecting*. Camelot Publishing Company, P.O. Box 1357, Ormond Beach, FL 32175.

ivory, French, 27, 119
ivory turners, 112

K

"Keep Your Temper," 8, 88–89
Kendall, John M., 29
Kernan Manufacturing Co., 415–416
Kettle, Henry, 7
King, T. R. Co., 18, 35

L

labels, chip box, 53–61
Langworthy Co., 18
Lauer, Ludwig C., 7
leather chips, 27
loo (game), 11, 12
low-ball clubs, 21

M

machined chips, 15, 16
manufacturers, chip, 7, 27, 28, 29–30,
    112–120
markers, 22
marshalling of arms, 85
Mason & Co., 18, 117, 118
metal chips, 8–10, 21, 39, 46
Meyer, John, 116
miniature chips, 16, 47
Mississippi River Boat gambling, 13,
    109–112
molds, chip, 14, 29
Monarch chip, 17
Monarch border, 18
monogrammed chips, 42, 66, 147–155,
    285–294
Monte Carlo, 28, 391
mother-of-pearl counters, 12, 28, 33, 34,
    41, 50, 65–105, 353

counter reverse, 94–95
dedications, mementos, souvenirs, 88–89
French style, 97–105
games, 92–93
heraldry, 84–87
numbers, 89–91
peers, barons, landed gentry, 86–87
Myers, Allan, 44

N

nacre, 67
Nafew, Samuel, 407–409
Napoleon, 33, 88
Nevada gaming tokens, 21
numeral chips, 42, 90–91, 109–110,
    157–186, 295–300

O

ocean liner chips, 21
Ogden Co., 412–413
ombre (game), 12, 92
ordinaries, 85
organizing chips, 42

P

paper chips, 20, 41, 357–358
Paranoid chips, 16
paste-on chips, 15
patents, design, 22–26
Paulson Co., 18
Peabody Museum, 88
people chips, 263–267
Phyfe, Duncan, 113
Phyfe, John, 113, 115
Piping Rock Club, 365
plain chips, 15, 197, 261
plant chips, 269–275
plaques, 28, 82